RF and Microwave Circuit Design

Updated and Revised

with

100 Keysight **(ADS)** Workspaces

RF and Microwave Circuit Design

Updated and Revised
with
100 Keysight **(ADS)** Workspaces

Ali A. Behagi

Techno Search

Ladera Ranch, CA 92694

RF and Microwave Circuit Design
Updated and Revised
with 100 Keysight **(ADS)** Workspaces

ISBN 978-0-996-4466-4-8

Copyright ©2017 by Ali A. Behagi

First Published, February 2017

Published in USA
Techno Search
Ladera Ranch, CA 92694

Foreword

Unlike many traditional textbooks written mainly for the classroom teaching, the updated and revised RF and Microwave Circuit Design textbook adopts a practical hands-on approach to quickly familiarize university students and professional engineers to the theory and application of high frequency circuit design topics.

Professor Behagi's book is invaluable in that it marries RF and microwave circuit design with 100 practical design examples using the latest Keysight ADS software. Additionally, the book develops and frequently uses the MATLAB Scripts to analytically design complex impedance matching problems.

Keysight ADS is today's most widely used RF and microwave EDA software used by the world's leading companies to design MMICs, RFICs, RF Modules and RF boards in every smart-phone, tablet, Wi-Fi router as well as Radar and satellite communication systems.

Keysight ADS tools featured in the textbook include; lowpass and highpass Filter Design Guide, Filter Transformation Assistant, Passive Circuit Design Guide, Impedance Matching Utility, Momentum EM Simulation, Simulation Wizard, Smart Components, Tuning, and Optimization. No other textbook uses this many EDA tools in one book. University students and professional engineers will find the book as a potent learning tool as well as a reference guide to quickly setup designs using the ADS software.

The investment in learning the foundational skills of RF and microwave circuit design and the Electronic Design Automation techniques taught in this book provides students and engineers with valuable knowledge that will remain relevant for a long time to come.

Joe Civello
Keysight Technologies
ADS Planning and Marketing Manager
1400 Fountaingrove Parkway
Santa Rosa, CA 95403, USA

Preface

The updated and revised RF and Microwave Circuit Design textbook familiarizes the reader with a solid understanding of the RF and Microwave Concepts, Components, Transmission Lines, Network Parameters, Smith Charts, Resonant Circuits, Filters, Power Transfers, Discrete and Distributed Impedance Matching Networks, Single-Stage and Multi-Stage Amplifier Designs. The book also shows how to use the Keysight Electronic Design Automation (EDA) tools in the design of RF and microwave circuits in a manner that is practiced in industry. The EDA techniques ensures that the skills learned in this book can be easily and immediately put into practice without any barriers. The organization of the book is as follows:

In chapter 1, a thorough analysis of RF and microwave concepts and components are presented. Components such as, straight wire, flat ribbon, physical resistors, physical capacitors, and physical inductors are analyzed and their input impedance are simulated.

In chapter 2, propagation of the plane waves in different media is introduced. Popular types of transmission lines such as coaxial, microstrip, stripline, and waveguides are defined and their parameters are analyzed. Several transmission line components are modeled and their electrical performance are discussed. Microstrip bias feed and directional couplers are also designed.

In Chapter 3, derivation of RF and microwave network parameters, development and use of the network S parameters, and the movement of the lumped and distributed elements on the Smith chart are presented.

In the first half of Chapter 4, the subject of series and parallel resonant circuits, the effect of load resistance on the bandwidth, the tuning and optimization of the circuit components, and design of the tapped capacitor and inductor are discussed. In the second half of the chapter, design of the lowpass and highpass filters, generation of the physical models, and construction of the filter prototypes are presented. Finally the electromagnetic analysis of the stepped impedance filter, the microstrip edge-coupled bandpass filter design are also treated in this chapter.

In Chapter 5, the conditions for maximum power transfer and the equations for matching any two impedances with are derived. Both analytical and graphical techniques are used to design narrowband and broadband matching networks. In some examples the Impedance Matching Utility in ADS is used to solve any impedance matching problem. Derivation of equations for the Q factor and the number of L-networks, designing with Q curves on the Smith chart, Fano's limit theorem, and the effect of finite Q on the matching networks are also treated in this chapter.

In Chapter 6, analytic design equations for quarter-wave transformer and single-stub matching networks are derived. Narrowband and broadband distributed matching networks are designed. For the broadband case, the cascaded quarter-wave transformer and the single-stub matching networks are used.

In Chapter 7, single-stage amplifiers are designed by utilizing four different impedance matching objectives. The first amplifier is designed for maxim gain where the input and the output are conjugately matched to the source and load impedance; the second amplifier is designed for specific gain where the input or the output is mismatched to achieve a specific gain less than its maximum; the third amplifier is a low noise amplifier where the transistor is selectively mismatched to achieve a specific Noise Figure; and the fourth amplifier is a power amplifier where the transistor is selectively mismatched to achieve a specific amount of output power. Quarter-wave transformer networks,

In Chapter 8, a two-stage amplifier is designed by utilizing a direct inter-stage matching network. Finally a brief introduction to LNA cascade analysis is presented.

Ali A. Behagi, Ph.D.
February 2017

Table of
Contents

Table of ADS
Design Examples

Chapter 5: Power Transfer and Impedance Matching   227

Chapter 1

RF and Microwave Concepts and Components

1.1 Introduction

An electromagnetic wave is a propagating wave that consists of electric and magnetic fields. The electric field is produced by stationary electric charges while the magnetic field is produced by moving electric charges. A time-varying magnetic field produces an electric field and a time-varying electric field produces a magnetic field. The characteristics of electromagnetic waves are frequency, wavelength, phase, impedance, and power density. In free space, the relationship between the wavelength, frequency, and velocity of light is given by Equation (1-1).

$$\lambda = \frac{c}{f} \qquad (1\text{-}1)$$

In the MKS system, λ is the wavelength in meters, c is approximately 300,000 kilometers per second, and f is in cycles per second, or Hz.

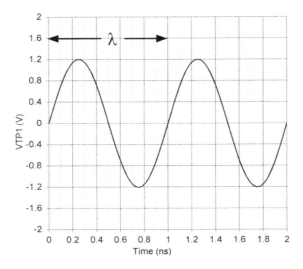

Figure 1-1 A time varying voltage waveform

The electromagnetic spectrum is the range of all possible frequencies of electromagnetic radiation. They include radio waves, microwaves, infrared radiation, visible light, ultraviolet radiation, X-rays and gamma rays. In the field of RF and microwave engineering the term RF generally refers to Radio Frequency signals with frequencies in the 3 KHz to 300 MHz range. The term Microwave refers to signals with frequencies from 300 MHz to 300 GHz having wavelengths from 1 meter to 1 millimeter. The RF and microwave frequencies form the spectrum of all radio, television, data, and satellite communications. Figure 1-2 shows a chart highlighting the RF and microwave frequencies from 3 KHz to 300 GHz. This text will focus on the RF and microwave frequencies as the foundation for component design techniques. The application of Keysight ADS software in the text will enhance the student's understanding of the underlying principles presented in the text. Both students and practicing engineers will find the text an invaluable reference to the RF and microwave theory and techniques by using the ADS software. The numerous ADS examples enable the setup and design of many RF and microwave circuit design problems.

Figure 1-2 Electromagnetic spectrums from VLF to EHF

The spectrum chart of Figure 1-2 is intended as a general guideline to the commercial nomenclature for various sub bands. There is typically overlap across each of the boundaries as there is no strict dividing line between the categories. The RF frequencies typically begin in the very low frequency, VLF, range through the very high frequency, VHF, range. Microwaves are typically the ultra high frequency, UHF, super high frequency, SHF and extremely high frequency, EHF, frequency ranges. During World War II microwave engineers developed a further detailed classification of the microwave frequencies into a band-letter designation. In 1984 the Institute of Electrical and Electronics Engineers, IEEE, agreed to standardize the letter designation of the microwave frequencies. These designators and their frequency ranges are shown in Table 1-1.

Band Designator	L Band	S Band	C Band	X Band	Ku Band	K Band	Ka Band
Frequency Range GHz	1 to 2	2 to 4	4 to 8	8 to 12	12 to 18	18 to 27	27 to 40

Table 1-1 Microwave band letter designators

Engineering students spend much of their formal education learning the basics of inductors, capacitors, and resistors. Many are surprised to find that as we enter the high frequency, HF, part of the electromagnetic spectrum these components are no longer a singular (ideal) element but rather a network of circuit elements. Components at RF and microwave frequencies become a network of resistors, capacitors, and inductors. This leads to the complication that the component's characteristics become quite frequency dependent. For example, we will see in this chapter that a capacitor at one frequency may in fact be an inductor at another frequency.

In section 1.2 we will begin with the calculation of the straight wire inductance and move into more complete ADS analysis of straight wire inductance, skin depth in conductors, and calculation of flat ribbon inductance. In section 1.3 we will discuss the analysis of physical resistors and chip resistors. In sections 1.4 and 1.5 we discuss the analysis and design of various physical inductors and capacitors and their implementation at RF and microwave frequencies. Discrete resistors, capacitors, and inductors are often referred to as lumped elements. RF and microwave engineers use the terminology to differentiate these elements from those designed in distributed printed circuit traces. Distributed component design is introduced in Chapter 2 and used throughout the book.

1.2 Straight Wire, Flat Ribbon, and Conductors

Straight Wire Inductance

A conducting wire carrying an AC current produces a changing magnetic field around the wire. According to Faraday's law the changing magnetic field induces a voltage in the wire that opposes any change in the current flow. This opposition to change is called self inductance. At high frequencies even a short piece of straight wire possesses frequency dependent resistance and inductance behaving as a circuit element.

Example 1-1: Calculate the inductance of a three inch length of AWG #28 copper wire in free space.

Solution: The straight wire inductance can be calculated from the empirical Equation (1-2) [1].

$$L = K\ell \left(\ln \frac{4\ell}{D} - 0.75 \right) nH \qquad (1-2)$$

Where:

  ℓ = Length of the wire
  D = Diameter of the wire (from Appendix A).
  $K = 2$ for dimensions in cm and $K=5.08$ for dimensions in inches

Using Appendix A the diameter of the AWG#28 wire is found to be 0.0126 inches. Solving Equation (1-2) the inductance is calculated.

$$L = 5.08 \ (3) \left(\ln \frac{4 \ (3)}{0.0126} - 0.75 \right) = 93.1 \ nH$$

It is interesting to examine the reactance of the wire. We know that the reactance is a function of the frequency and is related to the inductance by the following equation.

$$X_L = 2\pi f L \quad \Omega \tag{1-3}$$

Where: f is the frequency in Hz and L is the inductance in Henries

Calculating the reactance at 60Hz, 1MHz, and 1GHz we can see how the reactive component of the wire increases dramatically with frequency. At 60Hz the reactance is well below 1Ω while at microwave frequencies the reactance increases to several hundred ohms.

60 Hz: $X_L = 2\pi \left(60\right)\left(93.1 \cdot 10^{-9}\right) = 35 \ \mu\Omega$

500MHz: $X_L = 2\pi \left(10^6\right)\left(500\right)\left(93.1 \cdot 10^{-9}\right) = 292 \ \Omega$

1 GHz: $X_L = 2\pi \left(10^9\right)\left(93.1 \cdot 10^{-9}\right) = 585 \ \Omega$

Analysis of Straight Wire Inductance

The procedure for the analysis and simulation of straight wire in ADS is as follows.

- Start ADS and create a new workspace

- Name the workspace Ex1-1_wrk

- From the ADS Main window create a New Schematic in cell_1

- In the Schematic window, click on Insert > Template >ads-templates:S_Params

- Delete the DisplyTemplate icon

- Type in WIRE in the part selection box and place the wire component between the input and output Terminations

- Insert the input impedance, Zin1, from the Simulation-S_Param Palette to analyze the input impedance as a function of frequency.

- Double click on the S-PARAMETERS icon and set the frequency range as shown in Figure 1-3.

Figure 1-3 Frequency setting for simulation of wire impedance

- Wire up the schematic as shown in Figure 1-4.

Figure 1-4 ADS schematic of the straight wire

In ADS, the input termination, TERM_1, represents a signal source in series with the source impedance and the output termination, TERM_2, represents the load impedance connected to ground. Set the wire diameter to 12.6 mils and the length to 3 inches. Accept the value of 1 for Rho. Rho is not the actual resistivity of the wire but rather the resistivity of the wire relative to copper. Because we are modeling a copper wire the value should be set to one. It is a common practice in most commercial microwave software programs to specify resistivity in relative terms, compared to copper. Table 1-2 provides a reference of the materials used in microwave engineering.

Material	Resistivity Relative to Copper	Actual Resistivity Ω-meters	Actual Resistivity Ω-inches
Copper, annealed	1.00	$1.68 \cdot 10^{-8}$	$6.61 \cdot 10^{-7}$
Silver	0.95	$1.59 \cdot 10^{-8}$	$6.26 \cdot 10^{-7}$
Gold	1.42	$2.35 \cdot 10^{-8}$	$9.25 \cdot 10^{-7}$
Aluminum	1.64	$2.65 \cdot 10^{-8}$	$1.04 \cdot 10^{-6}$
Tungsten	3.25	$5.60 \cdot 10^{-8}$	$2.20 \cdot 10^{-6}$
Zinc	3.40	$5.90 \cdot 10^{-8}$	$2.32 \cdot 10^{-6}$
Nickel	5.05	$6.84 \cdot 10^{-8}$	$2.69 \cdot 10^{-6}$
Iron	5.45	$1.00 \cdot 10^{-7}$	$3.94 \cdot 10^{-6}$
Platinum	6.16	$1.06 \cdot 10^{-7}$	$4.17 \cdot 10^{-6}$
Tin	52.8	$1.09 \cdot 10^{-7}$	$4.29 \cdot 10^{-6}$
Nichrome	65.5	$1.10 \cdot 10^{-6}$	$4.33 \cdot 10^{-5}$
Carbon	2083.3	$3.50 \cdot 10^{-5}$	$1.38 \cdot 10^{-3}$

Table 1-2 Resistivity of common materials relative to copper

ADS has a built-in function Zin to measure the port impedance of the circuit at each analysis frequency. Insert a built-in function Zin1 from the Simulation-S_Param palette to measure the input impedance of the wire versus frequency. When simulation is run in ADS the results are written to a Dataset. The results of a Dataset may then be sent to a graph or tabular output for visualization. More complex workspaces may have multiple Datasets. It is a good practice to specify which Dataset is used to collect data for post processing.

In this example two equations are used to post process the information in the Dataset. In Data Display Window add equations to calculate the reactance and inductance of the straight wire, as shown in Table 1-3. We know that the reactance is the imaginary part of the impedance. The first Equation defines the reactance as the imaginary part of the input impedance, Zin1. The second Equation calculates the inductance of the wire from the reactance using Equation (1-3). The frequency, freq, is the independent variable created by the linear analysis. In Table 1-3 there is a calculated array value for each independent variable. The Equations are interactive mathematical processor similar to MATLAB by MathWorks. The mathematical language is compatible with the m-file syntax that is used in MATLAB. It is very convenient for students and engineers that are proficient in MATLAB. Table 1-3 shows the tabular output of the simulation. To select the equations, double click anywhere on the Table to open the "Plot Traces & Attributes" window. From the "Datasets and Equations" select the Equations as the data source and then select both variables, reactance and inductance.

Eqn reactance=im(Zin1)

Eqn inductance=reactance/(freq*2*pi)

freq	Zin1	reactance	inductance
60.00 Hz	50.023 + j3.366E-5	3.366E-5	8.929E-8
500.0 MHz	50.538 + j280.501	280.501	8.929E-8
1.000 GHz	50.755 + j561.001	561.001	8.929E-8

Table 1-3 Table showing input impedance, reactance and inductance

Compare the results of the simulation of Table 1-3 with the calculated values of Example 1-1. We can see that at 60 Hz the reactance and resulting inductance are very close to the calculated values. At 500 MHz and 1 GHz however, the values greatly diverge. Equation (1-2) was useful for calculating the basic inductance at low frequency but as the frequency enters the microwave region, the value begins to change. This is due to the skin effect of the conductor. The skin effect is a property of conductors where, as the frequency increases, the current density concentrates on the outer surface of the conductor.

Skin Depth in Conductors

At RF and microwave frequencies, due to the larger inductive reactance caused by the increase in flux linkage toward the center of the conductor, the current in the conductor is forced to flow near the conductor surface. As a result the amplitude of the current density decays exponentially with the depth of penetration from the surface. Figure 1-5 shows the cross section of a cylindrical wire with the current density area shaded.

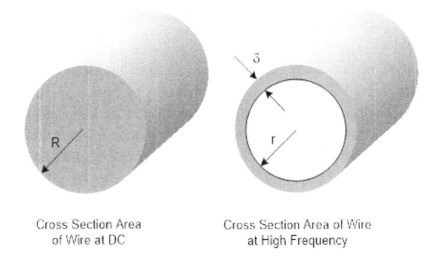

Cross Section Area
of Wire at DC

Cross Section Area of Wire
at High Frequency

Figure 1-5 Cross section of current flow in the conductor showing effect of skin depth

At low frequencies the entire cross sectional area is carrying the current. As the frequency increases to the RF and microwave region, the current flows much closer to the outside of the conductor. At the higher end of microwave frequency range, the current is essentially carried near the surface with almost no current at the central region of the conductor. The skin depth, δ, is the distance from the surface where the charge carrier density falls to 37% of its value at the surface. Therefore 63% of the RF current flows within the skin depth region. The skin depth is a function of the frequency and the properties of the conductor as defined by Equation (1-4). As the cross sectional area of the conductor effectively decreases the resistance of the conductor will increase [7].

$$\delta = \sqrt{\frac{\rho}{\mu\,\pi f}}$$

(1-4)

Where:

> δ = skin depth
> ρ = resistivity of the conductor
> f = frequency
> μ = permeability of the conductor

Use caution when solving Equation (1-4) to keep the units of ρ and μ consistent. Table 1-2 contains values of resistivity in units of Ω-meters and Ω-inches. The permeability μ is the permeability of the conductor. It is a property of a material to support a magnetic flux. Some reference tables will show relative permeability. In this case the relative permeability is normalized to the permeability of free space which is: $4\pi \cdot 10^{-7}$ Henries per meter. The relationship between relative permeability to the actual permeability is given in Equation (1-5). Most conductors have a relative permeability μ_r very close to one. Therefore conductor permeability μ is often given the same value as μ_o.

$$\mu = \mu_r \ \mu_o \qquad\qquad (1\text{–}5)$$

Where:

> μ = actual permeability of the material
> μ_r = relative permeability of material
> μ_o = permeability of free space

For example to calculate the skin depth of copper wire at a frequency of 25 MHz, we use Equation (1-4), and by converting the permeability from H/m to H/inch, the skin depth is:

$$\delta = \sqrt{\frac{6.61 \cdot 10^{-7}}{\left(3.19 \cdot 10^{-8}\right)\pi \left(25 \cdot 10^{6}\right)}} = 5.14 \cdot 10^{-4} \ inches$$

Although we have been considering the skin depth in a circular wire, skin depth is present in all shapes of conductors. A thick conductor is affected more by skin effect at lower frequencies than a thinner conductor. One of the reasons that engineers are concerned about skin effect in conductors is the fact that as the resistance of the conductor increases, so does the thermal heating in the wire. Heat can be a destructive force in high power RF circuits causing burn out of conductors and potentially hazardous conditions to personnel. Also the frequency dependence of the skin effect may make it difficult to maintain the impedance of a transmission line structure. This effect will be examined in Chapter 2 with the study of transmission lines.

As the frequency increases, the current is primarily flowing in the region of the skin depth. It can be visualized from Figure 1-5 that a wire would have greater resistance at higher frequencies due to the skin effect. The resistance of a length of wire is determined by the resistivity and the geometry of the wire as defined by Equation (1-6).

$$R = \frac{\rho \ell}{A} \qquad \Omega \qquad\qquad (1\text{-}6)$$

Where:

ρ = Resistivity of the wire

ℓ = Length of the wire

A = Cross sectional area

Also to calculate the DC resistance of a 12 inch length of AWG #24 copper wire we use the radius of the wire in Appendix A and calculate the DC resistance by using Equation (1-6).

$$R_{DC} = \frac{\left(6.61 \cdot 10^{-7}\right) \cdot 12}{\pi \left(\dfrac{0.0201}{2}\right)^2} = 0.025 \ \ \Omega$$

To calculate the resistance of the same wire at 25 MHz the cross sectional area of the conduction region must be redefined by the skin depth of Figure 1-5. We can refer to this as the effective area, A_{eff}.

$$A_{eff} = \pi \ (R^2 - r^2)\qquad\qquad(1\text{-}7)$$

Where: $r = R\text{-}\delta$.

For the AWG#24 wire at 25 MHz the A_{eff} is calculated as:

$$A_{eff} = \pi \left(\frac{0.0201}{2}\right)^2 - \pi \left(\left(\frac{0.0201}{2}\right) - 5.14 \cdot 10^{-4}\right)^2 = 3.14 \cdot 10^{-5} \ in^2$$

Then apply Equation (1-6) to calculate the resistance of the 12 inch wire at 25 MHz.

$$R_{25MHz} = \frac{12 \ \left(6.61 \cdot 10^{-7}\right)}{3.14 \cdot 10^{-5}} = 0.253 \ \Omega$$

Notice the resistance at 25 MHz is mote than 10 times greater than DC resistance.

Calculation of Flat Ribbon Inductance

Flat ribbon style conductors are very common in RF and microwave engineering. Flat ribbon conductors are encountered in RF systems in the form of low inductance ground straps. Flat ribbon conductors can also be encountered in microwave integrated circuits (MIC) as gold bonding straps. When a very low inductance is required the flat ribbon or copper strap is a good choice. The flat ribbon inductance can be calculated from the empirical Equation (1-8).

$$L = K \ \ell \left[\ln\left(\frac{2\ell}{W+T}\right) + 0.223 \left(\frac{W+T}{\ell}\right) + 0.5 \right] \ nH \qquad(1\text{-}8)$$

Where:

> ℓ = The length of the wire
> K = 2 for dimensions in cm and K=5.08 for dimensions in inches
> W = the width of the conductor
> T = the thickness of the conductor

Example 1-2: Calculate the inductance of the 3 inch Ribbon at 60 Hz, 500 MHz, and 1 GHz. Make the ribbon 100 mils wide and 2 mils thick.

Solution: Follow the procedure in Section 1.2 to create the flat ribbon schematic. The schematic of the Ribbon is shown in Figure 1-6 along with the Zin1 and S-Parameter simulation.

Figure 1-6 Flat ribbon schematic

Simulate the schematic to open the data display window. In the data display window add equations to calculate the reactance and inductance of the flat ribbon. Select a tabular List and add Zin1 plus reactance and inductance equations to the list, as shown in Table 1-4.

Eqn reactance=im(Zin1)   Eqn inductance=reactance/(freq*2*pi)

freq	Zin1	reactance	inductance
60.00 Hz	50.006 / 2.997E-5	2.616E-5	6.939E-8
500.0 MHz	220.786 / 76.883	215.026	6.844E-8
1.000 GHz	432.905 / 83.348	429.990	6.844E-8

Table 1-4. Flat ribbon tabular output Zin1, reactance, and inductance

Compare Table 1-4 with Table 1-3 and notice that the same length of ribbon as the AWG#28 wire has almost half of the reactance value. Also note that in Table 1-4 the inductance value of 68.44 nH does not change over the 500 MHz to 1 GHz range. It is why the ribbon is desirable as a low inductance conductor for use in RF and microwave applications.

1.3 Analysis of Physical Resistors

The resistance of a material determines the rate at which electrical energy is converted to heat. In Table 1-2 we have seen that the resistivity of materials is specified in Ω-meters rather than Ω/meter. This facilitates the calculation of resistance using Equation (1-6). When working with low frequency or logic circuits we are used to treating resistors as ideal resistive components.

Example 1-3: Plot the impedance of a 50 Ω ideal resistor in ADS over a frequency range of 0 to 2 GHz.

Solution: First we look at the input impedance of an ideal resistor with no parasitics at RF and microwave frequencies. Create a workspace in ADS and open a new schematic. Place a 50 Ohm resistor and measure the input impedance of the resistor from 0 to 2 GHz. Complete the schematic as show in Figure 1-7.

Figure 1-7 schematic of a 50 Ω ideal resistor

Simulate the schematic and display the input impedance over a frequency range of 0 to 2 GHz, as shown in Figure 1-8. The plot shows a constant resistance at all frequencies.

Figure 1-8 Ideal 50Ω resistor impedance versus frequency

Example 1-4: Plot the impedance of a 5 Ω leaded resistor in ADS over a frequency range of 0 to 2 GHz.

Solution: At RF and microwave frequencies, resistors also possess inductive and capacitive elements. The stray inductance and capacitance associated with a resistor are often called parasitic elements. Consider the leaded resistor model shown in Figure 1-9. For a 1/8 watt leaded resistor it is not uncommon for each lead to have about 10 nH of inductance. The body of the resistor may exhibit 5 pF capacitance between the leads, as shown in Figure 1-9.

Figure 1-9 Schematic of a 5 Ω leaded resistor with parasitic elements

Create Figure 1-9 in ADS and simulate the schematic. Plot the input impedance as a function of frequency as shown in Figure 1-10.

Figure 1-10 Impedance of the leaded resistor versus frequency

Notice the resonance of the leaded resistor at 500 MHz is 800 Ohm.

Chip Resistors

Thick film resistors are used in most contemporary electronic equipment. The thick film resistor, often called chip resistor, comes close to eliminating much of the inductance that plagues the leaded resistor. The chip resistor works well with popular surface mount assembly techniques preferred in modern electronic manufacturing. Figure 1-11 shows a typical thick film chip resistor along with a cross section of its design.

Figure 1-11 Thick film chip resistors and dimensions (*courtesy of KOA Speer Electronics*)

There are many types of chip resistors designed for specific applications. Common sizes and power ratings are shown in Table 1-5.

Size	Length x Width	Power Rating
0201	20mils x 10mils	50mW
0402	40mils x 20mils	62mW
0603	60mils x 30mils	100mW
0805	80mils x 50mils	125mW
1206	120mils x 60mils	250mW
2010	200mils x 100mils	500mW
2512	250mils x 120mils	1W

Table 1-5 Standard thick film resistor size and approximate power rating

The thick film resistor is comprised of a carbon based film that is deposited onto the substrate. Contrasted with a thin film resistor that is typically etched onto a substrate or printed circuit board, the thick film resistor can usually handle higher power dissipation. The ends of the chip have metalized wraps that are used to attach the resistor to a circuit board. ADS does not include native models for thick film resistors. Some manufacturers may provide models that can be incorporated into ADS. There are also companies that specialize in developing CAD models of components such as Modelithics, Inc. Modelithics has a wide variety of component model libraries that can be incorporated into ADS.

Example 1-5: Plot the impedance of 1 kΩ, 0603 size chip resistor, manufactured by KOA, from 0 to 3 GHz. This model is available in the Modelithics evaluation model kit.

Solution: Create a schematic in ADS, select the Modelithics Library in the ADS Part Selector and place the KOA0603 resistor on the schematic, as shown with an arrow in Figure 1-12.

Figure 1-12 Modelithics chip component library in ADS

Complete the schematic as shown in Figure 1-13.

Figure 1-13 Modelithics chip resistor model schematic

Simulate the schematic and display input impedance as a function of frequency, as shown in Figure 1-14.

Figure 1-14 Modelithics chip resistor impedance versus frequency

Note the roll off of the impedance with increasing frequency. This suggests that the chip resistor does have a parasitic capacitance that is in parallel with the resistor similar to the discrete model of Figure 1-9.

1.4 Analysis of Physical Inductors

In section 1.2 we introduced the topic of inductance. The inductance of straight cylindrical and flat ribbon conductors was examined. The primary method of increasing inductance is not to simply keep increasing the length of a straight conductor but rather form a coil of wire. Forming a coil of wire increases the magnetic flux linkage and greatly increases the overall inductance. Because of the greater surrounding magnetic flux, inductors store energy in the magnetic field. Lumped element inductors are used in bias circuits, impedance matching networks, filters, and resonators. As we will see throughout this section inductors are realized in many forms including: air-core, toroidal and very small chip inductors. The concept of Q factor is introduced and will come up frequently in RF and microwave circuit design. It is a unit-less figure of merit that is used in circuits in which both reactive and resistive elements coexist. Because we know that individual air wound inductors, shown in Figure 1-15, are actually networks that are made up of resistors, inductors, and capacitors, each individual component is also characterized by a Q factor.

Figure 1-15 Air wound inductor showing the wire resistance and inter-winding capacitance

Basically, the higher the Q factor, the less loss or resistance exists in the energy storage property. The inductor quality factor Q is defined as:

$$Q = \frac{X}{R_s} \qquad (1\text{-}9)$$

Where X is the reactance and R_s is the resistance in the inductor

At low RF frequencies the resistance is primarily from the resistivity of the wire and as such is quite low. At higher frequencies the skin effect and inter-winding capacitance begin to influence the resistance and reactance thus causing the Q factor to decrease. In most applications we want a high Q component as possible. We can increase the Q of inductors by using larger diameter wire or by silver plating the wire. In a multi-turn coil, the windings can be separated to reduce the inter-winding capacitance which in turn increases the Q factor.

Air Core Inductors

Forming a wire on a removable cylinder is the basic realization of the air core inductor. When designing an air-core inductor, use the largest wire size and close spaced windings to result in the lowest series resistance and high Q. The basic empirical equation to calculate the inductance of an air core inductor is given by Equation (1-10) [2].

$$L = \frac{(17) N^{1.3} (D + D1)^{1.7}}{(D1 + S)^{0.7}} \qquad (1\text{-}10)$$

Where:

   N = Number of turns of wire

   D = Core form diameter in inches

   $D1$ = Wire diameter in inches

   L = Coil inductance in nH

   S = Spacing between turns in inches

As an interesting comparison with Example 1.2.1 calculate the amount of inductance that we can realize in that same three inches of wire if we wind it around a core to form an inductor. Choose a core form of 0.095 inches diameter as a convenient form to wrap the wire around.

For the solution first we calculate the approximate number of turns that we expect to have with the three inch length of wire. We know that the circumference of a circle is related to the diameter by the following equation.

$$Circumference = \pi \left(Diameter\right) = \pi \left(0.095\right) = 0.2985 \quad inches$$

With a circumference of 0.2985 inches we can calculate the approximate number of turns that we can wrap around the 0.095 inch core with three inches of wire.

$$N = \frac{3}{0.2985} = approximately\ 10\ turns$$

From Equation (1-10) we can see that the spacing between the turns has a strong effect on the value of the inductance that we can expect from the coil. When hand winding the coil, it may be difficult to maintain an exact spacing of zero inches between the turns. Therefore it is useful to solve Equation (1-10) in terms of a variety of coil spacing so that we can see the effect on the inductance. We can solve Equation (1-10) in MATLAB for a variety of coil spacing, as follows.

1. Enter design parameters

D=.095; D1=.0126; N=10; Spacing = [0; .002; .004; .006; .008; .010]

2. Calculate the coil length and inductance in nano Henries

Inductance_nH = (17*(N^1.3)*((D + D1)^1.7))/((D1 + Spacing)^.7)
Coil_Length = (D1*N) + (Spacing*(N-1))

Note that the coil spacing is variable and Spacing has been defined as an array variable. Placing a semicolon between the values makes the array organized in a column format. This is handy for viewing the results in tabular format. Placing a comma between the values would organize the array in a row format. As an aid in forming the coil, the overall coil length is also calculated. The coil length is simply the summation of the overall wire thickness times the number of turns and the spacing between the turns. Add the calculated inductance, spacing, and coil length to the table as shown in Table1-6.

Index	Inductance_nH	InductanceCalculator.Spacing	InductanceCalculator.Coil_Length
1	163.784	0	0.126
2	147.735	2e-3	0.144
3	135.037	4e-3	0.162
4	124.701	6e-3	0.18
5	116.097	8e-3	0.198
6	108.806	0.01	0.216

Table 1-6 Coil inductance, spacing and coil length

The Table shows that the coil inductance with no spacing between the turns is 163.784 nH and it is 0.126 inches long. Contrast this to the 93.1 nH inductance with the same three inches of wire in a straight length. We can clearly see the dramatic impact of the magnetic flux linkage in increasing the inductance by forming the wire into a coil. The Figure also shows the strong influence of the inter-winding capacitance in influencing the inductance of the coil. Just 10 mils spacing between the turns reduces the coil's inductance from 163.784 nH to 108.806 nH. It is clearly important to consider the turn spacing when analyzing the inductor's performance. In practice this is an effective means to tune the inductor's value in circuit. When designing and building the inductor it is necessary to solve Equation (1-10) for the number of turns given a desired value of inductance. The procedure in MATLAB script follows.

1. Enter design parameters

D=.095; D1=.0126; Inductance_nH=163.784; Spacing = [0; .002; .004; .006; .008; .010]

2. Calculate the number of turns and coil length

$N = ((((D1 + Spacing)^{0.7}*Inductance\_nH)/(17*((D + D1)^{1.7})))^{0.7692}$

$Coil\_Length = (D1*N) + (Spacing.*(N-1))$

Note that there is one subtle difference namely the calculation of the coil length. In this case both variables, Spacing and N, are array variables. When multiplying array variables use a period in front of the multiplication sign to signify that this is an operation on arrays. This makes sure that the correct array index is maintained between the variables. In the previous equations this notation was not necessary because N was a constant.

Index	N	Number_of_Turns.Spacing	Number_of_Turns.Coil_Length
1	9.999	0	0.126
2	10.825	2e-3	0.156
3	11.599	4e-3	0.189
4	12.332	6e-3	0.223
5	13.029	8e-3	0.26
6	13.696	0.01	0.3

Table 1-7 Number of turns, coil spacing, and length

Modeling of the Air Core Inductor

Example 1-6: Calculate the input impedance of an air core inductor.

Solution: The air core inductor model is shown in Figure 1-16.

Figure 1-16 ADS model of the air core inductor

Note the required parameters: number of turns, wire diameter, core diameter, and the coil length. The coil spacing cannot be entered directly but is accounted for by the overall coil length for a given number of turns.

Set up a linear frequency sweep over a range of 0 to 1.3 GHz. Plot the impedance of the inductor across the frequency range as shown in Figure 1-17. Note the interesting spike, or increase in impedance that occurs around 1.170 GHz. This is the parallel, self resonant frequency, of the inductor.

Figure 1-17 Impedance of the air core inductor as a function of frequency

The inductor is not an ideal component or a pure inductance but rather a network that includes parasitic capacitance and resistance.

Example 1-7 Create an RLC network that gives an equivalent impedance response similar to Figure 1-17.

Solution: One such circuit is shown in Figure 1-18.

Figure 1-18 Equivalent network of the air core inductor

The simulated response is given in Figure 1-19.

Figure 1-19 Input impedance of equivalent air core inductor

Resonant circuits are covered in detail in chapter 4 but it is important to understand that each individual component such as the air core inductor has its own resonant frequency. The resonant frequency is the frequency at which the inductive reactance and capacitive reactance are equal and cancel one another. When this condition occurs in the inductor it is a parallel resonant circuit which results in a very high real impedance. If we plot the reactance along with the impedance a very interesting response is obtained. This response is shown in Figure 1-20.

Figure 1-20 Impedance and reactance of the equivalent air core inductor

The reactance, up to the resonant frequency, is positive but beyond resonance the reactance becomes negative. From basic circuit theory we know that a negative reactance is associated with a capacitor. Therefore above the Self Resonant Frequency, SRF, the inductor actually becomes a capacitor. In practice we want to make sure that our inductor really behaves like an inductor. A good design practice is to keep this self resonant frequency about four times higher than the frequency of operation. However using the inductor near its resonant frequency might make a good choke. A choke is a high reactance inductor often used to feed voltage to a circuit in which all RF energy is blocked from the DC side of the circuit. The inductor manufacturer will typically specify SRF of the inductor. It is important to remember that the inductor's SRF is the parallel resonant frequency; not the series resonant frequency.

Inductor Q Factor

Example 1-8: Calculate and plot the Q factor of the air core inductor shown in Figure 1-16.

Solution: The plot of the Q factor for the air core inductor is shown in Figure 1-21.

Figure 1-21 Air core inductor model Q factor versus frequency

It is interesting to note that the Q factor peaks at a frequency well below the self resonant frequency of the inductor. The actual frequency at which the Q factor peaks will vary among inductor designs but is usually ranges from 2 to 5 times less than the SRF. Close winding spacing results in inter-winding capacitance, which lowers the self-resonant frequency of the inductor. Thus there is a tradeoff between maximum Q factor and high self resonant frequency. It is also noteworthy that the Q factor goes to zero at the self resonant frequency. Figure 1-21 shows the Q factor monotonously increasing beyond the self resonant frequency. This is erroneous and is due to the fact that the model used to simulate the inductor's performance is invalid beyond the self resonance. The Air Core inductor model uses a simplified network similar to the one shown in Figure 1-18. Beyond self resonance the complexity and number of ideal elements need to increase in order to accurately model the inductor. A resistor needs to be added in series with the capacitor to begin to model the Q factor because the inductor is becoming a capacitor above self resonance. For most practical work however the native model will work fine because we should be using the inductor well below the self resonant frequency. A technique used by microwave engineers to increase the Q factor of an inductor is to silver plate the wire. This can be modeled by setting Rho = 0.95 in the inductor model.

Chip Inductors

The inductor core does not have to be air. Other materials may be used as the core of an inductor. Similar in size to the chip resistor there is a large assortment of chip inductors that are popular in surface mount designs. The chip inductor is a form of dielectric core inductor. There are a variety of modeling techniques used for chip inductors. One of the more popular modeling techniques is with the use of S parameter files. The subject of S parameters is covered in chapter 3. At this point consider the S parameter file as an external data file that contains an extremely accurate network model of the component. Most component manufacturers provide S parameter data files for their products. It is a good practice to always check the manufacturer's website for current S parameter data files. Coilcraft, Inc is one manufacturer of chip inductors. A typical chip inductor is built with extremely small wire formed on a ceramic form as shown in Figure 1-22.

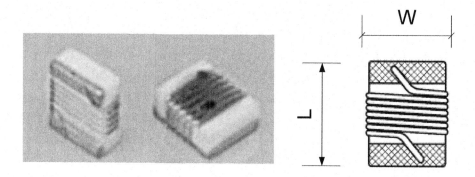

Figure 1-22 chip inductors (*courtesy of Coilcraft, Inc*)

Chip inductors are manufactured in many standard chip sizes as shown in Table 1-8.

Size	Length x Width
0201	20mils x 18mils
0302	34mils x 15mils
0402	44mils x 20mils
0603	69mils x 30mils
0805	90mils x 50mils
1008	105mils x 80mils
1206	140mils x 56mils
1812	195mils x 100mils

Table 1-8 Standard chip inductor size

The characteristic differences among the various sizes are more difficult to quantify than the chip resistors. A careful study of the data sheets is required for the proper selection of a chip inductor. In general the larger chip inductors will have higher inductance values. Often the smaller chip inductors will have higher Q factor. The impedance and self resonant frequency can vary significantly across the sizes as well as the current handling capability.

Chip Inductor Simulation in ADS

The ADS library has a collection of S parameter files for the Coilcraft chip inductors.

Example 1-9: Calculate and plot the inductance and Q factor of the Coil Craft 180 nH series 0603CS chip inductor from 1 MHz to 1040 MHz.

Solution: From the ADS schematic window select Modelithics MDLX_SELECT palette and insert Coil Craft CLC0603 component. Change the inductor value to L=180 nH as shown in Figure 1-23.

Figure 1-23 Coil Craft chip inductor and the circuit schematic

Simulate the schematic and display the inductance in a rectangular graph as shown in Figure 1-24. Place a marker at 150 MHz and at the self resonance frequency.

Figure 1-24 Plot of the 180 nH chip inductor inductance

From the markers we see that the simulation of the S parameter file measures 179.6 nH at 150 MHz and the SRF= 577 MHz. From Figure 1-25 we see that the manufacturer specifies a minimum Q of 45 at 100 MHz.

Figure 1-25 180 nH chip inductor Q factor versus frequency

The plot of the Q factor derived from the S parameter file shows that the maximum Q is 41.262 near 192 MHz. Manufacturers will often plot the Q vs frequency on a logarithmic scale. It is easy to change the x-axis to a logarithmic scale on the rectangular graph properties window in ADS. This allows us to have a visual comparison to the manufacturer's plot.

Magnetic Core Inductors

We have seen that the inductance of a length of wire can be increased by forming the wire into a coil. We can make an even greater increase in the inductance by replacing the air core with a magnetic material such as ferrite or powdered iron. Two popular types of magnetic core inductors are the rod core and toroidal core inductors shown in Figure 1-26.

Figure 1-26 Rod and toroidal magnetic core inductors

The magnetic field around an inductor is characterized by the magnetic force H, and the magnetic flux B. They are related by the level of the applied signal and the permeability, μ, of the core material. This relationship is given by Equation (1-11).

$$B = \mu\, H \qquad\qquad (1\text{-}11)$$

Where:

B = Flux density in Gauss

H = Magnetization intensity in Oersteds

μ = Permeability in Webers/Ampere-turn

This relationship is nonlinear in that as H increases, the amount of flux density will eventually level off or saturate. We will consider the linear region of this relationship throughout the discussion of this text. In an iron core inductor the permeability of the magnetic core is much higher than an air core and produces a high flux density. This magnetic flux density for each type of inductor is shown in Figure 1-27.

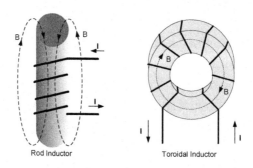

Rod Inductor   Toroidal Inductor

Figure 1-27 Magnetic flux densities for rod and toroidal inductors

The rod inductor has magnetic flux outside of the core as well as inside the core. Rod inductors that are used in tuned circuits generally require a metal shield around the inductor to contain this magnetic flux so that it does not interfere or couple to adjacent circuits and other inductors. The toroidal inductor flux remains primarily inside the core material. This suggests that the toroidal inductor experiences less loss and should have higher Q factor. This also gives the toroidal inductor a self shielding characteristic and does not require a metallic enclosure. Because of its self-shielding properties and high Q factor the toroidal inductor is one of the most popular of all magnetic core inductors. However one advantage of the rod inductor is that it is much easier to tune. The coil can be wound on a hollow plastic cylindrical form in which the magnetic rod can be placed inside. The rod is then free to move longitudinally which can tune the inductance value. Core materials are characterized by their permeability. Core permeability can vary quite a bit with frequency and temperature and can be confusing to specify for a given application. The stability of the permeability can change with the magnetic field due to DC current or RF drive through the inductor. As the frequency increases the permeability eventually reduces to the same value as air. Therefore iron core inductors are used only up to about 200

MHz. In general powdered iron can handle higher RF power without saturation and permanent damage. Ferrite cores have much higher permeability. The higher permeability of ferrite results in higher inductance values but lower Q factors. This characteristic can be advantageous in the design of RF chokes and broadband transformers. For inductors used in tuned circuits and filters, however, the higher Q factor of powdered iron is preferred. The powdered iron cores are manufactured in a variety of mixes to achieve different characteristics. The iron powders are made of hydrogen reduced iron and have greater permeability and lower Q factor. These cores are often used in RF chokes, electromagnetic interference (EMI) filters, and switched mode power supplies. Carbonyl iron tends to have better temperature stability and more constant permeability over a wide range of power. At the same time the Carbonyl iron maintains very good Q factor making them very popular in RF circuits. These characteristics lead to the popularity of toroidal inductors of Carbonyl iron for the manufacture of RF inductors. There is a wide variety of sizes and mixtures of Carbonyl iron that are used in the design of toroidal inductors, as shown in Table 1-9.

Core Designato r	OD, inches	ID, inches	Height, inches
T30	0.307	0.151	0.128
T37	0.375	0.205	0.128
T44	0.440	0.229	0.159
T50	0.500	0.303	0.190
T68	0.690	0.370	0.190
T80	0.795	0.495	0.250
T94	0.942	0.560	0.312
T106	1.060	0.570	0.437
T130	1.300	0.780	0.437
T157	1.570	0.950	0.570
T200	2.000	1.250	0.550
T300	3.040	1.930	0.500
T400	4.000	2.250	0.650

Table 1-9 Partial listing of popular toroidal cores with designators

The inductance per turn of a toroidal inductor is directly related to its permeability and the ratio of its cross section to flux path length as given by Equation (1-12) [4].

$$L = \frac{4 \pi N^2 \mu A}{length} \quad nH$$

(1-12)

Where:

L_{nH} = inductance

μ = permeability

A = cross sectional area

$length$ = flux path length

N = number of turns

As Equation (1-12) shows the inductance is proportional to the square of the turns. A standard specification used by toroid manufacturers for the calculation of inductance is the inductive index, A_L. The inductive index is typically given in units of nH/turn. The inductance can then be defined by Equation (1-13).

$$L = N^2 A_L \quad nH$$

(1-13)

Some manufacturers specify the A_L in terms of uH or mH. To convert among the three quantities use the following guideline.

$$\frac{1 \, nH}{turn} = \frac{10 \, uH}{100 \, turns} = \frac{1 \, mH}{1000 \, turns}$$

(1-14)

The various powdered iron mixes are optimized for good Q factor and temperature stability over certain frequency bands. A partial summary of some popular mixtures is shown in Table 1-10. Powdered Iron cores have a standard color code and material sub-type designator. The toroid is painted with the appropriate color so that the mixture can be identified. A given A_L is dependent on both the size of the toroid and the material mix.

Material Mix Designator	Material Permeability	Magnetic Material	Color Code	Frequency Range	Temperature Stability (ppm/°C)
-17	4.0	Carbonyl	Blue/Yellow	20 – 200 MHz	50
-10	6.0	Carbonyl W	Black	10 – 100 MHz	150
-6	8.5	Carbonyl SF	Yellow	2.0 – 30 MHz	35
-7	9.0	Carbonyl TH	White	1.0 – 20 MHz	30
-2	10.0	Carbonyl E	Red	0.25 – 10 MHz	95
-1	20.0	Carbonyl C	Blue	0.15 – 2.0 MHz	280
-3	35.0	Carbonyl HP	Grey	0.02 – 1.0 MHz	370

Table 1-10 Partial listing of powdered iron core mixes and suggested frequency range

Because of the complex properties of the core material, the determination of the Q factor of a toroidal inductor can be difficult. It is not simply the magnetic material properties alone, but also the wire winding loss as well that determines the overall Q factor. These losses can then vary greatly with frequency, flux density, and the toroid and wire size. The optimal Q factor occurs when the winding losses are equal to the core losses [4]. In general for a given inductance value and core mix a larger toroid will produce larger Q factors. Conversely for a given toroid size higher Q factor is achieved at higher frequency as the permeability decreases. The skin effect of the wire in the windings can have a significant impact on the achievable Q factor. Just as we have seen with the air core inductor, the inter-turn capacitance will also have a limiting effect on the resulting Q factor as well as the self resonant frequency. Manufacturers often provide a set of Q curves that the designer can use as a design guide for determining the toroidal inductor Q factor. Figure 1-28 shows a typical set of optimal Q curves for Carbonyl W core material at various toroid sizes.

Figure 1-28 Optimal Q factor versus toroid size (*courtesy Micrometals Inc.*)

Example 1-10: Design a 550 nH inductor using the Carbonyl W core of size T30. Determine the number of turns and model the inductor in ADS.

Solution: From the manufacturer's data sheet the A_L value is 2.5 for a T30-10 toroidal core. Rearranging Equation (1-13) to solve for the number of turns we find that 14.8 turns are required.

$$N = \sqrt{\frac{L}{A_L}} = \sqrt{\frac{550 \ nH}{2.5}} = 14.8$$

To reduce the winding loss we want to use the largest diameter of wire that will result in a single layer winding around the toroid. Equation (1-15) will give us the wire diameter.

$$d = \frac{\pi \ ID}{N + \pi} \qquad\qquad (1\text{-}15)$$

Where:

      d = Diameter of the wire in inches

      ID = Inner diameter of the core in inches (from Table 1-9)

      N = Number of turns

Therefore,

$$d = \frac{\pi\,(0.151)}{14.8 + \pi} = \frac{0.4744}{19.942} = 0.0238 \quad inches$$

From Appendix A, AWG#23 wire is the largest diameter wire that can be used to wind a single layer around the T30 toroid. Normally AWG#24 is chosen because this is a more readily available standard wire size. The toroidal inductor model in ADS requires a few more pieces of information. The ADS model requires that we enter the total winding resistance, core Q factor, and the frequency for the Q factor, F_q. As an approximation, set F_q to about six times the frequency of operation. In this case set F_q to (6)(25) MHz = 150 MHz. Then tune the value of Q to get the best curve fit to the manufacturer's Q curve. We know that we have 14.8 turns on the toroid but we need to calculate the length of wire that these turns represent. The approximate wire length around one turn of the toroid is calculated from the following equation.

$$Length = \left[(2)\,Height + (OD - ID)\right](\#turns) \qquad (1\text{-}16)$$

Using the dimensions for the T30 toroid from Table 1-10 we can calculate the total length of the wire as 6.10 inches.

$$\left[(2)(0.128) + (0.307 - 0.151)\right] \cdot 14.8 = 6.10 \quad inches$$

Then use the techniques covered in section 1.2.3 to calculate the resistance of the 6.10 inches of wire taking into account the skin effect. To get a better estimate of the actual inductor Q, use the F_q frequency rather than the operating frequency for the skin effect calculation. The resistance at 150 MHz for the AWG#24 wire is calculated as 0.30 Ω. Figure 1-29 shows the schematic of the toroidal inductor and the simulated Q.

Figure 1-29 Schematic of the toroidal inductor in ADS

The simulated Q factor is shown in Figure 1-30.

Figure 1-30 ADS toroidal inductor simulated Q factor

The Q parameter of the model has been tuned to give a reasonably good fit with the manufacturer's (T30) curve of Figure 1-28. Figure 1-31 shows that the simulated self resonant frequency of the inductor model is near 150 MHz.

Figure 1-31 Impedance of toroidal inductor model

Figure 1-32 shows the inductance that was calculated from the impedance. The inductance is exactly 550 nH at 10 MHz and begins to increase slightly to 563 nH at the design frequency of 25 MHz. Given the myriad of variables associated with the toroidal inductor, this simple model gives a good first order model of the actual inductor and will enable accurate simulation of filter or resonator circuits.

Figure 1-32 Inductance value of the toroidal inductor model

1.5 Analysis of Physical Capacitors

The capacitor is an electrical energy storage component. The amount of energy that can be stored is dependent on the type and thickness of the dielectric material and the area of the electrodes or plates. Capacitors take on many physical forms throughout electrical circuit designs. These range from leaded bypass capacitors in low frequency applications to monolithic forms in millimeter wave applications. Table 1-11 summarizes many of the applications in which capacitors are found. The table also shows some of the types of materials in which the capacitors are manufactured.

Application	Dielectric Type	Notes
Audio Frequency Coupling	Aluminum Electrolytic Tantalum Polyester/ Polycarbonate	Very High Capacitance High Capacitance for given size Medium capacitance, low cost
Power Supply Filtering	Aluminum Electrolytic	High Capacitance, high ripple current
RF Coupling	Ceramic NPO (COG) Ceramic X7R Polystyrene	Small, low loss, low cost Small, low cost, higher loss than COG Very low loss in RF range, larger than ceramic
Tuned Circuits, Resonators	Silver Mica Ceramic NPO (COG)	Low loss, low tolerance for RF applications Low loss, low tolerance, not as good as mica.

Table 1-11 Applications for various types of capacitors

As Table 1-11 shows, the ceramic capacitors dominate the higher RF and microwave frequency applications. Two of the most popular of the ceramic capacitors are the single layer and multilayer ceramic capacitors, as shown in Figure 1-33. These capacitors are available with metalized terminations so that they are compatible with a variety of surface mount assembly techniques from hand soldering to wire bonding and epoxy attachment.

Figure 1-33 Single layer and multi-layer chip capacitor dimension

Single Layer Capacitor

The single layer capacitor is one of the simplest and most versatile of the surface mount capacitors. It is formed with two plates that are separated by a single dielectric layer as shown in Figure 1-34. Most of the electric field (E) is contained within the dielectric however there is a fraction of the E field that exists outside of the plates. This is known as the fringing field.

Figure 1-34 Single layer parallel plate capacitor

The capacitance formed by a dielectric material between two parallel plate conductors is given by Equation 1-17 [1].

$$C = (N-1)\left(\frac{KA\varepsilon_r}{t}\right)(FF) \quad pF \tag{1-17}$$

Where,

A = plate area

ε_r = relative dielectric constant

t = separation

K = unit conversion factor; 0.885 for cm and 0.225 for inches

FF = fringing factor; 1.2 when mounted on microstrip

N = number of parallel plates.

The ceramic dielectrics used in capacitors are divided into two major classifications. Class 1 dielectrics have the most stable characteristics in terms of temperature stability. Class 2 dielectrics use higher dielectric constants which result in higher capacitance values but have greater variation over temperature. The temperature coefficient is specified in either percentage of nominal value or parts per million per degree Celsius (ppm/°C). Ceramic materials with a high dielectric constant tend to dominate RF applications with a few exceptions. NPO (negative-positive-zero) is a popular ceramic that has extremely good stability of the nominal capacitance versus temperature.

Dielectric Material	Dielectric Constant
Vacuum	1.0
Air	1.004
Mylar	3
Paper	4 - 6
Mica	4 - 8
Glass	3.7 - 19
Alumina	9.9
Ceramic (low ε_r)	10
Ceramic (high ε_r)	100 – 10,000

Table 1-12 Dielectric constants of materials

Example 1-11: Design a single layer capacitor from a dielectric that is 0.010 inches thick and has a dielectric constant of three. Each plate is cut to 0.040 inches square. Calculate the capacitor value and plot its Q factor from 1 to 10 GHz.

Solution: When the capacitor is mounted with at least one plate on a large printed circuit board track, a value of 1.2 is typically used in calculation of fringing factor.

$$C = (2-1)\left(\frac{(.225)(0.04 \cdot 0.04)(3)}{0.010}\right)(1.2) = 0.13 \, pF$$

The single layer capacitor can be modeled in ADS using the Thin Film Capacitor model as shown in Figure 1-35.

Figure 1-35: Thin Film Capacitor model in ADS

The Q factor plot of the capacitor is shown in Figure 1-36.

Figure 1-36: Capacitor Q factor

Multilayer Capacitors

Multilayer capacitors, shown in Figure 1-37, are very popular in surface mount designs. They are physically larger than single layer capacitors and can be attached by hand or by automatic pick-and-place machines. As Figure 1-35 shows, the multilayer chip capacitor is a parallel array of capacitor plates in a single package. Due to this type of construction the chip capacitor can handle higher voltages than the single layer capacitor. The insulation resistance of the capacitor is its ability to oppose the flow of electricity and is a function of the dielectric material and voltage. The insulation resistance is typically specified as a minimum resistance value in MΩ at a specified working voltage. The working voltage rating, WVDC, is the maximum DC voltage at which the capacitor can operate over the lifetime of the capacitor. The AC voltage rating is approximately one half of the WVDC value. The dielectric withstand voltage (DWV) is the electrical strength of the dielectric at 2.5 times the rated voltage. This is a maximum short term over-voltage rating and is usually specified as a length of time that the dielectric can withstand the 2.5 times the WVDC value without arcing through [6].

Figure 1-37 Multilayer chip capacitor construction

There is no physical model for the multilayer chip capacitor in ADS. The designer must rely on S parameter files or Modelithic models as we have used for the chip resistor in section on Chip Resistors. Two of the major manufacturers of multilayer chip capacitors are American Technical Ceramics, ATC, and Dielectric Laboratories Inc., DLI. These manufacturers provide S parameter files for their capacitors that are readily available on the company websites. They also provide helpful software applications that can aid the designer in making decisions for the proper selection of chip capacitors in specific applications.

Capacitor Q Factor

RF losses in the dielectric material of a capacitor are characterized by the dissipation factor. The dissipation factor is also referred to as the loss tangent and is the ratio of energy dissipated to the energy stored over a period of time. It is essentially the capacitor's efficiency rating. The dissipation factor and other ohmic losses lead to a parameter known as the Equivalent Series Resistance, ESR. The dissipation factor is the reciprocal of the Q factor. Just as we have seen with resistors and inductors, the physical model of a capacitor is a network of R, L, and C components.

Example 1-12: Calculate the Q factor versus frequency for the physical model of an 8.2 pF multilayer chip capacitor shown in Fig. 1-38.

Figure 1-38 Physical model of the 8.2 pF chip capacitor

Solution: The input impedance of the physical model versus frequency is shown in Figure 1-39.

Figure 1-39 Physical 8.2 pF chip capacitor impedance

As Figure 1-38 shows the capacitor model has 0.28 nH inductor in series with 0.145 Ohm resistor along with a parallel 38400 Ohms resistor. The parallel resistor sets the losses in the dielectric material and the series resistance and inductance represent any residual lead inductance and ohmic resistances. The values entered for the physical model and the Q factor can be obtained from the capacitor manufacturer.

The plot of Figure 1-39 shows the impedance of the capacitor versus frequency. Note that the impedance decreases as would be expected until the self resonant frequency is reached. Above the self resonant frequency the impedance begins to increase suggesting that the capacitor is behaving as an inductor. The self resonant frequency is due to the series inductance resonating with the capacitance. At resonance frequency the reactance cancels leaving only the resistances R1 and R2. The parallel resistance, R2, can be converted to an equivalent series resistance by Equation (1-18).

$$R2' = \frac{1}{1+Q^2} \ R2 \qquad (1\text{-}18)$$

These two series resistances can then be added to find the equivalent series resistance, ESR, as defined by Equation (1-19).

$$ESR = R1 + R2' \qquad (1\text{-}19)$$

The capacitor Q factor is then calculated by Equation (1-20) where X_T is the total series reactance of the inductive and capacitive reactance.

$$Q = \frac{X_T}{ESR} \qquad (1\text{-}20)$$

As Figure 1-39 shows, the 8.2 pF multilayer chip capacitor has a series resonant frequency of 3323 MHz. A marker is placed on the trace indicating the impedance at the SRF as 0.146 Ω. Because the reactance is cancelled at the SRF, this impedance essentially becomes the ESR of the capacitor.

The resistor R2 of Figure 1-38 is extremely frequency dependent. This means that the capacitor's Q factor is also extremely frequency dependent. An improved model for analyzing the capacitor's characteristics over a wide frequency range is to use the ADS model for capacitor with Q. Using this model the Q factor of the capacitor can be made proportional to the square root of the applied frequency. The inductance, capacitance, and Q factor can be calculated from the impedance using the following equations.

Reactance = im(Zin1)

Resistance = re(Zin1)

Inductance = abs((Reactance)/(freq*2*pi))

Qfactor = abs(Inductance/Resistance)

Capacitance = 1/(abs(Reactance)*freq*2*pi)

Example 1-13: Calculate the Q factor versus frequency for the modified physical model of an 8.2 pF multilayer chip capacitor shown in Figure 1-40.

Figure 1-40 Modified physical model of 8.2 pF chip capacitor

Solution: The capacitor Q factor of the modified model versus frequency is plotted in Figure 1-41.

Figure 1-41 Calculated Q factor of 8.2 pF chip capacitor

Figure 1-41 shows the large dependence of the capacitor Q on frequency. The Q factor goes to zero at the self resonant frequency. Above the self resonant frequency the Q factor is undefined.

Calculate the effective capacitance from the total reactance of the model using Equation (1-21).

$$C = \frac{1}{2 \pi F X_T}$$

(1-21)

The plot of Figure 1-40 reveals some interesting characteristics about the chip capacitor. From 100 MHz to 300 MHz the capacitance value is fairly constant. As the frequency increases we see that the capacitance actually increases. The parasitic inductive reactance of the capacitor package actually makes the effective capacitance greater than its nominal value.

Figure 1-42 Effective capacitance of the 8.2 pF chip capacitor

This is a property of the capacitor that is not always intuitive. As the frequency approaches the self resonant frequency (SRF) the capacitance rapidly approaches infinity. The capacitor actually becomes nearly a short circuit to RF at the self resonant frequency. This is an important property of the capacitor that is used frequently in RF and microwave design. In RF coupling or bypass capacitor applications, capacitors are very often used at or near their self resonant frequency. The capacitor's self resonant frequency is due to the series resonant circuit. In applications requiring bypassing over a wide range of frequencies it is often necessary to use several capacitors each selected to have a uniquely spaced self resonant frequency. In filter and other tuned circuit applications where we want the chip capacitor to appear as an 8.2 pF capacitor, we clearly must stay well below the self resonant frequency of the capacitor. A typical rule-of-thumb is to use the capacitor over a frequency range up to 35% of the self resonant frequency. Therefore the 8.2 pF chip capacitor with a self resonant frequency of 3321 MHz would be used as a capacitor in tuned circuits up to a frequency of about 1006 MHz. Figure 1-42 shows that at frequencies above 1006 MHz the capacitance is extremely nonlinear. However the capacitor could be used as a DC blocking, RF coupling capacitor that would efficiently pass microwave energy near its SRF of 3300 MHz.

References and Further Readings

[1]   Besser Associate's _Applied RF Techniques Course_, 480 San Antonio Road, Mountain View, CA. 94040

[2]   Paul Lorrain, Dale P. Corson, and Francois Lorrain, _Electromagnetic Fields and Waves_, W.H. Freeman and Company, New York, 1988

[3]   _Design Guide, Microwave Components_ Inc., P.O. Box 4132, South Chelmsford, MA 01824

[4]   _Iron Powder Cores for High Q Inductors_, Micrometals, Inc.

[5]   Keysight Technologies, Manuals for Advanced Design System, *ADS 2015.07 Documentation Set*, EEsof EDA Division, Santa Rosa, California www.keysight.com

[6]   *Capacitors for RF Applications,* Dielectric Laboratories, Inc.,2777 Rt.20 East, Cazenovia, NY. 13035

[7]   R. Ludwig and P. Bretchko, *RF Circuit Design -Theory and Applications*, Prentice Hall, New Jersey, 2000

[8]   William Sinnema and Robert McPherson, *Electronic Communication,* Prentice Hall Canada, 1991

[9]   M.F. "Doug" DeMaw, *Ferromagnetic Core Design & Application Handbook*, MFJ Publishing Co., Inc. Starkville, MS. 39759, 1996

[10]   *The RF Capacitor Handbook,* American Technical Ceramics, One Norden Lane, Huntington, New York 11746

[11]   Ali A. Behagi and Stephen D. Turner, *Microwave and RF Engineering,* A Simulation Approach with Keysight Genesys Software, BT Microwave LLC, State College, PA , March 2015

Problems

1-1.   Calculate the wavelength of an electromagnetic wave operating at a frequency of 428MHz.

1-2.   Calculate the inductance of a 5 inch length of AWG #30 straight copper wire.

1-3.   Calculate the reactance of the wire from Problem 2 at 10 Hz, 10 MHz, and 10 GHz. Create a Linear analysis in ADS and display the wire impedance vs. frequency.

1-4.   Calculate the resistance of a 12 inch length of AWG #24 copper wire at DC and at 25MHz

1-5.   Find the skin depth and the resistance of a 2 meter length of copper coaxial line at 2 GHz. The inner conductor radius is 1 mm and the outer conductor is 4 mm.

1-6.   Calculate the inductance of a 5 inch length of copper flat ribbon conductor. The dimensions of the ribbon are 0.100 inches in width and 0.002 inches thick.

1-7.   Model a chip resistor (size 0603) with a resistance of 50Ω in ADS. Consider an application in which 50Ω impedance must be maintained with +10%. Create a linear analysis and determine the maximum usable frequency of the chip resistor.

1-8.   Design an air core inductor with an inductance value of 84 nH. Use a copper wire of 0.050 inch diameter wound on a core diameter or 0.100 inch. Determine the number of turns required assuming a tight spaced winding.

1-9.   Using the inductor from Problem 1-8 and the techniques developed in Section 1.4.1 examine the change in the coil inductance as the turn spacing is increased from zero to 0.10 inch in 0.002 inch increments.

1-10.   Using the inductor from Problem 8, determine the self resonant frequency of the inductor and comment on the maximum frequency in which the inductor may be used in a tuned circuit application.

1-11.   Using the inductor from Problem 1-8, determine the maximum Q factor of the inductor and the frequency at which the maximum Q factor is obtained.

1-12.   In ADS, select a chip inductor from the CoilCraft library with an inductance value of 80nH. Determine the maximum Q factor of the inductor and comment on the maximum usable frequency of the inductor in a filter application.

1-13. Design a 1 mH toroidal inductor on a Carbonyl W core size T30. Determine the maximum wire size that could be used to realize a single layer winding.

1-14. Using the inductor from Problem 1-13, model the inductor in ADS and determine the approximate self resonant frequency. Comment on the maximum usable frequency of the inductor in the front end of a radio receiver.

1-15. A 0.05pF capacitor is required to couple a transistor to the resonator of a microwave oscillator. Design a single layer capacitor using a 0.020 inch thick dielectric with e_r=2.2. Determine the dimensions of the capacitor assuming square footprint is desired.

1-16. For the single layer capacitor of Problem 15, determine the dimensions of the capacitor with a dielectric constant e_r=10.2.

1-17. In ADS, model a 47pF chip capacitor using the ATC 0603 model from the Modelithics library. Determine the Q factor of the capacitor at a frequency of 1000MHz.

1-18. Determine the self resonant frequency of the capacitor in Problem 17 and comment on the maximum frequency that this capacitor could be used in a tuned circuit. At what frequency does the capacitor have the lowest amount of energy loss?

Chapter 2

Transmission Lines

2.1 Introduction

Transmission lines play an important role in designing RF and microwave networks. In chapter 1 we have seen that, at high frequencies where the wavelength of the signal is smaller than the dimension of the components, even a small piece of wire acts as an inductor and affects the performance of the network. In this chapter we present the lumped-element equivalent model of a transmission line and analytically define several important transmission line parameters such as transmission and reflection coefficients, characteristic impedance, propagation constant, attenuation constant, phase constant, voltage standing wave ratio, return loss, velocity factor and group delay. It is demonstrated how to simulate and measure these parameters using the ADS software. Popular types of transmission lines, such as: coaxial lines, microstrip lines, strip lines, and waveguides are discussed. Several methods of characterizing reflection coefficients and the characteristic impedance of these transmission lines are examined. Field coupling between adjacent (coupled) transmission lines is introduced. The chapter concludes with the design of a microstrip directional coupler.

2.2 Analysis of Plane Waves

Plane waves are the simplest form of electromagnetic waves in which the electric field intensity, E, is perpendicular to magnetic field intensity, H, and both are perpendicular to the direction of propagation (E and H are represented by vectors). Such a wave is also called transverse electromagnetic or TEM wave.

Plane Waves in a Lossless Medium

In rectangular coordinates, assuming that electric field E is a vector in the x direction and varies as it moves along the z direction, the Wave Equation for the electric field in a lossless medium can be written as [1]:

$$\frac{\partial^2 E_x}{\partial z^2} + k^2 E_x = 0 \tag{2-1}$$

Where,

$k = \omega\sqrt{\mu\varepsilon}$ is the wave number

ω is the angular frequency in radians per second

μ is permeability of the medium in Henries per meter

ε is permittivity of the medium in Farads per meter

In a lossless medium μ and ε are positive real numbers, therefore k is also positive and real. The solution to Equation (2-1) is of the following form.

$$E_x(z) = E^+ e^{-jkz} + E^- e^{+jkz} \tag{2-2}$$

Where E^+ and E^- are arbitrary constants determined by the boundary conditions. For the sinusoidal waveforms at frequency ω, Equation (2-2) can be written as:

$$\mathcal{E}_x(z,t) = E^+ \cos(\omega t - kz) + E^- \cos(\omega t + kz) \tag{2-3}$$

Where:

$E^+ \cos(\omega t - k z)$ *is the wave traveling in the forward direction*

$E^- \cos(\omega t + k z)$ *is the wave traveling in the reverse direction*

Some of the wave characteristics are as follows:

1. Phase velocity is the velocity of a fixed point on the wave that is obtained by setting the derivative of the phase, with respect to t, equal to zero:

$$\omega - k\frac{\partial z}{\partial t} = 0$$

$$v_p = \frac{\partial z}{\partial t} = \frac{\omega}{k} = \frac{1}{\sqrt{\mu \varepsilon}} \tag{2-4}$$

In free space: $\mu = \mu_0 = 4\pi(10^{-7})$ H/m and $\varepsilon = \varepsilon_0 = 8.854(10^{-12})$ F/m, therefore,

$$v_p = \frac{1}{\sqrt{\mu_o \varepsilon_o}} = 2.998\,(10^8) = c \qquad meters/second$$

Where c is the velocity of light in free space.

2. The wavelength, λ, is defined as the distance between two successive Maximum or minimum, points on the wave at a fixed instant of time. Therefore $k\,\lambda = 2\pi$ which leads to Equation (2-5).

$$\lambda = \frac{2\,\pi}{k} = \frac{v_p}{f} \tag{2-5}$$

3. The plane wave impedance, η, is defined as the ratio between electro-magnetic field components travelling in the same direction. Therefore, if:

$$E_x^+ = E^+ \cos(\omega\,t - k\,z)$$

$$H_y^+ = H^+ \cos(\omega\,t - k\,z)$$

Then,

$$\eta = \frac{E_x^+}{H_y^+} = \frac{E^+}{H^+} \tag{2-6}$$

Here E^+ and H^+ represent the electric and magnetic field amplitude travelling in the positive z direction in units of Volt/meter and Ampere/meter. Based on Maxwell's curl equations the plane wave impedance is given by:

$$\eta = \sqrt{\frac{\mu}{\varepsilon}} \qquad (2\text{-}7)$$

In free space the plane wave impedance is,

$$\eta_0 = \sqrt{\frac{\mu_0}{\varepsilon_0}} = 377 \ \Omega$$

Plane Waves in a Good Conductor

Metallic conductors used in microwave networks are not perfect but they are considered to be very good conductors. In a material with conductivity σ the current density due to conduction is given by:

$$J = \sigma E \qquad (2\text{-}8)$$

Where σ is the conductivity of the conductor in S/m.

In a good conductor the conductive current is much greater than the displacement current, therefore, by ignoring the displacement current, the propagation constant can be written as [1]:

$$\gamma = \alpha + j\beta = \sqrt{\frac{\omega\mu\sigma}{2}} + j\sqrt{\frac{\omega\mu\sigma}{2}} \qquad (2\text{-}9)$$

The skin depth for a good conductor is defined as the inverse of the attenuation constant:

$$\delta = \frac{1}{\alpha} = \frac{1}{\sqrt{\pi f \mu \sigma}} \qquad (2\text{-}10)$$

Where:

δ is the skin depth in meters
f is the frequency in Hertz

μ is the permeability in H/m

σ is the conductivity in S/m

In a good conductor the positive traveling wave is of the form:

$$e^{-\alpha z}\cos(\omega t - \beta z) \qquad (2\text{-}11)$$

Notice that when the wave travels a distance equal to the skin depth, $\delta = \frac{1}{\alpha}$, the signal amplitude drops to $e^{-1}\cos(\omega t - \beta z) = 0.368\cos(\omega t - \beta z)$ which is 36.8% of the original signal's amplitude at z = 0.

2.3 Lumped Element Representation of Transmission Lines

A lumped model of a small section of parallel wire transmission line, of physical length dz, is shown in Figure 2-1. Any transmission line of a given length can be considered a cascade of many sections of the length dz.

Figure 2-1 Lumped model representation of transmission line section

In Figure 2-1, R is the per unit length series resistance of both lines in Ω/m, L is the per unit length series inductance of both lines in Henries/meter, G is the per unit length shunt conductance of the line in Siemens/meter, and C is the per unit length capacitance of the line in Farads/meter. At higher frequencies, where the wavelength of the signal is smaller than the physical dimension of the network, the voltages and currents along a uniform transmission line are functions of position and time. For a TEM wave traveling in the z direction, the voltage and current are given by:

$$V(z,t) = re\left[V(z)e^{j\omega t}\right] \tag{2-12}$$

$$I(z,t) = re\left[I(z)e^{j\omega t}\right] \tag{2-13}$$

The quantities $V(z)$ and $I(z)$ are complex functions of z along the transmission line and ω is the frequency of the source in radians per second.

2.4 Transmission Line Equations and Parameters

For sinusoidal steady-state excitations, Kirchhoff's voltage and current laws along the line yield the following equations:

$$\frac{dV(z)}{dz} + (R + j\omega L)\, I(z) = 0 \tag{2-14}$$

$$\frac{dI(z)}{dz} + (G + j\omega C)\, V(z) = 0 \tag{2-15}$$

By taking the derivative of both sides of Equation (2-14) with respect to z, and substituting for $\frac{dI(z)}{dz}$ from Equation (2-15), we have:

$$\frac{d^2V(z)}{dz^2} - (R + j\omega L)(G + j\omega C)\, V(z) = 0 \tag{2-16}$$

Similarly, by taking the derivative of both sides of Equation (2-15) with respect to z, and substituting for $\frac{dV(z)}{dz}$ from Equation (2-14), we have:

$$\frac{d^2I(z)}{dz^2} - (R + j\omega L)(G + j\omega C)\ I(z) = 0 \tag{2-17}$$

By defining the complex propagation constant:

$$\gamma = \sqrt{(R + j\omega L)\ (G + j\omega C)} \tag{2-18}$$

Equations (2-16) and (2-17) can be redefined as:

$$\frac{d^2V(z)}{dz^2} - \gamma^2 V(z) = 0 \tag{2-19}$$

$$\frac{d^2I(z)}{dz^2} - \gamma^2 I(z) = 0 \tag{2-20}$$

Equations (2-19) and (2-20) are known as voltage and current wave equations respectively. It is easy to show that the solution to Equation (2-19) is of the form:

$$V(z) = Ae^{-\gamma z} + Be^{\gamma z} \tag{2-21}$$

Where:

A and B are constants

$Ae^{-\gamma z}$ is the incident voltage traveling in the +z direction

$Be^{\gamma z}$ is the reflected voltage traveling in the -z direction

Similarly it can be shown that the solution to Equation (2-20) is of the form:

$$I(z) = \frac{\gamma}{(R + j\omega L)}\left[Ae^{-\gamma z} - Be^{\gamma z}\right] \tag{2-22}$$

Where:

$$\frac{\gamma}{R + j\omega L} \, Ae^{-\gamma z} \qquad \text{Incident current traveling in the } +z \text{ direction}$$

$$\frac{\gamma}{R + j\omega L} \, Be^{\gamma z} \qquad \text{Reflected current traveling in the } -z \text{ direction}$$

Definition of Attenuation and Phase Constant

The complex propagation constant defined in Equation (2-18), is written as:

$$\gamma = \alpha + j\beta \qquad\qquad (2\text{-}23)$$

Where the real part α is defined as the attenuation constant in Nepers per meter (1 Neper = 8.686 dB) and the imaginary part β is defined as the phase constant in radians per meter.

Definition of Transmission Line Characteristic Impedance

The characteristic impedance of a transmission line, Z_0, is defined as the ratio of the incident voltage to incident current. Therefore by dividing the incident voltage by the incident current, in Equations (2-21) and (2-22), and replacing γ from Equation (2-18), the transmission line characteristic impedance is written as:

$$Z_o = \frac{(R + j\omega L)}{\gamma} = \sqrt{\frac{R + j\omega L}{G + j\omega C}} \qquad\qquad (2\text{-}24)$$

Definition of Transmission Line Reflection Coefficient

It is important to understand the concepts of incident (forward) and reflected (backward) wave propagation in transmission lines. In high power RF systems there can be potentially dangerous high voltage peaks that can occur at points along the transmission line when the incident and reflected waves are in phase and add together. The voltage reflection coefficient, $\Gamma(z)$, of a transmission line along the z axis is defined as the ratio of reflected to incident voltage as shown in Equation (2-25).

$$\Gamma(z) = \frac{Be^{\gamma z}}{Ae^{-\gamma z}} = \frac{B}{A}e^{2\gamma z} = \Gamma_o e^{2\gamma z} \tag{2-25}$$

Where Γ_o is the load reflection coefficient at z = 0, namely:

$$\Gamma_o = \Gamma(0) = \frac{B}{A} \tag{2-26}$$

Notice that when there is no reflection the load reflection coefficient $\Gamma_o = 0$.

Definition of Voltage Standing Wave Ratio, VSWR

VSWR is the ratio of the maximum to minimum value of the standing wave. The VSWR is a very common quantity for describing the percentage of power reflected by a given load impedance. The forward and reflected waves travel in opposite directions to form a standing wave pattern. The maximum value of the standing wave is given by Equation (2-27) while the minimum value is given by Equation (2-28).

$$|V(z)|_{max} = |A|\left(1+|\Gamma_o|\right) \tag{2-27}$$

$$|V(z)|_{min} = |A|\left(1-|\Gamma_o|\right) \tag{2-28}$$

The ratio of the maximum to minimum voltage is related to the reflection coefficient as shown in Equation (2-29).

$$VSWR = \frac{|V(z)|_{max}}{|V(z)|_{min}} = \frac{1+|\Gamma_o|}{1-|\Gamma_o|} \tag{2-29}$$

Solving the equation for the magnitude of the reflection coefficient, Γ_o results in Equation (2-30).

$$|\Gamma_o| = \frac{VSWR-1}{VSWR+1} \tag{2-30}$$

Notice that when the reflection coefficient is zero, VSWR = 1. This VSWR is commonly presented as 1:1 ratio.

Definition of Return Loss

When the transmission line is mismatched to the load, a portion of the incident power is reflected back to the source. This can be considered a loss of power absorbed by the load. Therefore the return loss is defined as:

$$RL\ (dB) = -20\log|\Gamma| \tag{2-31}$$

For a matched line $|\Gamma| = 0$ and RL = ∞ dB whereas for $|\Gamma| = 1$, RL = 0 dB.

Lossless Transmission Line Parameters

From Figure 2-1 we can see that a transmission line is considered lossless when R = G = 0. For a lossless transmission line the propagation constant reduces to:

$$\gamma = j\beta = j\omega\sqrt{LC} \tag{2-32}$$

Therefore,

$$\beta = \omega\sqrt{LC} \tag{2-33}$$

And,

$$\alpha = 0 \tag{2-34}$$

The characteristic impedance of a lossless transmission line i.e. R = G = 0 is obtained from Equation (2-24) as:

$$Z_o = \sqrt{\frac{L}{C}} \tag{2-35}$$

Similarly the voltage reflection coefficient in Equation (2-25) reduces to:

$$\Gamma = \Gamma_o e^{2j\beta z} \tag{2-36}$$

Where: $\Gamma_0 = B/A$, the load reflection coefficient.

Notice from Equations (2-32) through Equation (2-34) for lossless transmission lines the attenuation constant is zero and the phase constant is linearly proportional to frequency. The propagation constant is purely imaginary, and the characteristic impedance is a positive real number.

Lossless Transmission Line Terminations

When a lossless transmission line of length d and characteristic impedance Z_0 is terminated in an arbitrary load Z_L, the input impedance of the line is given by [1]:

$$Z_{in} = Z_o \frac{Z_L + j Z_o \tan \beta d}{Z_o + j Z_L \tan \beta d} \tag{2-37}$$

Where β is the phase constant of the line.

In the following sections we discuss the input impedance of terminated transmission lines.

1. Transmission Line Terminated in Z_0

When a lossless transmission line of characteristic impedance Z_0 is terminated in a load equal to Z_0, Equation (2-37) shows that the input impedance becomes equal to Z_0. Such a line behaves like an infinitely long transmission line with no reflection. In this case all of the incident power is absorbed by the load.

2. Transmission Line Terminated in a Short Circuit

When a lossless transmission line of characteristic impedance Z_0 is terminated in a short circuit, $Z_L = 0$, Equation (2-37) shows that the input impedance becomes a purely imaginary number equal to:

$$Z_{in} = jZ_o \tan \beta d \qquad (2\text{-}38)$$

Depending on the length of the line the input impedance takes any possible reactive value from minus to plus infinity.

3. Transmission Line Terminated in an Open Circuit

When a lossless transmission line of characteristic impedance Z_0 is terminated in an open circuit, $Z_L = \infty$, Equation (2-37) shows that the input impedance becomes equal to:

$$Z_{in} = -jZ_o \cot \beta d \qquad (2\text{-}39)$$

In this case Z_{in} is also purely imaginary. Depending on the length of the line the input impedance takes any possible reactive value from minus to plus infinity.

4. Half Wavelength Transmission Lines

For a lossless transmission line of characteristic impedance Z_0 with the length $d = \lambda/2$, the input impedance from Equation (2-37) becomes equal to:

$$Z_{in} = Z_L \qquad (2\text{-}40)$$

This means that the input impedance of a transmission line of one half wavelength is equal to the load impedance regardless of the line characteristic impedance.

5. Quarter Wavelength Transmission Lines

For a lossless transmission line with the length $d = \lambda/4$, the input impedance from Equation (2-37) becomes equal to:

$$Z_{in} = \frac{Z_o^2}{Z_L} \qquad (2\text{-}41)$$

In this case the transmission line transforms the load impedance to a different impedance as defined by Equation (2-41). Such a line is called a quarter-wave transformer. Equation (2-41) can be rewritten to solve for the characteristic impedance of a quarter-wave matching section as:

$$Z_o = \sqrt{Z_{in}\,Z_L} \qquad (2\text{-}42)$$

Simulation of Reflection Coefficient and VSWR

The ADS software has built-in functions to directly display the common measurements of VSWR, return loss, and reflection coefficient. The following example explores the simulation of series RLC circuit and measurement of VSWR, input reflection coefficient in dB, and S(1,1).

Example 2-1: For the series RLC elements in Figure 2-2 simulate the schematic and measure the reflection coefficients and VSWR from 100 to 1000 MHz in 100 MHz steps.

Solution: The procedure for the analysis of Example 2-1 in ADS is as follows. Similar procedure will be used throughout the book.

- Start ADS and create a new workspace
- Name the workspace Ex2-1_wrk
- From the Main window create a new schematic in cell_1
- In the schematic window, click Insert and select S_Params Template
- Delete the DisplyTemplate icon
- Type in SRLC in the part selection box and place the series RLC component between the input and output Terminations
- Set R=55 Ω, L=15 nH, and C=20 pF
- Type in VSWR in the part selection box and place it on the schematic to measure the voltage standing wave ratio as a function of frequency.
- Set the frequency range from 100 to 1000 MHz in 100 MHz step and wire up the schematic as shown in Figure 2-2

Figure 2-2 Schematic of the series RLC resonator

Simulate the schematic and display VSWR1 at the input port, the reflection coefficient S(1,1) in dB, and S(1,1) in Mag/Degrees formats, as shown in Table 2-1.

freq	VSWR1	dB(S(1,1))	S(1,1)
100.0 MHz	3.514	-5.084	0.557 / -52.176
200.0 MHz	1.503	-13.933	0.201 / -65.292
300.0 MHz	1.106	-25.945	0.050 / 18.321
400.0 MHz	1.420	-15.207	0.174 / 64.690
500.0 MHz	1.811	-10.796	0.289 / 64.345
600.0 MHz	2.245	-8.321	0.384 / 61.007
700.0 MHz	2.727	-6.682	0.463 / 57.292
800.0 MHz	3.260	-5.506	0.531 / 53.694
900.0 MHz	3.849	-4.620	0.588 / 50.344
1.000 GHz	4.494	-3.931	0.636 / 47.270

Table 2-1 Tabular output of VSWR, and reflection coefficient

Return Loss, VSWR, and Reflection Coefficient Conversion

Return Loss, VSWR, and Reflection Coefficient are all different ways of characterizing the wave reflection. These definitions are often used interchangeably in practice. Therefore it is important to be able to convert from one form of reflection to another. Return Loss is often used to characterize components such as filters, amplifiers, and networks. VSWR is normally used in systems such as radio and TV transmitters. Reflection coefficient is normally used in device characterization such as transistors, capacitors, inductors, etc. Equations (2-29), (2-30), and (2-31) give the conversions among these three parameters. Note, however, that the reflection coefficient is a vector quantity whose magnitude is all that is required to determine the VSWR or return loss. Therefore when calculating Γ from the VSWR or return loss we can only find the magnitude and not the angle of the reflection coefficient. Another useful parameter is the mismatch loss. The mismatch loss is a measure of power that is reflected from the load.

$$Mismatch \ \ Loss \ \ (dB) = -10\log\left(1 - \left|\Gamma\right|^2\right) \qquad (2\text{-}43)$$

Example 2-2: For the one port series RLC resonator in Figure 2-3, generate a table showing the input VSWR, the mismatch, the power loss, and the reflection coefficient from 100 MHz to 1 GHz in 100 MHz steps.

Solution: The schematic of the series RLC resonator is shown in Figure 2-3.

Figure 2-3 Schematic of the series RLC resonator

When the circuit is simulated write the following equations in the display window.

ReflCoef = (VSWR1 - 1)/(VSWR1 + 1)

Mismatch = 1 – (ReflCoef)*(ReflCoef)

PwrLoss = (1 – Mismatch)*100

Simulate the schematic and display the input VSWR, the Mismatch, the power loss, and the input reflection coefficient in a Table.

Eqn ReflCoef=(VSWR1 -1)/(VSWR1+1)

Eqn Mismatch=1-(ReflCoef)*(ReflCoef)   Eqn PwrLoss=(1-Mismatch)*100

freq	VSWR1	Mismatch	PwrLoss	ReflCoef
100.0 MHz	3.201	0.725	27.452	0.524
200.0 MHz	2.206	0.858	14.158	0.376
300.0 MHz	2.101	0.874	12.602	0.355
400.0 MHz	2.177	0.863	13.729	0.371
500.0 MHz	2.333	0.840	15.997	0.400
600.0 MHz	2.539	0.811	18.915	0.435
700.0 MHz	2.785	0.778	22.242	0.472
800.0 MHz	3.066	0.742	25.818	0.508
900.0 MHz	3.380	0.705	29.526	0.543
1.000 GHz	3.726	0.667	33.272	0.577

Table 2-2 VSWR, Mismatch, Power Loss and Reflection Coefficient

As you can see the mismatch power loss as a percentage of the available power that is reflected from the load.

2.5 Analysis of Physical Transmission Media

There are many physical transmission lines that are encountered in RF and microwave circuits and systems. In addition it should not be overlooked that free space is also a transmission medium. Therefore Equation (2-35) could be used to describe the characteristic impedance, Z_o, of free space. In order to define L and C we need to consider the inductive and capacitive properties of free space. Permeability is the ability of a transmission media to support a magnetic field. Considered as a density in free space the permeability is related to inductance and defined by Equation (2-44).

$$\mu_o = 4\pi \cdot 10^{-7} \quad Henries/meter \qquad (2-44)$$

Permittivity is the ability of a transmission media to support an electric field. Considered as a density in free space the permittivity is closely related to capacitance in equation (2-45.

$$\varepsilon_o = \frac{1}{36\pi} \cdot 10^{-9} \quad Farads/meter \qquad (2\text{-}45)$$

Therefore we can rewrite equation (2-35) as:

$$Z_o = \sqrt{\frac{\mu_o}{\varepsilon_o}} = \sqrt{\frac{4\pi \cdot 10^{-7}}{\frac{1}{36\pi} \cdot 10^{-9}}} = 377 \ \Omega \qquad (2\text{-}46)$$

Equation (2-46) shows that the characteristic impedance is related to the inductance and capacitance of the transmission media. The velocity of propagation is also related to inductance and capacitance. It can be shown that the time required for a sine wave to propagate through a unit length of lossless transmission line is related by Equation (2-47) [5].

$$t = \sqrt{LC} \qquad (2\text{-}47)$$

The velocity of propagation is related to the wavelength in one period T, by:

$$v = \frac{\lambda}{T} = \frac{1}{t} = \frac{1}{\sqrt{LC}} \qquad (2\text{-}48)$$

Where: T is the time period of the sine wave.

Using the free space permeability and permittivity the velocity of propagation through free space is:

$$v_o = \sqrt{\mu_o \varepsilon_o} = 2.998 \cdot 10^8 \quad meters/second \qquad (2\text{-}49)$$

From Equations (2-46) and (2-49) we can see that the characteristic impedance and velocity of propagation can be defined for any transmission media based on the inductive and capacitive properties of that media.

Physical Transmission Lines

Free space can be used for the propagation of radio signals across long distances but may not be as useful for the point to point connection and isolation of specific RF signals. For this purpose engineers use a variety of different transmission line media. This text is focused on a few of the most commonly used transmission media in RF and microwave circuit and system design including, microstrip, stripline, coaxial, and waveguide transmission lines. As a general differentiator, transmission media may be divided among pure TEM, quasi TEM, and non TEM propagation modes. TEM refers to the transverse electromagnetic mode of wave propagation. Signals traveling through space propagate in the TEM mode. This simply means that the magnetic field, electric field, and the direction of propagation are all orthogonal to one another. This orthogonal relationship is depicted in Figure 2-4.

Figure 2-4 TEM wave propagation

The velocity with which a wave travels will almost always be slower in a physical transmission line than it is in free space. Engineers frequently need to trim a transmission line for a specific wavelength so it is essential that they know the velocity of propagation in the transmission line. Knowing the distributed inductive and capacitive properties of the media, Equation (2-48) could be used to determine the propagation velocity. However it is common for many transmission line manufacturers to specify a velocity factor. The velocity factor is a ratio of the actual transmission line velocity v, to the velocity of free space.

$$v_f = \frac{v}{v_o}$$

(2-50)

Similar to the velocity factor, manufacturers of transmission line media typically express the permittivity of the dielectric material as a relative dielectric constant. The relative dielectric constant, ε_r, is the ratio of the actual material dielectric constant to the dielectric constant of free space.

$$\varepsilon_r = \frac{\varepsilon}{\varepsilon_o}$$

(2-51)

Depending on the type of transmission media the manufacturer may choose to specify either the velocity factor, v_f, or the relative dielectric constant ε_r. The two quantities are related by Equation (2-52).

$$v_f = \frac{1}{\sqrt{\varepsilon_r}}$$

(2-52)

There are many types of physical transmission lines ranging from twisted wire pairs to fiber optic cables. There are many good reference sources to examine the characteristics and application of transmission lines [4]. In this chapter we will focus on just a few of these transmission lines that the RF and microwave engineer will frequently encounter. They include:

- Coaxial Transmission Lines
- Microstrip Transmission Lines

- Stripline Transmission Lines

- Waveguides

Note that coaxial, microstrip, and stripline transmission lines require two conductors to transfer power from a given source to its load while waveguides require only a single hollow conductor. A brief introduction to each of the above transmission media is followed by the techniques in which these transmission lines are modeled in the ADS software.

2.6 Coaxial Transmission Line

Coaxial transmission line, also known as coaxial cable, is one of the most common transmission lines used in electrical equipment interconnection. A typical coaxial line consists of an inner conductor inside another cylindrical conductor and a dielectric material in between, as shown in Figure 2-5. The outer conductor, or the shield, is usually grounded to minimize RF interference and radiation loss. The coaxial transmission line supports pure TEM propagation as shown in Figure 2-5. The dielectric material is typically a form of Teflon. Teflon has very good physical strength as well as low loss and high temperature operation. For very high power and low loss applications the dielectric material may be air. In this case there must be some dielectric spacer installed at certain intervals to support the center conductor and maintain concentricity. It is also common to introduce nitrogen into the air dielectric to help prevent condensation from forming inside the cable. Condensation would greatly increase the loss and lower the voltage breakdown. Coaxial cables that are used in very high power applications generally require a larger diameter to increase the voltage breakdown.

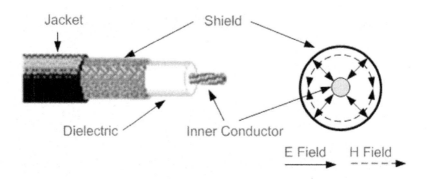

Figure 2-5 Coaxial cable construction and field orientation

Earlier in this chapter we dealt with reflective losses in transmission lines. This is mostly due to the impedance mismatch between the source and load impedance connected to each end of the coaxial cable. There also exists a dissipative loss in a coaxial cable that varies significantly with frequency. When a good impedance match exists between the source and the load it is only the cable loss that is significant. The losses in coaxial cable are primarily due to the conductor loss and the dielectric material loss. Because of its smaller cross sectional area the center conductor dominates the conductor loss contribution. The center conductor's diameter and resistivity determine the conductor loss. Skin effects which cause the RF currents to propagate near the surface of the conductor require that the center conductor have very good conductivity. Sometimes a copper conductor may have a silver plating to improve the surface conductivity. The characteristics of the dielectric material and its thickness determine the losses in the dielectric. Table 2-3 gives a brief listing of some commonly used flexible coaxial cables. Manufacturers typically specify the cable loss in dB per 100 foot lengths at various frequencies. This table gives the manufacturer's (Belden) part number along with an RG designation. The RG designation is an attempt by the U.S. government under MIL-C-17 specification to have a standard designation for the manufacture of coaxial cables [5]. The R means that the cable is intended for RF frequency usage. The G means that the cable is manufactured to general specifications. The number then identifies the unique specifications that the cable is designed to meet. Minor differences in the specification have a letter appended to the numerical designator. The characteristic impedance and velocity factor are also specified. It is not uncommon to have the cable's capacitance, per unit length, specified as well. Two physical characteristics included in Table 2-3 are the outer dimension (O.D.) and the shield percentage. The shield percentage is only applicable in flexible cables in which the outer conductor is actually a braid of several discrete wires that form a tight mesh. A 100% rating means that there are no air gaps in the wires that comprise the braid and therefore a perfect outer conductor is formed.

Coaxial Cable	Loss in dB/100ft. @ frequency in MHz					Z_o	V_f	Capac. per ft.	O.D. inch	Shield
	100 MHz	200 MHz	400 MHz	700 MHz	900 MHz					
Belden 9913	1.30	1.80	2.70	3.60	4.20	50	.84	24.6 pF	0.405	100%
Belden 9914	1.60	2.40	3.50	5.00	5.70	50	.82	24.8 pF	0.403	100%
Belden 8214 RG-8/U	1.80	2.70	4.20	5.80	6.70	50	.78	26.0 pF	0.405	97%
Belden 8238 RG-11/U	2.00	2.90	4.20	5.80	6.70	75	.66	20.5 pF	0.405	97%
Belden 8267 RG-213/U	1.90	2.70	4.10	6.50	7.60	50	.66	30.8 pF	0.405	97%
Belden 8242 RG-9/U	2.10	3.00	4.80	6.50	7.60	51	.66	30.0 pF	0.420	98%
Belden 9258 RG-8/X	3.70	5.40	8.00	11.10	12.80	50	.80	25.3 pF	0.242	95%
Belden 84142 RG-142	3.90	5.60	8.20	11.00	12.50	50	.695	29.2 pF	0.195	98%
Belden 9273 RG-223/U	4.10	6.00	8.80	12.00	13.80	50	.66	30.8 pF	0.212	95%
Belden 8240 RG-58/U	4.50	6.80	10.00	14.00	16.00	51.5	.66	29.9 pF	0.195	95%
Belden 8259 RG-58A/U	4.90	7.30	11.50	17.00	20.00	50	.66	30.8 pF	0.193	95%
Belden 9259 RG-59/U	3.00	4.50	6.60	8.90	10.1	75	.78	17.3 pF	0.242	95%
Belden 8241 RG-59/U	3.40	4.90	7.00	9.70	11.1	75	.66	20.5 pF	0.242	95%
Belden 8216 RG-174/U	8.40	12.50	19.00	27.00	31.00	50	.66	30.8 pF	0.101	90%
Belden 9228 RG-62A/U	2.70	3.80	5.30	7.30	8.20	93	.84	13.5 pF	0.242	95%

Table 2-3 Sample table of coaxial cable specifications

Parameters such as the characteristic impedance can be determined from the basic geometrical design of the coaxial cables. The characteristic impedance of a coaxial line is determined by the diameter of the inner conductor, d, and the outer conductor, b, along with the relative dielectric constant, as given by Equation (2-53).

$$Z_o = \frac{60}{\sqrt{\varepsilon_r}} \cdot \ln\left(\frac{b}{d}\right)$$

(2-53)

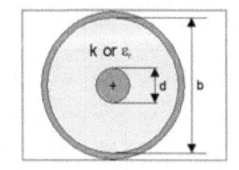

Figure 2-6 coaxial cable geometry

Coaxial Transmission Lines in ADS

There are two coaxial cable models In ADS known as COAX and COAX_MDS. Starting with ADS2005A, the COAX component is not available in the library or palette, but can be accessed from the Component History field. It is recommended to use COAX_MDS instead of COAX.

The symbol and illustration of the coaxial transmission line, COAX_MDS is shown in Figure 2-7.

Illustration

Figure 2-7 Symbol and illustration of COAX_MDS in ADS

2.7 Microstrip Transmission Lines

Microstrip is a planar transmission line media in which the transmission line is etched onto the top side of a printed circuit board. The bottom side of the printed circuit board is completely metalized and grounded. The printed circuit board has a low loss dielectric material that is suitable for microwave transmission. Figure 2-8 shows a sampling of microstrip lines that represent specific circuits. The top side of the dielectric substrate is shown with the copper conductor, microstrip transmission lines.

Figure 2-8 Examples of microstrip transmission lines on various dielectrics

Unlike the coaxial cable the center conductor is not shielded. This means that a portion of the electric and magnetic field is in the air space above the microstrip line as shown in Figure 2-9. Thus the propagation in microstrip is not purely TEM but rather quasi TEM. This also leads to the fact that the dielectric constant beneath the microstrip line is slightly less than the relative dielectric constant of the material. This is known as the effective dielectric constant, ε_{eff}, and is a function of the width of the microstrip line, W and the height of the substrate, h as shown in Figure 2-9. The thickness of the microstrip conductor, t, has a minor effect on ε_{eff} and is omitted from the computation. The effective dielectric constant is calculated in the empirical Equations (2-54) and (2-55) [6].

Figure 2-9 Microstrip cross section and electromagnetic field lines

For $\left(\dfrac{W}{h}\right) < 1$

$$\varepsilon_{eff} = \frac{\varepsilon_r + 1}{2} + \frac{\varepsilon_r - 1}{2} \cdot \left[\left(1 + 12 \left(\frac{h}{W} \right) \right)^{-0.5} + 0.04 \left(1 - \left(\frac{W}{h} \right) \right)^2 \right] \quad (2\text{-}54)$$

For $\left(\dfrac{W}{h}\right) \geq 1$

$$\varepsilon_{eff} = \frac{\varepsilon_r + 1}{2} + \frac{\varepsilon_r - 1}{2} \cdot \left(1 + 12 \left(\frac{h}{W} \right) \right)^{-0.5} \quad (2\text{-}55)$$

Similarly the characteristic impedance also has two solutions based on the ratio of the line width to substrate height [6].

For $\left(\dfrac{W}{h}\right) < 1$

$$Z_o = \frac{60}{\sqrt{\varepsilon_{eff}}} \; \ln\left(8 \cdot \frac{h}{W} + 0.25 \cdot \frac{W}{h}\right) \tag{2-56}$$

For $\left(\dfrac{W}{h}\right) \geq 1$

$$Z_o = \frac{120\pi}{\sqrt{\varepsilon_{eff}} \cdot \left[\dfrac{W}{h} + 1.393 + 0.6667 \; \ln\left(\dfrac{W}{h} + 1.444\right)\right]} \tag{2-57}$$

Equations (2-56) and (2-57) do not consider the conductor thickness of the line. The effective width, W_e, of a microstrip line is the equivalent width of the line with the conductor thickness taken into account. The effective line width is defined by Equations (2-58) and (2-59).

For $\left(\dfrac{W}{h}\right) \geq \dfrac{1}{2\pi}$

$$W_e = W + \frac{t}{\pi}\left(1 + \ln\frac{2h}{t}\right) \tag{2-58}$$

For $\left(\dfrac{W}{h}\right) < \dfrac{1}{2\pi}$

$$W_e = W + \frac{t}{\pi}\left(1 + \ln\left(\frac{4\pi \cdot W}{t}\right)\right) \tag{2-59}$$

Microstrip Transmission Lines in ADS

The symbol and illustration of the microstrip transmission line in ADS is shown in Figure 2-10.

Figure 2-10 Symbol and illustration of microstrip line in ADS

The width of a microstrip line for a given impedance and substrate can be calculated from above equations. The physical line width for a desired impedance is also dependent on the dielectric constant and substrate thickness. Given the line impedance there are two additional parameters that can affect the line width calculation. These are the conductor thickness, *t*, and the cover or box height. When using a thicker conductor for higher current handling it is recommended to model the actual conductor thickness, *t*, as it will have a slight impact on the line width. If the cover height becomes too close to the microstrip line it will add enough capacitance to lower the impedance of the line.

Before adding any microstrip transmission lines to an ADS workspace schematic, a dielectric substrate must be defined. The substrate's dielectric constant and height are the most important parameters to enter into the parameters window. The default settings can be accepted for the remaining parameters for most circuits. The dielectric loss tangent and conductor resistivity will dominate the microstrip losses of resonators, filters or other critical low loss circuits. A virtual catalog of microwave dielectrics is built into the ADS software. A comprehensive collection of the major manufacturers' soft substrate material is contained in the library. Substrates can be divided into hard substrate and soft substrate types. Hard substrates are very stiff and brittle and must be cut with diamond, tipped saws or lasers. Soft substrates are very pliable and can be cut with a razor knife or scissors. All of the circuit designs and components discussed in this book are based on soft substrates. Hard substrates arc normally used in semiconductor design i.e., transistors, and MMICs. Alumina is a hard substrate that is often used in microwave integrated circuit (MIC) designs. Because the top half of the microstrip is exposed it is very easy to attach discrete components. This has made microstrip the most popular form of transmission line for designing and building microwave components. There are many variants of the basic microstrip transmission line including suspended line, inverted line, and coplanar waveguide [8].

2.8 Stripline Transmission Lines

Stripline is a transmission line using planar dielectric material similar to microstrip. The major difference is that the top half of the line also consists of a dielectric of the same material as the bottom conductor. Therefore the transmission line is shielded in much the same way as the coaxial transmission line. As such the stripline transmission line supports a pure TEM propagation mode. Because of the presence of the top dielectric it is much more difficult to integrate discrete components such as transistors, and chip inductors and capacitors. Stripline does offer superior performance in distributed filters, directional couplers, and power combiners.

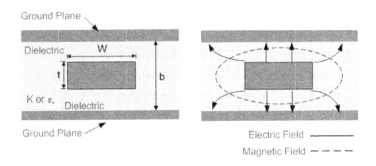

Figure 2-11 Cross section view of stripline transmission line and field lines

Because the propagation mode is pure TEM, there is no effective dielectric constant, just the relative dielectric constant of the substrate material. Soft substrates are almost entirely used for stripline transmission circuits. One popular variation is when an air dielectric is used. This is referred to as suspended substrate stripline (SSS) and is characterized by very low loss. Suspended substrate stripline is often used in filter and multiplexer circuit designs. The characteristic impedance of a stripline transmission line is given by the empirical Equation (2-60) [7].

$$ Z_o = \frac{94.2}{\sqrt{\varepsilon_r}} \ \ln \left[\frac{1 + \frac{W}{b}}{\frac{W}{b} + \frac{t}{b}} \right] \qquad (2\text{-}60) $$

In practice a 0.060 stripline media is realized by clamping or fusing two 0.030 dielectric halves together. The circuit pattern is etched on one of the 0.030 dielectrics similar to a microstrip circuit pattern. The top half dielectric would then have all metal removed on the side which meets the bottom half circuit patterns. A special bonding film can be used to effectively glue the halves together.

2.9 Waveguide Transmission Lines

A waveguide is a special form of transmission line that is used primarily at microwave frequencies above 2 GHz. The most important difference between waveguide and other forms of transmission line is the low loss and capability to transmit very high power. Waveguides do not have a separate conductor, ground plane, or shield as the previous transmission line structures. Rather waveguide is a hollow tube in which the wave propagates through. Even though the propagation is in the air space, enclosing an RF wave in a metallic boundary causes the wave to propagate quite differently than it would in free space. Waveguide tubes can be circular or rectangular but the rectangular tube is much more popular due to its ease of manufacture. Figure 2-12 shows a typical rectangular waveguide section with flanges on each end. The flanges allow a connection to be made to a mating piece of waveguide or waveguide component. The broad dimension of the waveguide is labeled as the 'a' dimension while the narrow side is labeled the 'b' dimension. The TEM propagation mode does not exist in waveguide. The propagation must be either transverse electric (TE) or transverse magnetic (TM). The propagation modes are quite complex with many subcategories of TE and TM propagation in existence.

Figure 2-12 Rectangular waveguide section showing inside dimensions

In TE mode the electric field is transverse to the direction of propagation. This means that there is no component of the electric field in the direction of propagation. In the TM mode there is no magnetic field component in the direction of propagation. Depending on how the RF energy is launched into the waveguide there are many variations of both TE and TM propagation modes. These sub-modes are designated with the subscripts m and n ($TE_{m,n}$). The sub-mode notation describes the field patterns that exist in the waveguide. The dominant sub-mode is the $TE_{1,0}$ mode. This is the lowest frequency that the waveguide will support. Figure 2-13 shows the field pattern for the $TE_{1,0}$ mode in a rectangular waveguide. The 1,0 index signifies that there is one field variation along the broad dimension and no field variations along the narrow dimension. The remaining discussion of rectangular waveguide properties is based on the $TE_{1,0}$ mode.

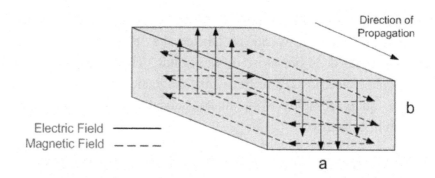

Figure 2-13 $TE_{1,0}$ dominant mode field pattern in rectangular waveguide

The wave pattern in a waveguide leads to an interesting condition where at or below a certain frequency the wave bounces from side-to-side or top-to-bottom in the waveguide tube and no longer travels in the direction of propagation. This frequency is known as the cutoff frequency. Below the cutoff frequency the waveguide transmits very little energy. As such the waveguide has a natural high pass filter characteristic. The cutoff frequency of the $TE_{1,0}$ in rectangular waveguide is given by Equation (2-61),

$$f_{c_{1,0}} = \frac{c}{2a} = \frac{3 \cdot 10^8}{2a} \tag{2-61}$$

Where: c is the speed of light and a is the wider dimension of the waveguide. The wavelength in a rectangular waveguide it then defined as.

$$\lambda_g = \frac{\lambda}{\sqrt{\left(1 - \left(\frac{\lambda}{(2a)^2}\right)\right)}} \tag{2-62}$$

The characteristic impedance of waveguide is based on the propagation mode. The characteristic impedance must be defined separately for the transverse electric and magnetic fields as given by equations (2-63) and (2-64).

$$Z_{o\,(TE_{m,n})} = \frac{\eta}{\sqrt{1 - \left(\dfrac{f_c}{f}\right)^2}} \tag{2-63}$$

$$Z_{o\,(TM_{m,n})} = \eta \sqrt{1 - \left(\frac{f_c}{f}\right)^2} \tag{2-64}$$

Waveguide is characterized by its cross section dimensions as shown in Table 2-4. The cross sectional dimension of commonly used rectangular waveguide is given a WR designator.

Frequency Band, GHz	U.S. (EIA) Designator	British WG Designator	Cut Off Freq. in GHz $TE_{1,0}$	a dimension inches	b dimension inches
1.12 - 1.70	WR 650	WG 6	0.908	6.500	3.250
1.45 - 2.20	WR 510	WG 7	1.158	5.100	2.550
1.70 - 2.60	WR 430	WG 8	1.375	4.300	2.150
2.20 - 3.30	WR 340	WG 9A	1.737	3.400	1.700
2.60 - 3.95	WR 284	WG 10	2.080	2.840	1.340
3.30 - 4.90	WR 229	WG 11A	2.579	2.290	1.145
3.95 - 5.85	WR 187	WG 12	3.155	1.872	0.872
4.90 - 7.05	WR 159	WG 13	3.714	1.590	0.795
5.85 - 8.20	WR 137	WG 14	4.285	1.372	0.622
7.05 - 10.00	WR 112	WG 15	5.260	1.122	0.497
8.2 - 12.4	WR 90	WG 16	6.560	0.900	0.400
9.84 - 15.0	WR 75	WG 17	7.873	0.750	0.375
11.9 - 18.0	WR 62	WG 18	9.490	0.622	0.311
14.5 - 22.0	WR 51	WG 19	11.578	0.510	0.255
17.6 - 26.7	WR 42	WG 20	14.080	0.420	0.170
21.7 - 33.0	WR 34	WG 21	17.368	0.340	0.170
26.4 - 40.0	WR 28	WG 22	21.100	0.280	0.140
32.9 - 50.1	WR 22	WG 23	26.350	0.224	0.112
39.2 - 59.6	WR 19	WG 24	31.410	0.188	0.094
49.8 - 75.8	WR 15	WG 25	39.900	0.148	0.074
60.5 - 91.9	WR 12	WG 26	48.400	0.122	0.061
73.8 - 112.0	WR 10	WG 27	59.050	0.100	0.050

Table 2-4 Standard rectangular waveguide characteristics

To interface waveguide with coaxial, microstrip, or stripline transmission lines a special transformer, known as an adapter, must be used. Waveguide to coax adapters come in many forms. Some adapters couple energy to the *E* field while others couple to the *H* field. The adapter shown in Fig. 2-14 is an *E* field waveguide to coax transition. The center conductor of the coaxial connector extends into the waveguide to excite the wave propagation in the waveguide. The center conductor is approximately $\lambda_g/4$ from the back wall.

Figure 2-14 Waveguide to coax transition adapter

Waveguide Transmission Lines in ADS

Because of the complex EM fields that can propagate in waveguide, modern computer aided design techniques are best handled by three dimensional EM solvers. ADS is limited in its ability to model waveguide propagation and waveguide components but does have two models that are useful to the engineer. The first model is a straight section of waveguide in which the $TE_{1,0}$ mode is utilized. The second model is a waveguide to TEM transition which is similar to the adapter of Figure 2-15. The input and output ports used in ADS can be thought of as coaxial ports supporting TEM propagation. Therefore we cannot attach a section of waveguide directly to a port because an impedance mismatch will exist.

Example 2-3 Consider the model of a one inch and a three inch length of the waveguide as used in the X Band satellite transmit system. Display the insertion loss of the waveguides from 4 to 8 GHz.

Solution: Make the length of the waveguide tunable. From Table 2-4 we can get the width (a) and height (b) dimensions to enter into the waveguide model. Set the source and load resistors equal to 377 Ω (simulating the waveguide to TEM adapter) representing the impedance of free space. Sweep the insertion loss (S21) from 4 GHz to 8 GHz as shown in Figure 2-16 and 2-17. Note that the use of the waveguide models does require a substrate definition. In this case however the waveguide models only use the dielectric constant Er, and Rho, the resistivity of the metal walls. Typically enter values of one for both the air dielectric and the resistivity normalized to copper. Figure 2-15 shows the schematic of the waveguide. The insertion loss of the waveguide in its pass band at 8 GHz is extremely low. This is one of the advantages of using waveguide transmission lines as they are practically the lowest loss microwave transmission line available. Also note that the insertion loss increases as we move below the cutoff frequency. A marker is placed at the -3 dB point of the insertion loss. Increase the length of the waveguide to 3 inches and note the dramatic increase in the rejection below the cutoff frequency. The insertion loss in band is still quite low. We can see that using the waveguide below the cutoff frequency is an effective method of achieving a very good microwave high pass filter.

Figure 2-15 One inch length of RWG waveguide

Figure 2-16 Insertion loss of one inch length of RWG waveguide

Figure 2-17 Insertion loss of three inch length of RWG waveguide

2.10 Group Delay in Transmission Lines

A frequently encountered concept related to the transmission line velocity factor is group delay. Group delay is a measure of the time that it takes a signal to traverse a transmission line, or its transit time. It is a strong function of the length of the line, and usually a weak function of frequency. It is expressed in units of time, picoseconds for short distances or nanoseconds for longer distances. Remember that in free space all electromagnetic signals travel at the speed of light, *c*, which is approximately 300,000 kilometers per second. Therefore, in free space, electromagnetic radiation travels one foot in one nanosecond, unless there is something to slow it down such as a dielectric. Mathematically the group delay is the derivative of phase versus frequency. In communication systems, the ripple in the group delay creates a form of distortion.

2.11 Transmission Line Components

There are many useful components that can be realized using transmission lines. These include power splitters, directional couplers, voltage and current insertion networks, as well as various filter networks. These networks can be realized with any of the physical transmission line structures. However, because of its popularity, we will explore many of these components in microstrip transmission line. These components are referred to as distributed components. It can be shown that the series inductance and shunt capacitance can be realized with distributed microstrip transmission lines. We will begin this section with an examination of the open and short-circuited microstrip transmission lines.

Short-Circuited Transmission Line

Equation (2-38) demonstrated that the input impedance of a lossless short-circuited transmission line is a pure imaginary function; therefore, the input reactance is given by the following equation.

$$X_{in} = Z_O \tan \theta \qquad (2-65)$$

Where $\theta = \beta d$ is the electrical length of the transmission line in degrees

From Equation (2-65) we can see that this reactance can change from inductive to capacitive depending on the length of the transmission line.

Example 2-4: In ADS measure the input impedance of a loss less quarter-wave short-circuited transmission line at 1500 MHz.

Solution: To measure the input impedance of a lossless quarter line short-circuited transmission line in ADS, create a schematic with a grounded transmission line. Make the electrical length of the transmission line 90 degrees. Setup a new S parameter simulation with a single frequency at 1500 MHz. Wire up the schematic as shown in Figure 2-18.

Figure 2-18 Short-circuited quarter-wave transmission line

Then simulate the schematic and display the input impedance in a table as shown in Fig. 2-19.

freq	Zin1	Zin1
1.500 GHz	-50.000 + j8.166E17	8.166E17 / 90.000

Figure 2-19 Short-circuited line reactance versus electrical length

From the input impedance data of Figure 2-19 we can see that at one quarter wavelength, $\lambda_g/4$, the short-circuited line looks like an open circuited line.

Modeling Short-Circuited Microstrip Lines

The short-circuited microstrip line can be modeled as a microstrip transmission line connected to a grounded via hole. A via hole is made by drilling a hole in the dielectric and metalizing the inside of the hole to form a conductive path to the ground side of the dielectric. To create a 90 degree line in the microstrip substrate we must know the effective dielectric constant so that the wavelength in the dielectric, λ_g, can be calculated. The relationships between line length and electrical degrees are as follows.

$$\theta = \frac{2\pi\ell}{\lambda_g} \tag{2-66}$$

$$\ell = \frac{\theta\lambda_g}{360\sqrt{\varepsilon_{eff}}} \tag{2-67}$$

Example 2-5: Calculate the input impedance of a quarter wave short-circuited microstrip transmission line at 1500 MHz.

Solution: In ADS simply place the microstrip transmission line on a schematic and enter the desired impedance, electrical length, and frequency. Figure 2-20 shows the correct method of modeling a microstrip short-circuited transmission line with a VIA hole.

Figure 2-20 Quarter wave short circuited line schematic

freq	Zin1	Zin1
1.500 GHz	768.602 - j3.067E3	3.161E3 / -75.930

Figure 2-21 Quarter wave short-circuited line impedance in two formats

As the numbers in Figure 2-21 show, the impedance of a quarter-wave section of short-circuited microstrip line is quite high, close to an open circuit. This type of line section could be used as a parallel resonant circuit.

Open-Circuited Transmission Line

Example 2-6: Calculate the input impedance of a quarter-wave open-circuited ideal transmission line at 1500 MHz.

Solution: The input impedance of a lossless quarter-wave open circuited transmission line is a pure imaginary function; therefore, the input reactance is given by the following equation.

$$X_{in} = Z_O \cot\theta = -jZ_O \cot(\beta d) \qquad (2\text{-}68)$$

Where: θ is the electrical length of the transmission line in degrees.

Simulate the circuit in Figure 2-22 to observe the behavior of the input impedance at 1500 MHz. Note that the transmission line is terminated with a $10^6\,\Omega$ load to emulate an open circuit termination on the transmission line.

Figure 2-22 Quarter wave 0pen circuited transmission line schematic

Notice that the small real part is due to losses in the large termination resistor.

freq	Zin1	Zin1
1.500 GHz	0.003 - j3.062E-15	0.003 / -7.017E-11

Figure 2-23 Reactance of open circuit line versus electrical length

Modeling Open-Circuited Microstrip Lines

Care must be used when modeling the open circuit microstrip line due to the radiation effects from the end of the transmission line. The E fields that exist in the air space of the microstrip line add capacitance to the microstrip transmission line. On an open circuit microstrip line this fringing capacitance is referred to as an end effect. The end effect makes the line electrically longer than the physical length. This requires that the physical line length be shortened to achieve the desired reactance. The 'microstrip end' model accurately accounts for this end effect capacitance for the specified substrate. The end effect fringing field is visualized in Figure 2-24.

Figure 2-24 Fringing E fields in microstrip open circuit and gaps

Example 2-7: Calculate the input impedance of a quarter-wave open-circuited microstrip transmission line using termination with end effects.

Solution: Figure 2-25 shows the correct method of modeling a microstrip open circuit transmission line using an end effect. As Figure 2-26 shows, the impedance of a quarter-wave section of open circuit line is quite low, close to a short circuit. This type of line section could be used as a series resonant circuit.

Figure 2-25 Quarter wave open circuited line schematic

freq	Zin1	Zin1
1.500 GHz	0.045 + j0.835	0.837 / 86.935

Figure 2-26 Quarter wave open circuited line impedance

Distributed Inductive and Capacitive Elements

Thus far we have dealt with only 50 Ω transmission lines. It is possible to synthesize series inductance by using short lengths of transmission lines that have considerably higher impedance than 50 Ω. It is possible to synthesize shunt capacitors by using short lengths of transmission lines that have considerably lower impedance than 50 Ω. Typical impedances would range from approximately 20 Ω for capacitive elements and 80 Ω for inductive elements. The actual impedance used is a compromise between the substrate height and dielectric constant and the ability to physically realize the distributed element. For example an 80 Ω line on a thin substrate or a high dielectric constant substrate may be too narrow to etch on a printed circuit board. In such a case it may be necessary to use a 70 Ω impedance to realize the inductive element. These elements are successfully used in narrow bandwidth applications. These distributed elements are useful in the design of filters, bias feed, and impedance matching networks.

Distributed Microstrip Inductors and Capacitors

For short lengths of high impedance transmission line use the following equations to calculate the length of microstrip line [2].

$$Inductive \ \ Line \ \ Length = \frac{f \, \lambda_g \, L}{Z_L} \qquad (2\text{-}69)$$

$$Capacitive \ \ Line \ \ Length = f \, \lambda_g \, Z_C \, C \qquad (2\text{-}70)$$

Where:

f = frequency and which inductance is calculated

L= nominal inductance value

C=nominal capacitance value

Z_L= impedance of inductive transmission line

λ_g =wavelength using the effective dielectric constant

Example 2-8: Convert the capacitors and inductors to districted elements.

Solution: Use Equations (2-69) and (2-70) to convert the lumped element capacitor and inductor in Figure 2-27 to low, (20 Ohm),and high, (80 Ohm), impedance microstrip equivalent circuits in Figure 2-28. The PCB layout shows the line width relationship among the microstrip lines. The microstrip Step elements are added between high and low impedance lines.

Figure 2-27 Lumped element circuit

The capacitor has been converted to low impedance (large width) and the inductor has been converted to high impedance (narrow width) microstrip lines.

Figure 2-28 Distributed capacitive and inductive lines

The PCB layout is shown in Figure 2-29.

Figure 2-29 Capacitive and inductive lines in PCB layout

Step Discontinuities

Examine the printed circuit board (PCB) layout of the transmission lines in Figure 2-29. Note the change in geometry as the impedance transitions from 50 Ω to 20 Ω and then to 80 Ω.

These changes in geometry are known as discontinuities. Discontinuities in geometry result in fringing capacitance and parasitic inductance that will modify the frequency response of the circuit. At RF and lower microwave frequencies (up to about 2 GHz) the effects of discontinuities are minimal and sometimes neglected [4]. As the operation frequency increases, the effects of discontinuities can significantly alter the performance of a microstrip circuit. ADS has several model elements that help to account for the effects of discontinuities. These include: T-junctions, cross junctions, open circuit end effects, coupling gaps, bends, and slits. A Microstrip Step element (STP) can be placed between series lines of abruptly changing geometry to account for the step discontinuity. The ADS schematic of Figure 2-28 shows the proper placement of a microstrip step element between the low impedance and high impedance lines.

Microstrip Bias Feed Networks

Another useful purpose for high impedance and low impedance microstrip transmission lines is the design of bias feed networks. Often it is necessary to insert voltage and current to a device that is attached to a microstrip line. Such a device could be a transistor, MMIC amplifier, or diode. The basic bias feed or "bias decoupling network" consists of an inductor (used as an "RF Choke") and shunt capacitor (bypass capacitor). At lower RF frequencies (< 200 MHz) these networks are almost entirely realized with lumped element components. Even at these low frequencies it is very important to account for the parasitics in the components.

Example 2-9: Design a lumped element bias feed network and display the frequency response.

Solution: Fig. 2-30 shows a typical design of the series inductor, shunt capacitor, lumped element bias feed network.

Figure 2-30 Inductor and bypass capacitor bias insertion network

The frequency response of the bias feed network is shown in Figure 2-31.

Figure 2-31 Response of the bias feed network

Design of the Distributed Bias Feed Network

A high impedance microstrip line of $\lambda_g/4$ can be used to replace the lumped element inductor. Similarly a $\lambda_g/4$ of low impedance line can be used to model the shunt capacitor.

Example 2-10: Calculate the physical length of the $\lambda_g/4$ sections of 80 Ω and 20 Ω microstrip lines at a frequency of 2 GHz. Create a schematic of a distributed bias feed network and display its response.

Solution: Use the 80 Ω high impedance quarter wave section and a shunt capacitance as shown in Figure 2-32. A microstrip taper, TP1, is used to connect the low impedance line to the high impedance line. Note the use of the microstrip tee junction, TE2. The tee junction accurately models the electrical length of the junction and includes all parasitic effects of the discontinuity. An end-effect element is used on the open circuit line. The response of the bias feed is characterized by the null in the return loss and very low insertion loss near the design frequency of 2 GHz. The return loss null occurs at 1.85 GHz suggesting that the high impedance line length should be decreased to center the design on 2 GHz.

Figure 2-32 Bias feed modeled with distributed transmission line elements

Figure 2-33 Bias feed response

A modified version of the open circuited transmission line is the radial stub. The radial stub can be used in applications where an open circuit transmission line is needed. Fig. 2-34 shows the use of the radial stub replacing the open circuit transmission line in the bias feed. Comparing the responses we can see that the network using the radial stub achieves a slightly wider bandwidth. This is one of the advantages of using the radial stub. The radial stub may also result in a slightly smaller PCB pattern.

Figure 2-34 Bias feed with open circuited line replaced with the radial stub

2.12 Coupled Transmission Lines

There are three primary methods in which coupled lines are used in microwave circuit design as shown in Figure 2-35.. These are end-coupled, edge-coupled, and broadside coupled line structures. End coupled lines are often used to realize microstrip resonators and filters. Edge coupled lines are used in both coupler and filter designs. Broadside coupled lines are popular with various coupler designs.

| End Coupled | Edge Coupled | Broadside Coupled |

Figure 2-35 Types of coupled line structures

Current flow in the edge-coupled and broadside coupled sections can be difficult to quantify. Because of the coupling between the lines there exist two modes of impedance required to characterize the circuit. These are known as the even mode, Z_{oe}, and odd mode, Z_{oo}, impedance. Figure 2-36 shows the field distribution on the edge coupled lines for both conduction modes. In the even mode, a common displacement current flows from the conductors as shown by the E fields of the same polarity. In the odd mode, a component of the electric field is at opposite direction with respect to the two conductors. Therefore, the magnitude of the even and odd mode impedance is strongly dependent on the separation between the lines which also determine the electrical coupling between the lines. The coupling between the lines, in dB, is defined by Equation (2-71).

$$C = 20 \, \log \left| \frac{Z_{oe} - Z_{oo}}{Z_{oe} + Z_{oo}} \right| \qquad (2\text{-}71)$$

The even and odd mode impedances are then defined by the following equations [2].

$$Z_{oo} = Z_o \sqrt{\frac{1 - 10^{\left(\frac{-C}{20}\right)}}{1 + 10^{\left(\frac{-C}{20}\right)}}} \qquad (2\text{-}72)$$

$$Z_{oe} = Z_o \sqrt{\frac{1 + 10^{\left(\frac{-C}{20}\right)}}{1 - 10^{\left(\frac{-C}{20}\right)}}} \qquad (2\text{-}73)$$

$$Z = \sqrt{Z_{oo} \, Z_{oe}} \qquad (2\text{-}74)$$

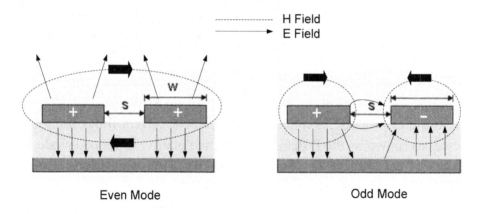

Figure 2-36 Edge coupled microstrip line field distribution

The ADS TLINE utility has the capability to perform the calculations for coupled line impedance. The even and odd mode impedance can be calculated for a given characteristic impedance, Z_o, and coupling ratio in dB.

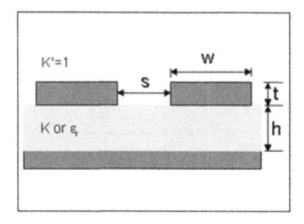

Figure 2-37 Microstrip edge coupled line

Directional Coupler Analysis

One important use of coupled lines is the design of directional couplers. Directional couplers are useful components for sampling an RF signal without significantly loading or perturbing the input signal. Simple directional couplers are often used to provide a sample of an RF signal for measurement. High quality, precision, directional couplers can separate incident and reflected signals and are the fundamental component used for the measurement of VSWR and return loss. Two directional couplers can be placed back-to-back to form a dual directional coupler as shown in Figure 2-38. This type of coupler forms a four port network that can provide a sample of the forward power and reflected power between a source and load. Some basic properties of directional couplers include:

Insertion Loss:

Insertion Loss is simply the ratio of the output power at P2 to the input power at P1. Expressed in dB:

$$Insertion\ Loss\ (dB)\ =\ P2_{dBm} - P1_{dBm} \tag{2-75}$$

Coupling:

The coupling factor is the ratio of the output power at P3 to the input power at P1. In microstrip and stripline circuits the coupled port is adjacent to the input line port. In waveguide couplers the coupled port is furthest from the input port.

$$Input\ Port\ Coupling\ (dB) = P1_{dBm} - P3_{dBm} \tag{2-76}$$

Isolation:

Isolation is the ratio of the output power at P4 to the input power at P1.

$$Isolation\ (dB) = P1_{dBm} - P4_{dBm} \tag{2-77}$$

Directivity:

Directivity is the difference between the isolation and the coupling when P2 is perfectly terminated in 50 Ω. Another way to think of a coupler's directivity is its ability to properly separate the forward and reflected waves.

$$Directivity\ (dB) = P3_{dBm} - P4_{dBm} \tag{2-78}$$

Figure 2-38 A dual directional coupler to measure VSWR, and return loss

A coupler will always have a finite amount of isolation. Ideally, all of the power input to P1 should be directed to P2 and P3. However some finite amount of power will show up at P4. This power will then add with any reflected power coming from P2 and being directed to P4. It is this finite isolation that limits the directivity of the directional coupler. Thus the power at P3 is the (Incident power at P1 – coupling factor) + the (Reflected power from P2 – isolation). For simple RF power sampling applications, the directivity is not that critical. But if we are using the directional coupler to measure VSWR, the directivity is very important. In VSWR measurement applications it is important to know the directivity of the directional coupler that is used to perform the measurement. A significant measurement error can exist when the coupler directivity is less than 40 dB. Figure 2-39 is a standard plot of measurement error vs. coupler directivity. The plot shows that when measuring a load that has an actual return loss of 20 dB with a directional coupler of 40 dB directivity, an error of +0.8 to -0.9 dB exists. This means that our instrument may read (-19.2 dB to -20.9 dB). We can readily see that if we used a directional coupler with directivity of 20 dB the resultant error could be approximately +2.3 dB to –3.0 dB. The asymmetry is due to whether the reflected signal is in phase with the forward signal or 180 degrees out of phase.

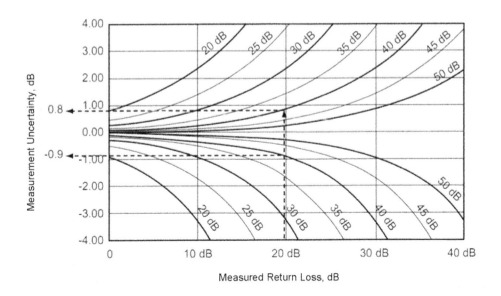

Figure 2-39 Error measurement versus coupler directivity (*Courtesy of Anritsu Corporation*)

Microstrip Directional Coupler Design

Example 2-11: Design an edge coupled microstrip directional coupler with a coupling factor of 10 dB at 5 GHz. Use Rogers RO3003 substrate with relative dielectric constant $\varepsilon_r = 3.0$ and 0.020-inch thickness.

Solution: Traditional coupler design required the computation of the even and odd mode impedance based on the characteristic impedance and coupling factor. Many references have tables and families of curves in which the line width and spacing could be obtained [2]. The ADS TLINE utility provides an exact solution for the coupled line parameters. Select the coupled microstrip line calculator from the Rectangular transmission lines in the TLINE utility. Enter the dielectric constant (ε_r), the dielectric thickness (h), and conductor thickness (t) as shown in Figure 2-40. Select the Synthesis mode and choose to synthesize a coupled line pair based on the input characteristic impedance, Z_o, and the coupling in dB. The coupled line width, W, is then calculated be 38.86 mils and the line spacing, s, is 6.16 mils.

Add the RO3003, 0.020-inch thick substrate and create the coupler schematic using the Coupled Microstrip Line (Symmetrical) element. On the coupled port side add a Microstrip Bend with Optimal Miter at 90° from the main path. It is important to keep this side orthogonal from the main path so that no further parallel line coupling can occur. The optimal miter element automatically optimizes the miter for the least amount of discontinuity traversing the 90° bend. Lastly add a short section of line to each port to complete the circuit as shown in Figure 2-40. Use a Linear Analysis to sweep the coupler from 4500 MHz to 5500 MHz. Simulate the circuit and display the insertion loss (S21), coupled response (S31), isolation (S41), and the directivity. The directivity must be calculated by using Equation 2-78. It is convenient to implement simple mathematical operations directly in the Graph Properties window as opposed to using an Equation block. The directivity is calculated by subtracting the coupled port response from the isolation. This computation is shown in the measurement properties of Figure 2-40.

Figure 2-40 Schematic of the microstrip directional coupler

The simulated coupling factor is 10.157 dB which is very close the 10 dB design goal. The isolation is found to be about 25 dB. The directivity of this Directional Coupler is about 15 dB. Clearly this type of directional coupler is not appropriate for VSWR measurement. This type of directional coupler is useful for obtaining a sample of the input signal without disturbing or loading down the input signal. High directivity directional couplers are typically realized with broadside coupled lines in stripline media or in waveguide.

Figure 2-41 Response of the microstrip directional coupler

References and Further Readings

[1]   David M. Pozar, *Microwave Engineering*, Third Edition, John Wiley and Sons, Inc. 2005

[2]   Foundations for Microstrip Circuit Design, T.C. Edwards, John Wiley & Sons, New York, 1981

[3]   Keysight Technologies, Manuals for Advanced Design System, *ADS 2015.07 Documentation Set*, EEsof EDA Division, Santa Rosa, California www.keysight.com

[4]   William   Sinnema   and   Robert   McPherson,   Electronic
        Communications, Prentice-Hall Canada, Inc., Scarborough, Ontario,
        1991

[5]   UHF/Microwave Experimenters Manual, American Radio Relay
        League, Newington, CT.1990

[6]   Reference: I. J. Bahl and D. K. Trivedi, "A Designer's Guide to
        Microstrip Line", Microwaves, May 1977, pp. 174-182.

[7]   Microwave Handbook Volume 1, Radio Society of Great Britain,
        The Bath Press, Bath, U.K., 1989.

[8]   Tatsuo Itoh, Planar Transmission Line Structures, IEEE Press, New
        York, NY, 1987

[9]   Ali A. Behagi and Stephen D. Turner, Microwave and RF
        Engineering, A Simulation Approach with Keysight Genesys
        Software, BT Microwave LLC, State College, PA , March 2015

Problems

2-1.   Determine the VSWR of a satellite antenna with a return loss of -
        11.4 dB.

2-2.   The input reflection coefficient of a transistor is measured to be 0.22
        at an angle of 32°. Determine the input VSWR of the device.

2-3.   Determine the impedance of a quarter-wave transformer to match a
        25 Ω load to a 50 Ω source.

2-4.   Design the quarter-wave transformer from Problem 3 using a
        microstrip transmission line. The frequency of operation is 2.05
        GHz. The dielectric constant is 3.0 with a thickness of 0.030 in.
        Determine the length and width of the microstrip line.

2-5.   A radio transmitter is operating into a transmission line that measures a 3:1 VSWR. Determine the percentage of power that would be expected to reflect back into the transmitter.

2-6.   A series RLC load, R = 75 Ω, L = 10 nH, C = 25 pF is connected to a 50 Ω transmission line. Setup a linear analysis in ADS to sweep the frequency from 200 MHz to 2000 MHz in 200 MHz steps. Display the input reflection Coefficient, S11, and VSWR in a Table.

2-7.   Create a simple schematic using the RG8 coaxial cable. Set the length to 50 ft. Calculate the insertion loss in a Table. Terminate the coaxial line with a 100 Ω resistor and display the input return loss and reflection coefficient in the same Table.

2-8.   Calculate the cutoff frequency of the TE1,0 mode in a rectangular waveguide with a height of 0.200 inches and a width of 0.470 inches. Also calculate the waveguide wavelength, λ_g.

2-9.   Design a distributed bias feed network for a C Band amplifier operating at 6.0 GHz. Use a microstrip substrate with a dielectric constant of 10.2 and a thickness of 0.025 inches. Plot the insertion loss and return loss from 2 GHz to 10 GHz.

2-10.   Determine the physical length of a $\lambda_g/4$ open circuit microstrip transmission line with an impedance of 20 Ω. The frequency of operation is 10 GHz. Use a microstrip dielectric constant of 2.2 and a thickness of 0.010 inches. Determine whether an end-effect model element should be used.

2-11.   Design a 35dB directional coupler to be used in a 100W transmitter operating at 4 GHz. Design the coupler in stripline. Use a dielectric constant of 3.0 and a thickness of 60 mils for each half of the stripline.

Chapter 3

Network Parameters and the Smith Chart

3.1 Introduction

At low frequencies below the VHF range, the terminal voltages V_1 and V_2 and the terminal currents I_1 and I_2 of a two-terminal network, shown in Fig. 3-1, can be related to each other by a different set of matrix parameters. The most common representations are the impedance matrix (Z parameters), the admittance matrix (Y parameters), the hybrid matrix (h parameters), and the transmission matrix (ABCD parameters).

Figure 3-1 Low frequency two-port network

Z Parameters

The network representation with Z parameters, relating the input and output voltages to input and output currents, is given by the following equations.

$$V_1 = Z_{11}I_1 + Z_{12}I_2 \tag{3-1}$$

$$V_2 = Z_{21}I_1 + Z_{22}I_2 \tag{3-2}$$

The Z parameters, also known as impedance parameters, are determined by making the following open circuit measurements:

$$Z_{11} = \left. \frac{V_1}{I_1} \right|_{I_2=0} \quad \textit{(Requires open circuit measurement)}$$

$$Z_{12} = \left. \frac{V_1}{I_2} \right|_{I_1=0} \qquad \textit{(Requires open circuit measurement)}$$

$$Z_{21} = \left. \frac{V_2}{I_1} \right|_{I_2=0} \qquad \textit{(Requires open circuit} \text{ measurement)}$$

$$Z_{22} = \left. \frac{V_2}{I_2} \right|_{I_1=0} \qquad \textit{(Requires open circuit measurement)}$$

The Z parameters are very useful when two-terminal networks are connected in series. In this case the overall Z parameters are simply the algebraic sum of the individual Z parameters.

Y Parameters

Similarly, the input and output currents can be related to input and output voltages by Y parameters as shown in Equations (3-3) and (3-4).

$$I_1 = Y_{11}V_1 + Y_{12}V_2 \qquad\qquad\qquad (3\text{-}3)$$

$$I_2 = Y_{21}V_1 + Y_{22}V_2 \qquad\qquad\qquad (3\text{-}4)$$

The Y parameters, also known as admittance parameters, are determined by making the following short circuit measurements.

$$Y_{11} = \left. \frac{I_1}{V_1} \right|_{V_2=0} \qquad \textit{(Requires short circuit measurement)}$$

$$Y_{12} = \left. \frac{I_1}{V_2} \right|_{V_1=0} \qquad \textit{(Requires short circuit measurement)}$$

$$Y_{21} = \frac{I_2}{V_1}\bigg|_{V_2=0} \qquad \textit{(Requires short circuit measurement)}$$

$$Y_{22} = \frac{I_2}{V_2}\bigg|_{V_1=0} \qquad \textit{(Requires short circuit measurement)}$$

The Y parameters are useful when two-terminal networks are connected in parallel. In this case the overall Y parameters are simply the algebraic sum of the individual Y parameters.

h Parameters

The network representation by Hybrid or h parameters, relating the input voltage and output current to input current and output voltage, is given by the following equations.

$$V_1 = h_{11}I_1 + h_{12}V_2 \qquad (3\text{-}5)$$

$$I_2 = h_{21}I_1 + h_{22}V_2 \qquad (3\text{-}6)$$

The h parameters can be determined from the following measurements.

$$h_{11} = \frac{V_1}{I_1}\bigg|_{V_2=0} \qquad \textit{(Requires short circuit measurement)}$$

$$h_{12} = \frac{V_2}{V_1}\bigg|_{I_1=0} \qquad \textit{(Requires open circuit measurement)}$$

$$h_{21} = \frac{I_2}{I_1}\bigg|_{V_2=0} \qquad \textit{(Requires short circuit measurement)}$$

$$h_{22} = \left.\frac{I_2}{V_2}\right|_{I_1=0} \qquad \textit{(Requires open circuit measurement)}$$

The h parameters are often used to characterize the low frequency characteristics of transistor circuits. The parameter, h_{21}, defines the forward current gain while the parameter, h_{12}, defines the reverse voltage gain of the network. The parameter, h_{11}, is the input impedance and parameter, h_{22}, is the output admittance of the network.

ABCD Parameters

Another representation relating the input voltage and current to the output voltage and current, is by ABCD parameters.

$$V_1 = AV_2 - BI_2 \qquad\qquad\qquad (3\text{-}7)$$

$$I_1 = CV_2 - DI_2 \qquad\qquad\qquad (3\text{-}8)$$

The ABCD parameters are found by the following measurements.

$$A = \left.\frac{V_1}{V_2}\right|_{I_2=0} \qquad \textit{(Requires open circuit measurement)}$$

$$B = -\left.\frac{V_1}{I_2}\right|_{V_2=0} \qquad \textit{(Requires short circuit measurement)}$$

$$C = \left.\frac{I_1}{V_2}\right|_{I_2=0} \qquad \textit{(Requires open circuit measurement)}$$

$$D = -\left.\frac{I_1}{I_2}\right|_{V_2=0} \qquad \textit{(Requires short circuit measurement)}$$

The ABCD parameters in Equations (3-7) and (3-8) are often presented in matrix form and referred to as the transmission matrix [2].

$$\begin{bmatrix} V_1 \\ I_1 \end{bmatrix} = \begin{bmatrix} A & B \\ C & D \end{bmatrix} \cdot \begin{bmatrix} V_2 \\ -I_2 \end{bmatrix}$$

The ABCD parameters are very useful to characterize networks when individual circuits are cascaded in a chain fashion. They have also been popular in the design of telephone networks. In this case the overall ABCD matrix is found by the product of the individual ABCD matrices. For example, if two networks are connected in cascade the overall ABCD matrix is the product of individual ABCD matrices.

$$\begin{bmatrix} A & B \\ C & D \end{bmatrix} = \begin{bmatrix} A_1 & B_1 \\ C_1 & D_1 \end{bmatrix} \cdot \begin{bmatrix} A_2 & B_2 \\ C_2 & D_2 \end{bmatrix} \qquad (3\text{-}9)$$

At microwave frequencies, due to the difficulty in making short circuit and open circuit measurements, the two-terminal network representation by Z, Y, h, or ABCD parameters is not practical. Therefore, at microwave frequencies, a new representation known as Scattering or S parameters has been developed.

3.2 Development of Network S Parameters

At RF and microwave frequencies, where the wavelength of the voltage and current waveforms are comparable or smaller than the physical dimensions of the network, it is difficult to obtain perfect open and short circuit terminations. It is also difficult to measure voltage and current in high frequency circuits, therefore, the usefulness of the parameters in Section 3.1 diminish. In high frequency networks it is much easier to measure power than voltage or current. For RF and microwave networks, a form of the transmission matrix has been defined based on power measurements into the system's characteristic impedance. These parameters are known as S parameters, named after their scattering matrix form. Consider a two-port network, shown in Figure 3-2, where Z_{01} is the real characteristic impedance and V_1^+ and V_1^-, respectively, are the incident and reflected voltage waveforms at the input port. Similarly, Z_{02} is the real characteristic impedance and V_2^+ and V_2^-, respectively, are the incident and reflected voltage waveforms at the output port.

Figure 3-2 Two-port network with incident and reflected voltage waveforms

In order to obtain measurable power relations in terms of wave amplitudes, we need to define a new set of waveforms by normalizing the voltage amplitudes with respect to the square root of the respective characteristic impedances, namely:

$$a_1 = \frac{V_1^+}{\sqrt{Z_{01}}} \tag{3-10}$$

$$b_1 = \frac{V_1^-}{\sqrt{Z_{01}}} \tag{3-11}$$

$$a_2 = \frac{V_2^+}{\sqrt{Z_{02}}} \tag{3-12}$$

$$b_2 = \frac{V_2^-}{\sqrt{Z_{02}}} \tag{3-13}$$

The two-port network with normalized waveforms is shown in Figure 3-3.

Figure 3-3 Two-port network with incident and reflected waveforms

Notice that:

$$|a_1|^2 = \frac{|V_1^+|^2}{Z_{01}} = \text{Incident power at the network input}$$

$$|b_1|^2 = \frac{|V_1^-|^2}{Z_{01}} = \text{Reflected power at the network input}$$

$$|a_2|^2 = \frac{|V_2^+|^2}{Z_{02}} = \text{Incident power at the network output}$$

$$|b_2|^2 = \frac{|V_2^-|^2}{Z_{02}} = \text{Reflected power at the network output}$$

The S parameters relate b_1 and b_2 to a_1 and a_2 by the following Equations [1].

$$b_1 = S_{11}a_1 + S_{12}a_2 \qquad (3\text{-}14)$$

$$b_2 = S_{21}a_1 + S_{22}a_2 \qquad (3\text{-}15)$$

In matrix form the scattering matrix is written as:

$$\begin{bmatrix} b_1 \\ b_2 \end{bmatrix} = \begin{bmatrix} S_{11} & S_{12} \\ S_{21} & S_{22} \end{bmatrix} \cdot \begin{bmatrix} a_1 \\ a_2 \end{bmatrix}$$

At RF and microwave frequencies the normalized voltage waveforms a_1, a_2, b_1, and b_2 represent vectors having both magnitude and phase. Terminating the output of the two-port network with a real load impedance that is equal to the real system characteristic impedance, $Z_{01} = Z_{02}$, forces $a_2 = 0$. Solving for the individual S parameters then gives the following relationships.

$$S_{11} = \frac{V_1^-}{V_1^+} = \left. \frac{b_1}{a_1} \right|_{a_2=0} \tag{3-16}$$

$$S_{21} = \frac{V_2^-}{V_1^+} = \left. \frac{b_2}{a_1} \right|_{a_2=0} \tag{3-17}$$

These measurements are better visualized using the network of Figure 3-4.

Figure 3-4 Measurement of S11 and S21 in a two-port network

Terminating the input of the two-port network with a real load impedance that is equal to the real system characteristic impedance, $Z_{01} = Z_{02}$, forces $a_1 = 0$. The S parameters S_{22} and S_{12} can be solved by Equations (3-18) and (3-19) as demonstrated in Figure 3-5.

$$S_{22} = \frac{V_2^-}{V_2^+} = \left. \frac{b_2}{a_2} \right|_{a_1=0} \tag{3-18}$$

$$S_{12} = \frac{V_1^-}{V_2^+} = \frac{b_1}{a_2}\Bigg|_{a_1=0}$$ (3-19)

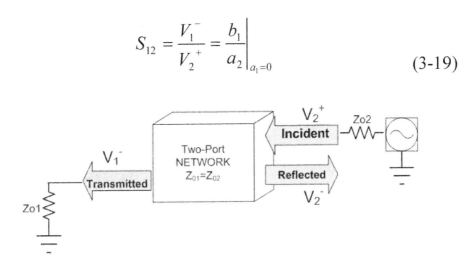

Figure 3-5 Measurement of S22 and S12 in a two-port network

S11 is often referred to as the input reflection coefficient and S22 as the output reflection coefficient of the network. S21 is the forward transmission and is often expressed as a gain or loss depending on whether S21, in dB, is positive or negative. S12 is the reverse transmission or isolation of the network. Because the S parameters are complex entities they must be measured with a Vector Network Analyzer, VNA, capable of measuring both amplitude and phase. A Scalar Network Analyzer is used to measure the magnitude of two-port networks only. Similar to the ABCD parameters, it is very easy to cascade S parameters to calculate the overall S parameters of a multi-stage network.

3.3 Using S Parameter Files in ADS

Chapter one touched upon the use of S parameters to describe the network models of lumped components such as resistors, inductors, and capacitors. Any linear RF and microwave network can be described by its S parameters. As such, the S parameters find extensive use throughout linear circuit modeling and simulation. The S parameter file can serve as a substitute for any element model in a circuit design. The file is loaded into the simulation engine via a data element model such as the one shown in Figure 3-6. This schematic symbol represents a generic two port S parameter data file. In the ADS parts selector there exists a variety of symbols that can represent S parameter files from one port to N-port scattering matrices. An N-port device will have N^2 S parameters. ADS allows any schematic symbol to be applied to a data file element model.

Figure 3-6 Two-port data file between two terminations

The generic data file element of Figure 3-6 can be changed to the symbol of a transistor, capacitor, or whatever element the S parameter data file represents. This is helpful for maintaining a more professional schematic.

Figure 3-7 Browsing to the location of S parameter

The data file element can be edited so that the designer can browse to the location of the saved S parameter data file, as shown in Figure 3-7. Figure 3-7 shows the S parameter file of a C Band amplifier. The S Parameter file is simply an ASCII text file that can be edited with any text editor. For a two-port network the filename should use the .s2p extension. Similarly a one port network would use the .s1p file extension. In S parameter files only one definition line is required and must begin with a (#) symbol. Any number of comment lines can be included and must begin with the (!) symbol. The only remaining requirement is the order in which the S parameters are entered into the text file. This order must be in the form of S_{11}, S_{21}, S_{12}, and $S_{22,}$ as shown in Figure 7-8.

```
!    S-Parameter File of 200W C-Band Amplifier
# GHz  S  MA  R  50
!FREQ     |S11|              |S21|              |S12|              |S22|
5.800    0.070   -52.367   65.436   59.242   0.001   49.912   0.151   -69.520
5.804    0.067   -58.549   64.997   49.393   0.002  -91.508   0.159   -69.723
5.807    0.078   -57.215   64.574   39.402   0.003   15.689   0.150   -70.922
5.811    0.071   -62.285   64.270   29.318   0.004  -46.869   0.161   -68.117
5.814    0.062   -63.434   64.010   18.336   0.003  100.039   0.155   -72.297
5.818    0.068   -68.539   63.737    9.254   0.002   55.959   0.154   -73.473
5.821    0.069   -68.652   63.011   -1.009   0.001  -49.662   0.153   -72.922
5.825    0.067   -75.742   63.067  -11.077   0.000   72.992   0.155   -73.332
5.828    0.067   -79.371   63.110  -20.816   0.001  -46.926   0.149   -73.844
5.832    0.066   -80.000   62.883  -30.369   0.001  163.273   0.153   -76.746
5.835    0.064   -80.039   62.700  -40.990   0.002   -0.501   0.146   -75.992
5.839    0.064   -83.637   62.461  -50.729   0.001   14.107   0.146   -77.883
5.842    0.065   -93.328   62.278  -61.002   0.002  168.805   0.153   -75.441
5.846    0.063   -89.715   61.721  -70.473   0.004  -33.932   0.151   -80.746
5.849    0.066   -91.605   62.152  -80.652   0.002   84.551   0.151   -79.625
5.853    0.060   -96.484   61.416  -90.824   0.001   78.816   0.143   -83.137
```

Figure 3-8 C band amplifier S parameter data file

As Figure 3-8 shows the definition line contains four descriptive parameters for the data file. The available options for these parameters are summarized below [5]. Only a single space is required between each entry on a line of the S parameter file. For better visual presentation a tab space can be used between entries.

GHz: Units for the swept frequency data column. Frequency can be GHz, MHz, KHz, or Hz.

S: Defines network parameter type. Parameters can be S, Y, Z, or h parameters format.

MA: Magnitude-Angle format for the parameter data. Available formats
       are DB for dB-angle, MA for magnitude-angle, or RI for real-
       imaginary format.

R: 50:   Reference resistance. This is the characteristic impedance in
       which the parameters have been measured. The parameters will be
       normalized to this resistance.

An S parameter simulation can be setup to analyze the amplifier's S
parameter data file over a frequency range of 5800 MHz to 5820 MHz in 1
MHz steps. Setup a tabular output and display each of the four S
parameters. On the Table Properties window, set the units to absolute (Abs)
and magnitude-angle format as shown in Figure 3-8. The resulting table is
shown in Figure 3-9. Note that even though the S Parameters in the data file
are recorded in increments greater than 1 MHz, ADS has interpolated the
values between each data point and can output the S parameters in 1 MHz
increments.

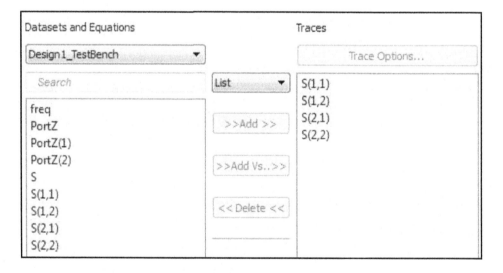

Figure 3-9 ADS measured data for display

	F (MHz)	mag(S[1,1]) (dB)	ang(S[1,1])	mag(S[2,1]) (dB)	ang(S[2,1])	mag(S[1,2]) (dB)	ang(S[1,2])	mag(S[2,2]) (dB)	ang(S[2,2])
1	5800	0.07	-52.367	65.436	59.242	1e-3	49.912	0.151	-69.52
2	5800.2	0.07	-52.676	65.414	58.75	1.05e-3	42.841	0.151	-69.53
3	5800.4	0.07	-52.985	65.392	58.257	1.1e-3	35.77	0.152	-69.54
4	5800.6	0.07	-53.294	65.37	57.765	1.15e-3	28.699	0.152	-69.55
5	5800.8	0.069	-53.603	65.348	57.272	1.2e-3	21.628	0.153	-69.561
6	5801	0.069	-53.913	65.326	56.78	1.25e-3	14.557	0.153	-69.571
7	5801.2	0.069	-54.222	65.304	56.287	1.3e-3	7.486	0.153	-69.581
8	5801.4	0.069	-54.531	65.282	55.795	1.35e-3	0.415	0.154	-69.591
9	5801.6	0.069	-54.84	65.26	55.302	1.4e-3	-6.656	0.154	-69.601
10	5801.8	0.069	-55.149	65.238	54.81	1.45e-3	-13.727	0.155	-69.611
11	5802	0.068	-55.458	65.217	54.318	1.5e-3	-20.798	0.155	-69.621
12	5802.2	0.068	-55.767	65.195	53.825	1.55e-3	-27.869	0.155	-69.632
13	5802.4	0.068	-56.076	65.173	53.333	1.6e-3	-34.94	0.156	-69.642
14	5802.6	0.068	-56.385	65.151	52.84	1.65e-3	-42.011	0.156	-69.652
15	5802.8	0.068	-56.694	65.129	52.348	1.7e-3	-49.082	0.157	-69.662
16	5803	0.068	-57.004	65.107	51.855	1.75e-3	-56.153	0.157	-69.672
17	5803.2	0.068	-57.313	65.085	51.363	1.8e-3	-63.224	0.157	-69.682
18	5803.4	0.067	-57.622	65.063	50.87	1.85e-3	-70.295	0.158	-69.693
19	5803.6	0.067	-57.931	65.041	50.378	1.9e-3	-77.366	0.158	-69.703
20	5803.8	0.067	-58.24	65.019	49.885	1.95e-3	-84.437	0.159	-69.713
21	5804	0.067	-58.549	64.997	49.393	2e-3	-91.508	0.159	-69.723
22	5804.2	0.068	-58.46	64.969	48.727	2.067e-3	-84.362	0.158	-69.803
23	5804.4	0.068	-58.371	64.941	48.061	2.133e-3	-77.215	0.158	-69.883
24	5804.6	0.069	-58.282	64.912	47.395	2.2e-3	-70.069	0.157	-69.963
25	5804.8	0.07	-58.193	64.884	46.729	2.267e-3	-62.922	0.157	-70.043

Figure 3-10 ADS tabular display of the S Parameter data file

Scalar Representation of the S Parameters

When working with a two-port network, such as an amplifier, the engineer is usually more interested in the magnitude in (dB's) of the S parameters rather than the absolute units. This is referred to as the Scalar representation of the S parameters and is readily measured on scalar network analyzers. Because the S parameters are based on voltage waveforms they must be multiplied by 20log to convert to dB format.

$$S_{11}(dB) = -20\log |S_{11}| \qquad \textit{Input return loss}$$

$$S_{21}(dB) = 20\log |S_{21}| \qquad \textit{Insertion gain (+) or insertion loss (-)}$$

$$S_{12}(dB) = 20\log |S_{12}| \qquad \textit{Reverse gain (+) or isolation (-)}$$

$$S_{22}(dB) = -20\log |S_{22}| \qquad \textit{Output return loss}$$

With the C Band amplifier in ADS, setup a rectangular graph and display the S Parameters in Scalar format. Assign each S parameter to the graph using the dB-magnitude format. The display is shown in Figure 3-10.

Figure 3-11 Scalar display of frequency swept amplifier S Parameters

3.4 Development of the Smith Chart

The most frequently used graphical tool used to visualize the vector properties of S parameters is the Smith chart. The Smith chart conformally maps the familiar rectangular impedance coordinates onto a polar plane. Essentially the reactive, normally the vertical axis, has been bent around in such a way that ± infinity is included within the boundary of the graph. Therefore any positive complex impedance can be plotted on the standard Smith chart shown in Figure 3-12. Negative impedances or gain is outside of the standard Smith chart. A compressed Smith chart must be used to plot negative impedances. Figure 3-12 shows the ADS standard Smith chart graph with impedance coordinates. A rectangular axis has been overlaid to show the relationship to the rectilinear grid system. The Smith chart can be normalized to any characteristic impedance. The chart of Figure 3-12 is normalized to 50 Ω. The normalized impedance is a pure resistance that is a single point at the center of the chart. The purely real impedances exist along the horizontal axis from 0 Ω to infinity. Note the locations of the short circuit (0 Ω) and open circuit (infinity) on the real axis. The concentric circles that intersect the real axis are known as the constant resistance circles. The constant reactance circles appear as arcs on the standard Smith chart. As shown in Figure 3-12 the reactance circles on the top half of the chart represent inductive reactance while the circles on the bottom half of the chart represent capacitive reactance. Any impedance defined by rectangular coordinates (R + jX) can be plotted as a point where the R value on the constant resistance circle intersects the X value on the reactance circle.

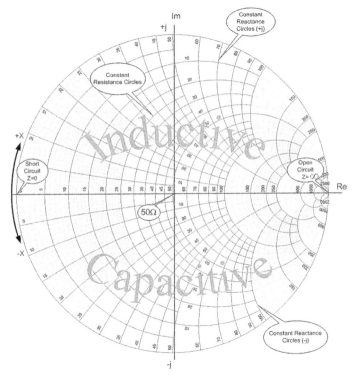

Figure 3-12 Standard Smith chart with impedance coordinates

Example 3-1: Use ADS to plot the impedance 25 + j25 Ω on the standard Smith chart.

Solution: To display the impedance on the Smith chart, create a new workspace in ADS and follow the procedure.

1. From the ADS Main window, create a new schematic and Insert S_Prams Template.
2. Connect a wire between the two Terminations and change the load impedance to 25 + j25 Ω.

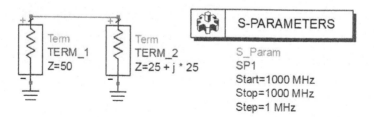

Figure 3-13 Schematic for plotting the impedance on the Smith chart

3. Simulate the schematic and select the Smith chart in data display window.
4. From the list of parameters Add S11 to display the impedance on the Smith chart, as shown in Figure 3-14.

freq (1.000GHz to 1.000GHz)

Figure 3-14 Plotting impedance on the Smith chart

Normalized Impedance on the Smith Chart

The impedance on a Smith chart is often presented in its normalized form. This means that the actual impedance is divided by the value of the characteristic impedance. The ADS Smith chart allows the selection of either normalized or actual impedance via the Properties window of the Smith chart. Equation (3-20) shows how the reflection coefficient, Γ, is related to the normalized impedance on the Smith chart.

$$\Gamma = \frac{\left(Z_{actual} - Z_o\right)}{\left(Z_{actual} + Z_o\right)} \tag{3-20}$$

Rearranging Equation (3-20) and defining $z = \frac{\left(Z_{actual}\right)}{\left(Z_o\right)}$, the reflection coefficient can be in terms of normalized impedance in Equation (3-21).

$$\Gamma = \frac{\left(z - 1\right)}{\left(z + 1\right)} \tag{3-21}$$

The normalized impedance is shown on the Smith chart of Figure 3-14. The normalized impedance is read as $z = 0.5 + j0.5$ Ω. The reflection coefficient on the Smith chart is the vector from the center of the chart to the normalized impedance. The transmission coefficient is the vector from the origin $(Z = 0)$ to the normalized impedance. The reflection S parameters, S_{11} and S_{22}, are measured as a reflection coefficient on the Smith chart. The transmission S parameters, S_{21} and S_{12}, are measured as transmission parameters on the Smith chart.

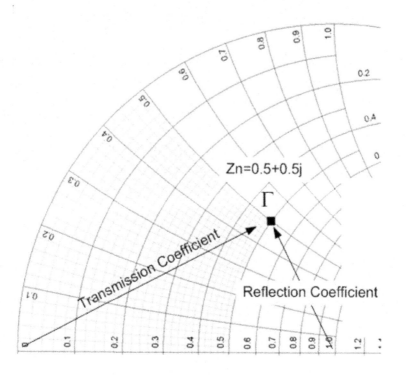

Figure 3-15 Impedance plotted with normalized impedance coordinates on the Smith chart

Knowing that the reflection coefficients and S parameters are vector quantities, there must be a method to measure the angular portion of the vector. Figure 3-16 shows the angular measurement convention on the Smith chart. Note that the reflection coefficient of a 50 Ω resistance (center of the chart) is equal to zero. A total reflection, like that due to a perfect short or open circuit, has a reflection coefficient equal to one. Therefore all positive impedances result in a reflection coefficient between 0 and 1. The reflection coefficient of the 25 + j25 Ω impedance can be determined in ADS by displaying the magnitude and angle of the S parameter, S11. As Figure 3-16 shows the reflection coefficient of this impedance is 0.447 at an angle of +116.565 degrees.

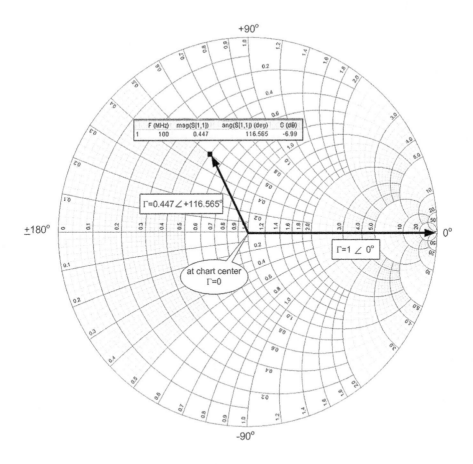

Figure 3-16 Angular measurement of reflection coefficients

Normalized Admittance on the Smith chart

Admittance circles can also be displayed on the Smith chart. The admittance circles can be enabled on the ADS Smith chart by their selection on the graph's Properties page. The admittance circles consist of constant conductance and susceptance circles which are inverted from the impedance circles. Subsequent chapters dealing with the subject of impedance matching will make frequent use of the admittance parameters. Having both impedance and admittance parameters displayed on the Smith chart makes it easy to design impedance matching networks that include both series and parallel (shunt) elements. It also becomes very easy to convert series impedance to its parallel admittance equivalent. The admittance of a network is the inverse of the impedance as given by Equation (3-22).

$$Y = \frac{1}{Z} = G \pm jB \qquad (3\text{-}22)$$

Where,

> G = conductance in mhos
>
> B = susceptance in mhos

The equivalent admittance of a network is read directly from the admittance circles on the Smith chart. For the normalized $0.5 + j0.5 \ \Omega$ series impedance the admittance is read directly from the chart as $1.0 - j1.0$ mho. It is important to remember that there is an inversion in the sign of the imaginary component when converting from impedance to admittance or vice versa.

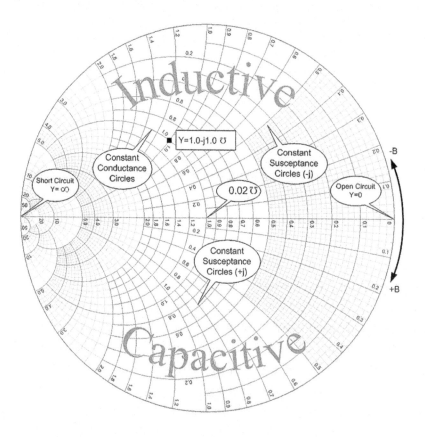

Figure 3-17 Admittance circles on the Smith chart

3.5 Lumped Element Movements on the Smith chart

Lumped element movements on the Smith chart form the basis for impedance matching. The Smith chart is a wonderfully intuitive tool, for visualization of moving from one impedance to another, without involving circuit synthesis mathematics. Understanding the basic movements around the Smith chart will build a foundation for the circuit designs covered in this text. It is helpful to display both the impedance and admittance coordinates simultaneously on the Smith chart.

Adding a Series Reactance to an Impedance

Adding a series reactance to an impedance point on the Smith chart causes the resulting impedance to move along the constant resistance circle in which the impedance intersects. A series inductance will move the impedance in a clockwise direction while a series capacitance will move the resulting impedance in a counter-clockwise direction on the constant resistance circle. The reactance that is added to the impedance by the series element can be read from the Smith chart by finding the difference between the lines of reactance that intersect the start point and end point on the constant resistance circle. This reactance can then be converted to a capacitance or inductance value using Equations (3-23) and (3-24) [4].

$$C(series) = \frac{1}{\omega Xn} \tag{3-23}$$

$$L(series) = \frac{Xn}{\omega} \tag{3-24}$$

Where,

X = reactance measured along the arc length

ω = the design frequency in radian per second, $2\pi f$

n = impedance normalizing value (50 Ω)

Example 3-2: Measure the amount of reactance required to move the impedance $Z = 25 + j25$ Ω on the Smith chart from point A to point B, as shown in Figure 3-19.

Solution: The amount of reactance required in the inductor can be measured from the reactance lines that intersect the start point (A) and end point (B). As Figure 3-19 shows the reactance is approximately 0.359. Using a design frequency of 1000 MHz and Equation (3-22) the inductance is calculated to as 2.86 nH.

$$L(series) = \frac{0.359 \cdot (50)}{2 \cdot \pi \cdot 1000 \cdot 10^6} = 2.86 \ nH$$

Add the inductor to the impedance element in ADS to verify that a 2.86 nH inductor moves the impedance to point B on the Smith chart. Make the inductor tunable and set the initial value to 0.1 nH and tune the value of inductance to move the impedance from point A to point B.

Figure 3-18 Series inductance added to 25 + j25 Ω impedance

Simulate the schematic and display S11 on the Smith chart, as shown in Figure 3-19.

m1	m2
freq=1.000GHz	freq=1.000GHz
Design1_TestBench..S(1,1)=0.447 / 116.565	S(1,1)=0.575 / 90.381
impedance = Z0 * (0.500 + j0.500)	impedance = Z0 * (0.500 + j0.859)

freq (1.000MHz to 1.000GHz)
freq (1.000GHz to 1.000GHz)

Figure 3-19 Moving point A to point B

Adding a Shunt Reactance to an Impedance

Adding a shunt element to an impedance point on the Smith chart causes the resulting impedance to move along the constant conductance circle in which the impedance intersects. A shunt inductance will move the impedance in a counter-clockwise direction while a shunt capacitance will move the resulting impedance in a clockwise direction on the constant conductance circle. The susceptance that is added to the impedance by the shunt element can be read from the Smith chart by finding the difference between the lines of susceptance that intersect the start point and end point on the constant conductance circle. This susceptance can then be converted to a capacitance or inductance value using Equations (3-25) and (3-26) [4].

$$L(shunt) = \frac{n}{\omega B}$$

(3-25)

$$C(shunt) = \frac{B}{\omega n}$$ (3-26)

Where,

    B = susceptance measured along the arc length

    ω = the design frequency $2\pi f$

    n = impedance normalizing value (50 Ω)

Example 3-3: Continuing with the previous example measure the susceptance required to move from point B to point C on the real axis.

 Solution: Add a shunt capacitance to move the impedance from point B to point C as shown in Figure 3-21. When adding a shunt element switch from the impedance grid to the admittance coordinates. The admittance follows the constant conductance circle in which the point lies by the difference between the intersecting susceptance lines. The susceptance as measured on the perimeter of the chart is about 0.865 mhos. Use Equation (3-26) to calculate the capacitance.

$$C\,(shunt) = \frac{B}{\omega n} = \frac{0.865}{2 \cdot \pi \cdot 1000 \cdot 10^6 \cdot (50)} = 2.75 \; pF$$

Alternatively you can add a shunt capacitor to the circuit and make the capacitance value tunable. Start with a very low value of approximately 0.1 pf and increase the value of capacitance until the admittance is moved from point B to point C.

Figure 3-20 Simulate added shunt capacitance to the network

Simulate the schematic and display the S11 on the Smith chart, as shown in Figure 3-21.

Figure 3-21 Moving point B to point C

The resulting admittance at point C is 0.5 mhos. This is the resulting normalized admittance looking into port one of the network shown in

Figure 3-21. The actual admittance is found by multiplying the normalized admittance by the Smith chart's characteristic admittance (1/50 Ω). Therefore the admittance at point C is 0.01 mhos or an impedance of 100Ω. These techniques form the basis for performing impedance transformations using the Smith chart. In this example a complex impedance of 25 + j25 Ω has been transformed to a pure resistance of approximately 100 Ω. The lumped element movement directions are summarized in Figure 3-22.

Example 3-4: Show the direction of movement on the Smith chart when adding a series or shunt element to an impedance.

Solution: By iterative addition of series and shunt elements an impedance point can be moved from one location to another on the Smith chart for a given frequency. This process forms the basis of the topic of impedance matching which is fundamental to RF and microwave engineering and will be used throughout the remainder of the text.

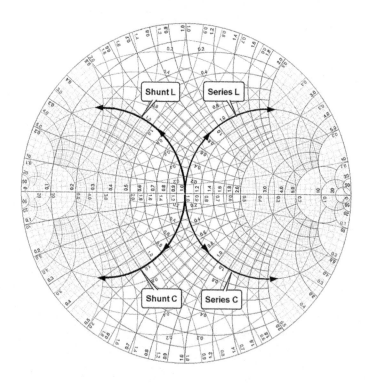

Figure 3-22 Lumped element movements on the Smith chart

3.6 VSWR Circles on the Smith chart

Equation (2-29) in Chapter 2 demonstrated that the VSWR of a network is related to the magnitude of the reflection coefficient, independent of the angle. From plotting the reflection coefficient on the Smith chart we know that the origin of the impedance vector is located in the center of the chart. This suggests that as the reflection coefficient vector rotates 360 degrees around the chart with a constant magnitude, the VSWR will remain constant. This locus of points around the center of the Smith chart is known as the constant VSWR circle [3]. Plotting constant VSWR circles on the Smith chart are frequently used for LNA design. In this example it is shown how to accomplish this task by using a few equations.

Example 3-5: Plot the 0utput VSWR circle on the Smith chart for VSWR value of 2.25.

Solution: Create a new workspace in ADS and open a new schematic to analyze the network at a fixed frequency as shown in Figure 3-23. Any frequency can be entered as the model uses a fix frequency.

Figure 3-23 S Parameter model in ADS

Enter the desired VSWR value in the Equation and notice the change in the radius of the VSWR circle. In Figure 3-24 a value of 2.25 for VSWR is chosen. Any reflection coefficient intersecting the circle has a VSWR equal to the value of the circle.

If the reflection coefficient is inside the circle, the VSWR is less than the value of the circle. Likewise if a reflection coefficient is outside of the circle, the VSWR is greater than the value of the circle. Figure 3-24 gives intuitive feel for relating reflection coefficients to their VSWR value. From the plot of the VSWR circles in Figure 3-24 we can see that the value of the VSWR is equal to the magnitude of the reflection coefficient as labeled on the horizontal axis to the right of the center of the chart. Conversely the horizontal axis values on the left-hand side of the chart represent $1/\Gamma$.

Eqn gs=polar(0.853,-27.25)   <== Change the value of GammaS here

Eqn VSWRout=2.25   <== Desired VSWR circle here

indep(VSWRout_circle) (0.000 to 51.000)

Figure 3-24 Output VSWR circle shown for VSWR value of 2.25

3.7 Adding a Transmission Line in Series with an Impedance

We have seen that adding a reactance in series with an impedance point causes the impedance to follow the constant resistance circles. Adding a transmission line of the same impedance as the Smith chart's normalized impedance, in series with an impedance point causes the resulting impedance to follow the constant VSWR circle in which the impedance lies. The impedance moves in a clockwise direction on the constant VSWR circle.

Example 3-6: Revisiting the 25+j25 Ω impedance in ADS, calculate the electrical length of a series transmission line moving the impedance at point A to point B on the Smith chart, as shown in Figure 3-27.

Solution: Add a series transmission line to the impedance and make the electrical length tunable. Increase the line length to move the impedance to point B. The electrical line length is 58.45 degrees. The impedance on the real axis (zero reactance) on the right hand side of the Smith chart would represent a point of maximum voltage-minimum current along the transmission line.

Figure 3-25 Series transmission line added to impedance

Transmission line lengths are sometimes referred to in terms of fractional wavelengths. Because one wavelength is equal to 360°, a 58.45° electrical length represents (58.45/360) 0.162λ. Continue to add electrical length to the transmission line to reach point C on the Smith chart. As Figure 3-27 shows, the real impedance (zero reactance) on the left side of the horizontal axis on the Smith chart represents a minimum voltage-maximum current point along the transmission line.

Figure 3-26 Series transmission line added to impedance

Simulate the schematic and display the response

Figure 3-27 Series line moves impedance to a minimum voltage point

Further increasing the length of the transmission line we find that we arrive back at point A at 180 degrees of electrical length. Therefore the electrical distance around the Smith chart is 180° or λ/2 wavelength. The points of maximum voltage and minimum voltage will repeat every λ/2 wavelength.

3.8 Adding a Transmission Line in Parallel with an Impedance

In Chapter 2 section 2.11 we have seen that the open and short-circuited transmission lines could take on the equivalence of an inductor, capacitor, or series and parallel resonant circuits depending on the electrical length of the line. Therefore the shunt transmission line will behave more like the lumped element movements on the Smith chart.

Short-Circuited Transmission Lines

At DC and low frequencies, a short circuit is a very low inductance but this is not the case at higher RF and microwave frequencies.

A transmission line with $0°$ length (perfect short) appears at the short circuit point on the Smith chart. As $45°$ of electrical length is added to the short circuit, the impedance moves clockwise along the outer circumference of the Smith chart to the position at the top of the chart. As the line length is increased to $90°$ we see that the short circuit has been transformed to an open circuit. At $180°$ line length the impedance will travel completely around the Smith chart and appear as a short circuit again. Therefore depending on the line length the short circuit transmission line can be transformed into a shunt capacitor or shunt inductor.

Open-Circuited Transmission Lines

At $0°$ electrical line length the open circuit transmission line appears as a perfect open circuit. As the electrical length is increased, the impedance moves clockwise around the circumference to the $45°$ position at the bottom of the chart. At $90°$ electrical length the open circuit now appears as a short circuit. This property of transforming open circuits to short circuits and vice versa is one that is used frequently throughout microwave circuit design.

3.9 Open and Short Circuited Shunt Transmission Lines

For small fractional wavelength transmission lines the open circuit shunt transmission line acts as a shunt capacitor.

Example 3-7: Measure the electrical length of an open circuited shunt transmission line, or the value of a shunt capacitor, to move the impedance $Z = 25 + j25 \ \Omega$ to the center of Smith chart at 1 GHz.

Solution: Create a new schematic and connect to the Z=25 +j25 load. Plotting the impedance on the Smith chart with the admittance circles shows that the impedance lies directly on the unit conductance circle, as shown in Figure 3-28.

```
m1
freq=1.000GHz
S(1,1)=0.447 / 116.565
impedance = Z0 * (0.500 + j0.500)
```

Figure 3-28 Marker m1 at Z = 25 + j25

Therefore, an open circuit shunt transmission line can move this impedance directly to the center of Smith chart. As the schematic of Figure 3-29 shows, a 50 Ohm transmission line of 43.38 electrical degrees moves the impedance to the center of the Smith chart.

Figure 3-29 Open circuit shunt transmission line added to an impedance

Simulate the schematic and display S11 to see that the impedance has moved to the center of Smith chart, as shown in Figure 3-30.

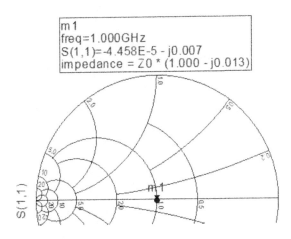

m1
freq=1.000GHz
S(1,1)=-4.458E-5 - j0.007
impedance = Z0 * (1.000 - j0.013)

Figure 3-30 Movement of the marker to the center of the chart

Similarly, the Figure 3-31 shows that a shorted 3.2 pF capacitor is equivalent to the open transmission line which moves the impedance to the center of Smith chart.

Figure 3-31 Short circuit capacitor equivalent to open circuit TLine

References and Further Readings

[1]   David M. Pozar, *Microwave Engineering*, Third Edition, John Wiley and Sons, Inc., 2005.

[2]   Franklin F. Kuo, Network Analysis and Synthesis, John Wiley and Sons Inc., 1966

[3]   William Sinnema, Electronic Transmission Technology, Prentice-Hall, Inc, Englewood Cliffs, New Jersey 07632, 1979

[4]   Chris Bowick, RF Circuit Design, Second Edition, Newnes, Elsevier, 2008

[5]   Keysight Technologies, Manuals for Advanced Design System, *ADS 2015.07 Documentation Set*, EEsof EDA Division, Santa Rosa, California www.keysight.com

[16]   Ali A. Behagi and Stephen D. Turner, Microwave and RF Engineering, A Simulation Approach with Keysight Genesys Software, BT Microwave LLC, State College, PA , March 2015

Problems

3-1.   Place a 20 + j30 Ω impedance at point A on the Smith chart. Add a series inductance to move the impedance along the constant resistance circle to point B having the impedance 20 + j50 Ω. Using a design frequency of 1000MHz, calculate the inductance that this reactance represents.

3-2.   Continuing with Problem 3-1, enable the admittance coordinates on the Smith chart to add a shunt element. Add a shunt capacitance to move the impedance to the real axis. Measure the susceptance required to move to the real impedance axis by the difference between the intersecting susceptance lines.

3-3.   Calculate the magnitude of reflection coefficient for a desired VSWR = 2.

3-4.   Using ADS, create a constant VSWR circle for a VSWR=20. Comment on the VSWR value required to place the VSWR circle on the circumference of the Smith chart.

3-5.   A load of 75 + j20 Ω is connected to a 50 Ω transmission line. Calculate the load admittance and the input impedance if the line is 0.2 wavelengths long.

3-6.   For the load impedance in Problem 3-4, determine the reflection coefficient and the transmission coefficient.

3-7.   For the load impedance in Problem 3-4, determine the normalized value of the load impedance if the impedance is normalized to 75 Ω.

3-8.   A series RLC load, R = 100 Ω, L = 20 nH, C = 25 pF is connected to a 50 Ω transmission line. Calculate the VSWR and reflection coefficient at the load at 100 MHz.

3-9.   Using the RLC load impedance of problem 3-8 determine the impedance with a series transmission line of characteristic impedance of 50 Ω and electrical length of 180 degrees.

3-10.   Determine the input impedance of a network that has a reflection coefficient of 0.5 at an angle of 112°.

3-11.   Create a one-port S parameter text file with the impedance of Problem 3-10 at a frequency of 1 GHz. Plot the S parameter, S11, on the Smith chart.

Chapter 4

Resonant Circuits and Filters

4.1 Introduction

The first half of this chapter examines resonant circuits. The second half is an introduction to the vast subject of filter networks. In the first half we discuss the lumped element resonant circuits and the lumped equivalent networks of mechanical and distributed resonators. Resonant circuits are used in many applications such as filters, oscillators, tuners, tuned amplifiers, and microwave communication networks. The analysis of basic lumped element series and parallel RLC resonant circuits is implemented using the ADS software. The discussion turns to microwave resonators with an analysis of the Q factor and transmission line resonators. Using the ADS software is demonstrated in the analysis and design of all resonant and filter networks. In the second half of the chapter the design of lumped element filters is followed by an introduction to distributed element filters. The chapter concludes with the design of microstrip coupled line filters.

4.2 Resonant Circuits

Near resonance, RF and microwave resonant circuits can be represented either as a lumped element series or parallel RLC network.

Series Resonant Circuits

In this section we analyze the behavior of the series resonant circuits in ADS.

Example 4-1: Consider the one port series resonator that is represented as a series RLC circuit of Figure 4-1. Analyze the circuit, with R = 10 Ω, L = 10 nH, and C = 10 pF.

Solution: The procedure for ADS analysis is as follows. This procedure will be repeated throughout the book.

- Start ADS and create a new workspace
- Name the workspace Ex4.2-1_wrk
- From the Main window create a new schematic in cell_1

- In the schematic window, click Insert > Template >ads-templates:S_Params

- Delete the DisplayTemplate icon

- Place R, L, and C elements from the Lumped-Components palette   on the schematic and connect them as shown in Figure 4-1.

- Set R=10 Ω, L=10 nH, and C=10 pF

- Type in Zin in the part selection box and place it on the schematic to measure the input impedance of the circuit.

- Set the frequency range from 450 to 550 MHz in 1 kHz step and wire up the schematic as shown in Figure 4-1

Figure 4-1 One-port series RLC resonator circuit

The plot of the resonator's input impedance in Figure 4-2 shows that the resonance frequency is about 503.3 MHz and the input impedance at resonance is 10 Ω, the value of the resistor in the network.

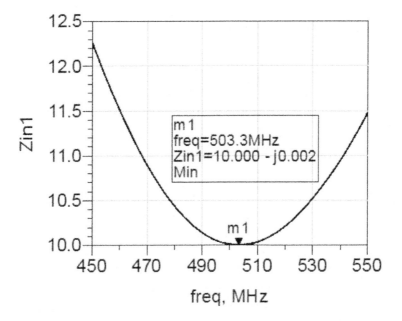

Figure 4-2 Input impedance plot showing the resonance frequency

The input impedance of the series RLC resonant circuit is given by,

$$Z_{in} = R + j\omega L - j\frac{1}{\omega C}$$

Where, $\omega = 2\pi f$ is the angular frequency in radian per second.

If the AC current flowing in the series resonant circuit is I, then the complex power delivered to the resonator is

$$P_{in} = \frac{|I|^2}{2} Z_{in} = \frac{|I|^2}{2}\left(R + j\omega L - j\frac{1}{\omega C}\right) \qquad (4\text{-}1)$$

At resonance the reactive power of the inductor is equal to the reactive power of the capacitor. Therefore, the power delivered to the resonator is equal to the power dissipated in the resistor

$$P_{in} = \frac{|I|^2 R}{2} \qquad (4\text{-}2)$$

Parallel Resonant Circuits

Example 4-2: Analyze a rearrangement of the RLC components of Figure 4-1 into the parallel configuration of Figure 4-3. The schematic of Figure 4-3 represents the lumped element representation of the parallel resonant circuit.

Solution: The one port parallel resonant circuit is shown in Figure 4-3.

Figure 4-3 One-port parallel RLC resonant circuit

Simulate the schematic and display the input impedance in a rectangular plot. The plot of the magnitude of the input impedance shows that the resonance frequency is still 503.3 MHz where the input impedance is R = 10 Ω. Again this shows that the impedance of the inductor cancels the impedance of the capacitor at

resonance. In other words, the reactance, X_L, is equal to the reactance, X_C, at the resonance frequency.

Figure 4-4 Input impedance of parallel RLC resonant circuit

The input admittance of the parallel resonant circuit is given by:

$$Y_{IN} = \frac{1}{R} + j\omega C - j\frac{1}{\omega L}$$

If the AC voltage across the parallel resonant circuit is V, then the complex power delivered to the resonator is

$$P_{in} = \frac{|V|^2}{2}Y_{in} = \frac{|V|^2}{2}\left(\frac{1}{R} + j\omega C - j\frac{1}{\omega L}\right) \qquad (4\text{-}3)$$

At resonance the reactive power of the inductor is equal to the reactive power of the capacitor. Therefore, the power delivered to the resonator is equal to the power dissipated in the resistor

$$P_{in} = \frac{|V|^2}{2R} \qquad (4\text{-}4)$$

The resonance frequency for the parallel resonant circuit as well as the series resonant circuit is obtained by setting $\omega_0 C = \frac{1}{\omega_0 L}$ or:

$$\omega_o = 2\pi f_o = \frac{1}{\sqrt{L C}} \tag{4-5}$$

Where, ω_0 is the angular frequency in radian per second and f_0 is equal to the frequency in Hertz.

Resonant Circuit Loss

In Figures 4-1 and 4-3 the resistor R1 represents the loss in the resonator. It includes the losses in the capacitor as well as the inductor. The Q factor can be shown to be a ratio of the energy stored in the inductor and capacitor to the power dissipated in the resistor as a function of frequency [6]. For the series resonant circuit of Figure 4-1 the unloaded Q factor is defined by:

$$Q_u = \frac{X}{R} = \frac{\omega_o L}{R} = \frac{1}{\omega_o RC} \tag{4-6}$$

The unloaded Q factor of the parallel resonant circuit in Figure 4-3 is simply the inverse of the unloaded Q factor of the series resonant circuit.

$$Q_u = \frac{R}{X} = \frac{R}{\omega_o L} = \omega_o RC \tag{4-7}$$

We can clearly see that as the resistance increases in the series resonant circuit, the Q factor decreases. Conversely as the resistance increases in the parallel resonant circuit, the Q factor increases.

The Q factor is a measure of loss in the resonant circuit. Thus a higher Q corresponds to lower loss and a lower Q corresponds to a higher loss. It is usually desirable to achieve high Q factors in a resonator as it will lead to lower losses in filter applications or lower phase noise in oscillators. Note that the resonator Q of

Equation (4-6) and (4-7) is defined as Q_u, the unloaded Q of the resonator. This means that the resonator is not connected to any load. Equations (4-6) and (4-7) would then have to be modified to include the source and load resistance. We might also surmise that any reactance associated with the source or load impedance may alter the resonant frequency of the resonator. This leads to two additional definitions of Q factor that the engineer must consider: the loaded Q and the external Q.

Using Equation (4-7) to define the Q factor for the circuit requires that we include the source and load resistance which is 'loading' the resonator. This leads to the definition of the loaded Q, Q_L, for the parallel resonator in Equation (4-8).

$$Q_L = \frac{R_S + R + R_L}{\omega_o L} \qquad (4\text{-}8)$$

Conversely we can define a Q factor in terms of only the external source and load resistance. This leads to the definition of the external Q, Q_E.

$$Q_E = \frac{R_S + R_L}{\omega_o L} \qquad (4\text{-}9)$$

The three Q factors are related by the inverse relationship of Equation (4-10).

$$\frac{1}{Q_L} = \frac{1}{Q_E} + \frac{1}{Q_U} \qquad (4\text{-}10)$$

At RF and microwave frequencies it is difficult to directly measure the Q_u of a resonator. We may be able to calculate the Q factor based on the physical properties of the individual inductors and capacitors as we have seen in chapter 1. This is usually quite difficult and the Q factor is typically measured using a Vector Network Analyzer, VNA. Therefore, the measured Q factor is usually the loaded Q, Q_L. External Q is often used with oscillator circuits that are generating a signal. In this case the oscillator's load impedance is varied so that the external Q can be measured. The loaded Q of the network is then related to the fractional bandwidth by Equation (4-11) [8].

$$Q_L = \frac{\sqrt{f_l f_h}}{BW_{-3dB}} \qquad (4\text{-}11)$$

Where, BW is the -3 dB bandwidth, f_l and f_h are the lower and upper frequencies in Hz at -3dB points.

Loaded Q and External Q

Example 4-3: Analyze the parallel resonator that is attached to a 50 Ω source and load as shown in Figure 4-5. Measure the loaded Q factor of the resonator.

Figure 4-5 Parallel resonator with source and load impedance

Solution: To measure the loaded Q factor of the resonator we plot the resonator insertion loss and measure the 3 dB bandwidth.

Figure 4-6: Resonator 3 dB bandwidth and frequencies

The loaded Q factor from Equation (4-11) is calculated with $f_l = 92.28$ MHz, $f_h = 108.3$ MHz, and BW $= 108.3 - 92.28 = 16.02$

$$Q_L = \frac{\sqrt{f_l f_h}}{BW} = \frac{99.97\,MHz}{16.02\,MHz} = 6.24$$

Notice that the loaded Q factor is quite low.

4.3 Lumped Element Parallel Resonator Design

Example 4-4: Analyze the following parallel resonator at 100 MHz having a source resistance of 100 Ω and a load resistance of 400 Ω.

Solution: Best accuracy would be obtained by using S parameter files or Modelithics models for the inductor and capacitor. However a good first order model can be obtained by using the ADS inductor and capacitor models that include the component Q factor. These models save us the work of calculating the equivalent resistive part of the inductor and capacitor model. The component Q factors are shown in the schematic of Figure 4-7.

Figure 4-7: Parallel resonator using components with assigned Q factors

Simulate the schematic and display the insertion loss in a rectangular plot.

Figure 4-8: Insertion loss and calculation of 3 dB bandwidth and Q factor

Note that markers have been placed on the plot of the insertion loss, S21, which gives readout of -3 dB bandwidth. To place markers m2 and m3 manually at -3dB points, first place marker m1 at the peak of S21 trace. Next place marker m2 at a point below marker m1. Select marker m2 and press the up and down arrows to move the marker m2 as close to -3dB point as possible. Repeat the process for marker m3. The loaded Q can be calculated using Equation (4-11).

$$Q_L = \frac{\sqrt{f_l f_h}}{BW} = \frac{99.98 MHz}{5.901 MHz} = 16.94$$

The designer must use caution when sweeping resonant circuits. Particularly high Q band pass networks require a large number of discrete frequency steps in order to achieve the necessary resolution required to accurately measure the 3dB bandwidth. In this example the Linear Analysis is set up to sweep the circuit from 90 MHz to 110 MHz using 1 kHz steps.

Effect of Load Resistance on Bandwidth and Q_L

In RF circuits and systems the impedances encountered are often quite low, ranging from 1 Ω to 50 Ω. It may not be practical to have a source impedance of 100 Ω and a load impedance of 400 Ω.

Example 4-5: In the parallel LC resonator of Example 4-4, change the load from 400 Ω to 50 Ω, **(a)** measure the loaded Q factor and the 3 dB bandwidth of the resonator, **(b)** tune the components values to increase the loaded Q factor while keeping the resonant frequency at 100 MHz, **(c)** optimize the resonator components to increase the loaded Q factor further.

Solution (a): Change the load from 400 Ω to 50 Ω as shown in Figure 4-9.

Figure 4-9 Parallel resonance circuit

Simulate the schematic, display the insertion loss, and measure the 3dB bandwidth. The loaded Q factor and the 3dB insertion loss measurements are shown in Figure 4-10.

Figure 4-10: Insertion loss of parallel resonance circuit

The bandwidth measurement at 3 dB insertion loss shows that bandwidth has increased to 12.88 MHz resulting in a decreased loaded Q factor of 7.76.

$$Q_L = \frac{\sqrt{f_l f_h}}{BW_{3dB}} = \frac{99.96 MHz}{12.88 MHz} = 7.76$$

Notice that the loaded Q factor has decreased by nearly half of the value in Example 4-4. We have increased the bandwidth or de-Q'd the resonator. This can also be thought of as tighter coupling of the resonator to the load.

Solution (b): The tuning feature in ADS is a fast way to lean how a circuit behaves when the component parameters are changed. In other words, the tuning feature enable us to change one or more the value of design parameters and quickly see the effect on the output without re-simulating the entire design.

When a component is made tunable, any change in the component value would automatically change the plot. To tune the resonator components in Figure 4-9, click on the Tuning Fork icon, to opens the Tune Parameters window, shown in Figure 4-11.

Figure 4-11: Tuning parameters

While the Tune Parameters window is open, select the capacitor and inductor in the resonator circuit, one by one, and add them to the Tune Parameters. Selection of the inductor is shown in Figure 4-12.

Figure 4-12: Selection of the inductor for tuning

After each selection you would see a small window with the slider, as shown in Figure 4-13.

Figure 4-13: Tuning of parameters for tuning

In the Tune Parameters window the values of the Maximum, Minimum, and Step can be changed to meet any other requirement.

Start tuning the resonator by moving the sliders up or down. For each slider setting you can see the movement of the simulation plots to a new position without the need for re-simulation. Parameter values can be swept in Linear or Log format. We can also Enable/Disable a parameter to tune by clicking on Enable/Disable button. Once we have achieved the desired or best possible results, we can click the Update Schematic button to update the tuning values on the schematic. If you accidentally click Close, the pop up window will appear checking whether you would like to update your Schematic or not. Figure 4-14 shows the new slider settings for the resonator.

Figure 4-14: New slider settings for the inductor and capacitor

Notice, in order to keep the frequency constant at 100 MHz, we have increased the capacitor value from 398 pF to 404 pF while the inductor value has been decreased from 6.37 nH to 6.27 nH. The result of tuning is shown in Figure 415.

Figure 4-15: Insertion loss, bandwidth, and loaded Q factor

Notice that the tuning has increased the loaded Q factor from 7.76 to 7.87.

Solution (c): We now want to optimize the parallel resonator circuit to achieve the desired performance without the need for tuning.

Pre-optimization process in ADS is achieved in 3 steps.

1. Setting up Optimization Goals

2. Placing Optimization Controller and selecting the Type of Optimizer

3. Selecting the number of iterations

To begin the process, we first make a copy of the tuned schematic cell so that we can perform optimization in the tuning workspace.

1. On the ADS main window right click on the Cell to be copied and select Copy Cell to open the Copy Cell window.

2. In the Copy Cell window check the "Include hierarchy" box and select the current library.

3. Select a New Name for the cell as shown in Figure 4-16. Click OK.

Figure 4-16: Copy Cell window

4. Go to the Main window and notice that the selected cell has been copied.

5. In the new schematic go to Opt/Stat/DOE library palette and place the Goal component on the schematic.

6. Double click on the Goal1 to open the Optim Goal Input window.

7. In the Optim Goal Input window, for the Expression enter dB(S(1,1)), which is the Y-axis of the optimization plot, for the Analysis select the S parameter analysis SP1, set the Weight equal to 1.0, and check the "freq" box from the Sweep Variables option.

8. In the Limit lines select the less than sign, <, and enter -20 for the Max.

9. For the frequency limits enter 9e7 "for freq min" and 1.1e8 for "freq max" which means from 90 MHz to 110 MHz, as shown in Figure 4-17.

Figure 4-17: Optimization Goal1 setup

10. Select Apply and click OK to open the schematic window.

Figure 4-18: Pre-optimization schematic-1

11. Place Goal2 on the schematic for S21 and repeat similar steps as done in defining the S(11) goal except for the Expression use dB(S(2,1)).

Figure 4-19: Optimization Goal2 setup

12. From Opt/Stat/DOE library palette place the Optimization Controller on the schematic, as shown in Figure 4-20.

Figure 4-20: Pre-optimization resonator schematic-2

13. Double-click on the Optimization controller and set the Optimization Type to Gradient and the Number of Iterations to 25

Figure 4-21: Optimization controller setup

14. Go to the Display tab and select Clear All which will uncheck all options.

15. Check the Optim Type and MaxIters to be displayed on the schematic.

16. Click OK. The schematic in Figure 4-22 is now ready for optimization.

Figure 4-22: Final Optimization schematic

The next step is to make the resonator components ready for optimization.

17. In the schematic window go to Simulate > Simulation Variables Setup to open the Simulation Variables Setup window.

18. Select the Optimization tab and check the capacitor and inductor for optimization, as shown in Figure 4-23.

Figure 4-23: Selection of components to be optimized

19. Enter the Max and Min values for the selected capacitor and inductor. Click OK.

20. Click the Optimize button ⬆ on the schematic toolbar to open the Optimization Cockpit and begin optimization. The final optimization Cockpit after 25 iteration is shown in Figure 4-24

Figure 4-24: Final Optimization Cockpit

21. Exit the Optimization Cockpit and update the schematic.
22. The optimized schematic is shown in Figure 4-25

Figure 4-25: Final Optimized schematic

23. Simulate the schematic and display the insertion loss in Figure 4-26.
24. Write equations for -3 dB bandwidth and the loaded Q factor.
25. Place markers at 100 MHz and -3dB points.
26. Display the -3 dB points and loaded Q factor in a Table.

Figure 4-26: Insertion loss, bandwidth, and loaded Q factor

Notice that the optimization has deceased the -3 dB bandwidth and increased the loaded Q factor further from 7.87 to 7.965.

4.4 Lumped Element Resonator Decoupling

To maintain the high Q of the resonator when attached to a load such as 50 Ω, it is necessary to transform the low impedance to high impedance presented to the load. The 50 Ω impedance can be transformed to the higher impedance of the parallel resonator thereby resulting in less loading of the resonator impedance. This is referred to as loosely coupling the resonator to the load. The tapped-capacitor and tapped-inductor networks can be used to accomplish this Q transformation in lumped element circuits.

Design of the Tapped Capacitor Resonator

Example 4-6: Rearrange the parallel LC network of Figure 4-8 with the tapped capacitor network shown in Figure 4-10. Re-examine the circuit's 3 dB bandwidth and loaded Q factor.

Solution: The new capacitor values for C1 and C2 can be found by the simultaneous solution of the following equations [2].

$$C_T = \frac{C1 \cdot C2}{C1 + C2} \tag{4-12}$$

$$R_{L1} = R_L \left(1 + \frac{C1}{C2}\right)^2 \tag{4-13}$$

R_{L1} is the higher, transformed, load resistance. In this example substitute R_{L1} = 400 Ω, the original load resistance value. C_T is simply the original capacitance of 398 pf. The capacitor values are found to be: C1 = 1126.23 pF and C2 = 616.1 pF. The new resonator circuit is shown in Figure 4-27.

Figure 4-27: Parallel LC resonator using tapped capacitor

Sweeping the circuit we see that the response has returned to the original performance of Figure 4-8.

Figure 4-28: Response of parallel LC resonator using a tapped capacitor

The 3 dB bandwidth has returned to 5.89 MHz making the Q_L equal to:

$$Q_L = \frac{\sqrt{f_l f_h}}{BW} = \frac{99.92 MHz}{5.897 MHz} = 16.94$$

The 50 Ω load resistor has been successfully decoupled from the resonator.
The tapped capacitor and inductor resonators are popular methods of decoupling RF and lower microwave frequency resonators. It is frequently seen in RF oscillator topologies such as the Colpitts oscillator in the VHF frequency range.

Design of the Tapped Inductor Resonator

Example 4-7: Design a tapped inductor network to decouple the 50 Ω source impedance from loading the resonator.

Solution: Replace the 100 Ω source impedance with a 50 Ω source and use a tapped inductor network to transform the new 50 Ω source to 100 Ω. Modify the circuit to split the 6.37 nH inductor, L_T, into two series inductors, L1 and L2. The inductor values can then be calculated by solving the following equation set simultaneously [2]. R_{S1} is the higher, transformed, source resistance. In this example substitute $R_{S1} = 100 \ \Omega$,

$$Rs1 = Rs\left(\frac{L_T}{L_1}\right)^2 \tag{4-14}$$

$$L_T = L_1 + L_2 \tag{4-15}$$

Solving the equation set results in values of L1=4.5 nH and L2=1.87 nH. The resulting schematic and response are shown in Figures 4-29 and 4-30.

Figure 4-29: Tapped-inductor parallel resonant circuit

Figure 4-30: Response of the parallel resonant circuit

The new response in Figure 4-30 is identical to the plot of Figure 4-8. Therefore we now have a source and load resistance of 50 Ω and have not reduced the Q of the resonator from what we had with the original source resistance of 100 Ω and a load resistance of 400 Ω.

4.5 Practical Microwave Resonators

At higher RF and microwave frequencies resonators are seldom realized with discrete lumped element RLC components. This is primarily due to the fact that the small values of inductance and capacitance are physically unrealizable. Even if the values could be physically realized we would see that the resulting Q factors would be unacceptably low for most applications. Microwave resonators are realized in a wide variety of physical forms. Resonators can be realized in all of the basic transmission line forms that were covered in Chapter 2. There are many specialized resonators such as ceramic dielectric resonator pucks that are coupled to a microstrip transmission line as well as Yittrium Iron Garnet spheres that are loop coupled to its load. These resonators are optimized for very high Q factors and may be tunable over a range of frequencies.

Figure 4-31: Ceramic dielectric resonator (puck) and coaxial resonator

Transmission Line Resonators

In chapter 2 Figure 2-20 we have seen that a quarter-wave short-circuited transmission line results in a parallel resonant circuit. Similarly Figure 2-22 showed that a half-wave open-circuited transmission line results in a parallel resonant circuit too. Such parallel resonant circuits are often used as one port resonators. Near the resonant frequency, the one port resonator behaves as a parallel RLC network as shown in Figure 4-3. As the frequency moves further from resonance the equivalent network becomes more complex typically involving multiple parallel RLC networks. One port resonators are coupled to one another to form filter networks or directly connected to a transistor to form a microwave oscillator. Knowing the losses due to the physical and electrical parameters of the transmission line, one can calculate the unloaded Q factor of the transmission line resonator. The microstrip resonator Q_u is comprised of losses due to the conductor metal, the substrate dielectric, and radiation losses. The Q_u is often dominated by the conductor Q. Unfortunately it can be quite difficult to accurately determine the conductor losses in a microstrip resonator. T. C. Edwards has developed a set of simplified expressions for the conductor losses [4]. Equation (4-16) is an approximation of the conductor losses that treats the transmission line as a perfectly smooth surface.

$$\alpha_c = 0.072 \frac{\sqrt{f}}{W_e Z_o} \lambda_g \qquad \text{dB/inch} \qquad (4\text{-}16)$$

Where,

   f = the frequency in GHz

   W_e = the effective conductor width (inches)

   Z_o = the characteristic impedance of the line

   α_c = Conductor loss in dB/inch

   λ_g = wavelength in dielectric in inches

A microstrip conductor is actually not perfectly smooth but exhibits a certain roughness. The surface roughness exists on the bottom of the microstrip conductor where it contacts the dielectric. This can be seen by magnifying the cross section of a microstrip line's contact with the dielectric material. The surface roughness is usually specified as an r.m.s. value.

Figure 4-32: Cross section of microstrip line showing surface roughness at the conductor to dielectric interface (courtesy of Tektronix)

Edwards modified Equation (4-16) to include the effects of the surface roughness as given by Equation (4-17).

$$\alpha'_c = \alpha_c \left[1 + \frac{2}{\pi} \tan^{-1} \left(1.4 \left(\frac{\Delta}{\delta_s} \right)^2 \right) \right] \quad \text{dB/inch} \qquad (4\text{-}17)$$

Where, Δ is the r.m.s. surface roughness and δ_s is the conductor skin depth.

The corresponding Q factor related to the conductor is then given by:

$$Q_c = \frac{27.3 \sqrt{\varepsilon_{eff}}}{\alpha_c \lambda_o} \qquad (4\text{-}18)$$

The dielectric loss is determined by the dielectric constant and loss tangent. It is calculated using Equation (4-19).

$$\alpha_d = 27.3 \, \frac{\varepsilon_r \left(\varepsilon_{eff} - 1 \right) \tan \delta}{\sqrt{\varepsilon_{reff}} \left(\varepsilon_r - 1 \right) \lambda_o} \quad \text{dB/inch} \qquad (4\text{-}19)$$

Where:

ε_r = the substrate dielectric constant

ε_{reff} = the effective dielectric constant

tanδ = the loss tangent of the dielectric

λ_o = wavelength in inches

The corresponding Q factor due to the dielectric is then given by:

$$Q_d = 27.3 \frac{\sqrt{\varepsilon_{\textit{eff}}}}{\alpha_d \lambda_o} \tag{4-20}$$

We know that a microstrip line will also have some radiation of energy from the top side of the line. The open circuit stub will also experience some radiation effect from the open circuited end. On low dielectric constant substrates, $\varepsilon_r \le 4.0$, the radiation losses are more significant for high impedance lines. Conversely for high dielectric constant substrates, $\varepsilon_r \ge 10$, low impedance lines experience more radiation loss [10]. The radiation Q factor is presented as Equation (4-21) [9].

$$Q_r = \frac{Z_o(f)}{480\pi \left(\dfrac{h}{\lambda_o}\right)^2 \left\{ \left(\dfrac{\varepsilon_{\textit{eff}(f)}+1}{\varepsilon_{\textit{eff}(f)}}\right) - \left[\dfrac{\left(\varepsilon_{\textit{eff}(f)}-1\right)^2}{2\left(\varepsilon_{\textit{eff}(f)}\right)^{3\!/\!2}} \ln\left(\dfrac{\sqrt{\varepsilon_{\textit{eff}(f)}}+1}{\sqrt{\varepsilon_{\textit{eff}(f)}}-1}\right)\right] \right\}} \tag{4-21}$$

Where, h = substrate thickness in cm.

Note that in Equation (4-21) the line impedance and effective dielectric constant are defined as functions of frequency. This includes the dispersion or frequency dependent effect of Z_o and $\varepsilon_{\textit{eff}}$. Dispersion tends to slightly increase the $\varepsilon_{\textit{eff}}$ as the frequency increases. This dispersive Z_o and $\varepsilon_{\textit{eff}}$ are given in Equations (4-22) and (4-23).

$$\varepsilon_{eff(f)} = \frac{\varepsilon_r - \varepsilon_{eff}}{1 + \left[(0.6 + 0.009Z_o)\left(\dfrac{f}{Z_o / 8\pi(h - 2t)}\right)^2\right]} \qquad (4\text{-}22)$$

Where,

h = substrate thickness in mils

t = conductor thickness in mils

And,

$$Z_{o(f)} = Z_o \sqrt{\frac{\varepsilon_{eff}}{\varepsilon_{eff(f)}}} \qquad (4\text{-}23)$$

Finally the resultant overall unloaded Q factor, Q_u, of the microstrip line can be determined by the reciprocal relationship of Equation (4.24).

$$\frac{1}{Q_u} = \frac{1}{Q_c} + \frac{1}{Q_d} + \frac{1}{Q_r} \qquad (4\text{-}24)$$

Microstrip Resonator

Example 4-8: Design a 5 GHz half wavelength open-circuited microstrip resonator. The resonator is realized with a 50 Ω microstrip line on Roger's RO3003 dielectric. Calculate the unloaded Q factor of the resonator. The substrate parameters are defined as:

Dielectric constant	$\varepsilon_r = 3$,	Substrate height	h = 0.030 in.
Conductor thickness	t = .0026 in.	Line Impedance	$Z_o = 50$ Ω
Conductor width	w = 0.075 in.	Loss tangent	tanδ = 0.0013

Solution: Using the simplified expression of Equation (4-16) for a smooth microstrip line the loss and conductor Q factor is calculated as:

$$\alpha_c = 0.072 \frac{\sqrt{5}}{0.077(50)} \cdot 1.52 = 0.063 \ dB/inch$$

$$Q_c = \frac{27.3\sqrt{2.41}}{(0.063)(2.36)} = 283.1$$

The dielectric loss and the Q factor are then calculated from Equation (4-19) and (4-20).

$$\alpha_d = 27.3 \frac{(3)(2.41-1)(0.0013)}{\sqrt{2.41}(3-1)(2.36)} = 0.021 \, dB/inch$$

$$Q_d = 27.3 \frac{\sqrt{2.41}}{(0.021)(2.36)} = 875.2$$

For simplicity the radiation Q factor will be omitted. We will model the resonator using the ADS Linear simulator. Linear simulators often do not model the radiation effects of the microstrip line. Therefore the overall unloaded Q factors then becomes.

$$\frac{1}{Q_u} = \frac{1}{283.1} + \frac{1}{875.2} = \frac{1}{213.9}$$

$$Q_u = 213.9$$

Microstrip Resonator Model in ADS

The half wave open-circuited microstrip resonator is modeled in ADS as shown in Fig 4-33. Note that the source and load impedance has been increased to 5000 Ω to avoid loading the impedance of the parallel resonant circuit. Perform a linear sweep of the resonator using 0.1 MHz step from 4500 MHz to 5400 MHz.

Figure 4-33: Half-wave open ended microstrip resonator

Simulate the schematic and display the S21, the -3 dB bandwidth, and the loaded Q factor, as shown in Figure 4-34.

Figure 4-34: Response of the half-wave open circuit microstrip resonator

Using the Equation (4-11), the 3dB bandwidth is measured to determine the loaded Q of the resonator.

$$Q_L = \frac{4974.88MHz}{68MHz} = 73.16$$

The insertion loss at the resonant frequency can be used to relate the loaded Q factor to the Q_u as shown by Equation (4-25).

$$InsertionLoss(dB) = 20\log\frac{Q_u}{Q_u - Q_L} \qquad (4\text{-}25)$$

Or:
$$0.76 = 20\log\frac{Q_u}{Q_u - 73.16}$$

Solving for Q_u we get.

$$Q_u = 882.7$$

4.6 Resonator Series Reactance Coupling

To reduce the loading on the half wave resonator of Figure 4-33, the source and load impedances of 5000 Ω were used. In practice the resonator is typically coupled to lower impedance circuits. If we attempt to examine the resonator on a network analyzer, most modern test equipment will have 50 Ω impedance levels. Such resonators are often coupled to the circuit by a highly reactive circuit element. This reactive element can be realized as a series capacitor or inductor. The resonator is then analyzed as a one port network.

Example 4-9: In the following capacitive coupled half-wave microstrip resonator change the value of the capacitor and find out when the resonator is critically coupled.

Figure 4-35 Capacitive coupled half-wave microstrip resonator

Solution: As the frequency is swept over a narrow frequency range around the resonant frequency, a circle is formed on the Smith chart. This trace is known as the Q circle of the resonator [5]. Figure 4-36 shows the Smith chart plot of the resonator's input reflection coefficient, S11. Three plots are shown each with a different value of coupling capacitance. We can see that as the coupling capacitance changes, the resonant frequency of the circuit also changes. The series capacitance acts to decrease the overall resonance frequency of the circuit. This new resonance frequency is known as the loaded resonance frequency. Because the series capacitance lowers the frequency, the length of the resonator is decreased to 0.736 inches to return the resonant frequency close to 5 GHz. With the coupling capacitance set at 0.027 pF the Q circle passes through the center of the Smith chart at the resonant frequency of 5GHz. This is known as critical coupling and is characterized by having the lowest return loss on the scalar plot of S11 in Figure 4-37. With the capacitance increased to 0.05 pF the resonator is more strongly coupled to the 50 Ω load. The scalar plot shows that the resonance frequency is decreased. The Smith chart shows a larger Q circle which is a characteristic of an over coupled resonator. With the coupling capacitor set to 0.015 pF the resonance frequency increases. The Smith chart shows that the Q circles become much smaller thus under coupling the resonator.

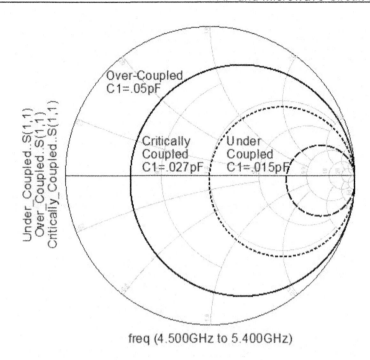

freq (4.500GHz to 5.400GHz)

Figure 4-36 Smith chart plots of the resonator input reflection coefficients

Figure 4-37 shows the scalar plot of the input reflection coefficients

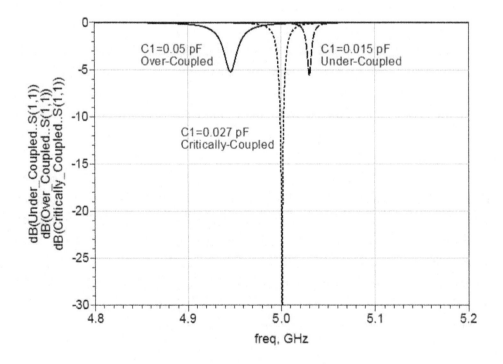

Figure 4-37: Scalar plots of the resonator input reflection coefficients

One Port Microwave Resonator Analysis

The microstrip half wave resonator was fairly easy to model and analyze in ADS. Many microwave resonators are not as easy to model. High Q microwave resonators are often realized as metallic cavities or dielectric resonators. The reactive coupling of the resonator to the circuit can be even more difficult to model. The coupling usually occurs by magnetic or electric coupling by a probe or loop inserted into the cavity. An E field probe coupled to a coaxial cavity resonator is shown in Figure 4-38. A dielectric resonator is coupled to a microstrip line by flux linkage in air as shown in Figure 4-39. The designer is left to develop approximate models based on a lumped RLC equivalent models and couple the resonator to the circuit using an ideal transformer model. Linear simulation can still be of value in the design and evaluation process if we have a measured S parameter file of the resonator's reflection coefficient. Just as we have used S parameter models to represent capacitors and inductors we can also use the measured S parameters of a resonator. All modern vector network analyzers have the ability to save an S parameter data file for any measurement that can be made by the instrument. This section will show how we can use ADS to analyze the S parameter file of a microwave resonator.

Figure 4-38: Coaxial cavity with E field probe coupled to center conductor

The coupling of microwave resonators is often characterized by a coupling coefficient k. The coupling coefficient is the ratio of the power dissipated in the load to the power dissipated in the resonator [5].

$$k = \frac{P_{load}}{P_{resonator}} = \frac{Q_o}{Q_{ext}} \qquad (4\text{-}27)$$

Where: Q_o is the unloaded Q of the resonator

                Q_{ext} is the external Q of the resonator

When P_{load} is equal to $P_{resonator}$, $k = 1$ and the critical coupling case exists. Substituting the reciprocal Q factor relationship of Equation (4-10) into Equation (4-27) we can relate the coupling coefficient to the loaded Q_L and unloaded Q_o of the resonator.

$$Q_L = \frac{Q_o}{1+k} \qquad (4\text{-}2$$

Figure 4-39: Dielectric resonator coupled to microstrip transmission line

Smith Chart Qo Measurement of Microstrip Resonator

Now the unloaded Q_o of the resonator can be calculated if the Q_L and k can be measured. Because the resonator is a one port device we cannot pass a signal through the device and measure the 3dB bandwidth as was done in section 4.5.3. Kajfez [5] has described a technique to extract the coupling coefficient k and Q_L values from the Q circle of the resonator. Consider the Q circle on the Smith chart of Figure 4-40. A line that is projected from the center of the Smith chart to intersect the Q circle with minimum length will intersect the circle at the loaded resonance frequency, f_L. The length of this vector is labeled as $|\Gamma_L|$. As the line projects along a path of the diameter of the circle it intersects the circle near the circumference of the Smith chart at a point defined as $|\Gamma_d|$. The input reflection coefficient of the Q circle can be defined using the following equation [5].

$$\Gamma_i = \Gamma_d \left| 1 - \frac{2k}{1+k} \cdot \frac{1}{1 + jQ_L 2 \dfrac{\omega - \omega_L}{\omega_o}} \right| \tag{4-29}$$

Lines that are projected from Γ_d through the Q circle at the angles $\pm\phi$ are related to the loaded Q by Equation (4-30).

$$Q_L = \frac{f_L}{f_1 - f_2} \tan\phi \tag{4-30}$$

If we set $\phi = 45^\circ$ then Equation (4-30) reduces to the straightforward definition of Q_L given by Equation (4-31).

$$Q_L = \frac{f_L}{f_1 - f_2} \tag{4-31}$$

Previously we have noticed that the diameter of the circle was directly related to the coupling coefficient. The circle diameter can be measured from:

$$\left| \Gamma_d \right| - \left| \Gamma_L \right| = d \tag{4-32}$$

The coupling coefficient is then derived from the diameter of the Q circle.

$$k = \frac{d}{2-d} \tag{4-33}$$

Finally the unloaded resonator Q_o is then calculated from Equation (4-28). We can also find the unloaded resonance frequency directly from the Q circle. Follow the reactive line on the Smith chart that intersects the Q circle at Γ_d to the next Q circle intersection. The frequency at this Q circle intersection is the unloaded resonance frequency, f_o.

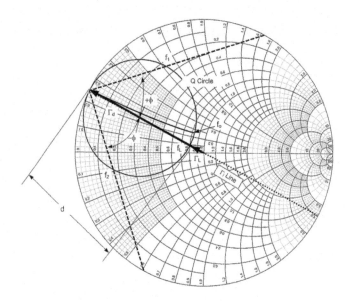

Figure 4-40 Resonator Q measurement from the resonator Q circle

4.7 Filter Design at RF and Microwave Frequency

In Section 4.3 we have seen that it is possible to change the shape of the frequency response of a parallel resonant circuit by choosing different source and load impedance values. Likewise multiple resonators can be coupled to one another and to the source and load to achieve various frequency shaping responses. These networks are referred to as filters.

Filter Topology

The subject of filter design is a complex topic and the subject of many dedicated texts [1–2]. This section is intended to serve as a fundamental primer to this vast topic. It is also intended to set a foundation for successful filter design using the ADS software. The four most popular filter types are: Low Pass, High Pass, Band Pass, and Band Stop. The basic transmission response of the filter types is shown in Figure 4-41. The filters allow RF energy to pass through their designed pass band. RF energy that is present outside of the pass band is reflected back toward the source and not transmitted to the load. The amount of energy present at the load is defined by the S21 response. The amount of energy reflected back to the source is characterized by the S11 response.

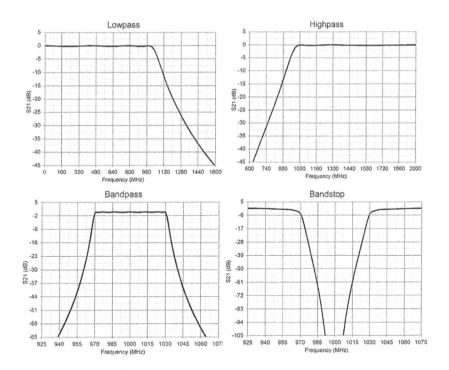

Figure 4-41 S21 versus frequency characteristic for the basic filter types

Filter Order

The design process for all of the major filter types is based on determination of the filter pass band, and the attenuation in the reject band. The attenuation in the reject band that is required by a filter largely determines the slope needed in the transmission frequency response. The slope of the filter's response is related to the order of the filter. The steeper the slope or 'skirt' of the filter; the higher is the order. The term order comes from the mathematical transfer function that describes a particular filter. The highest power of s in the denominator of the filter's Laplace transfer function is the order of the filter. For the simple low pass and high pass filters presented in this chapter the filter order is the same as the number of elements in the filter. However this is not the case for general filter networks. In more complex types of lowpass and highpass filters as well as bandpass and bandstop filters the filter order will not be equal to the number of elements in the filter. In the general case the filter order is the total of the number of transmission zeros at frequencies:

- $F = 0$ (DC)

- $F = \infty$

- $0 < F < \infty$ (specific frequencies between DC and ∞)

Transmission zeros block the transfer of energy from the source to the load. In fact the order of a filter network can be solved visually by adding up the number of transmission zeros that satisfy the above criteria. Figure 4-42 shows the relationship between the filter order and slope of the response for a Low Pass filter. Each filter of Figures 4-42, and 4-43 has the same cutoff frequency of 1000 MHz. The third order filter has an attenuation of about 16 dB at a rejection frequency of 2000 MHz. The fifth order filter shows an attenuation of 39 dB and the seventh order filter has more than 61 dB attenuation at 2000 MHz. It is therefore clear that the order of the filter is one of the first criteria to be determined in the filter design. It is dependent on the cutoff frequency of the pass band and the amount of attenuation desired at the rejection frequency.

Figure 4-42 A Relationship between filter order and the slope of S21

Figure 4-43: A Relationship between filter order and the slope of S21

Filter Type

The shape of the filter passband and attenuation skirt can take on different shape relationships based on the coupling among the various reactive elements in the filter. Over the years several polynomial expressions have been developed for these shape relationships. Named after their inventors, some of the more popular types include: Bessel, Butterworth, Chebyshev, and Cauer. Figures 4-44 and 4-45 show the general shape relationship among these filter types. The Bessel filter is a low Q filter and does not exhibit a steep roll off. The benefit of the Bessel filter is its linear phase or flat group delay response. This means that the Bessel filter can pass wideband signals while introducing little distortion. The Butterworth is a medium Q filter that has the flattest pass band of the group.

Figure 4-44: shape of Bessel and Butterworth filters

Figure 4-45: shape of Chebyshev, and Cauer filters

The Chebyshev response is a higher Q filter and has a noticeably steeper skirt moving toward the reject band. As a result it exhibits more transmission ripple in the pass band. The Cauer filter has the steepest slope of all of the four filter types. The Cauer filter is also known as an elliptic filter. Odd order Chebyshev and Cauer filters can be designed to have an equal source and load impedance. The even order Chebyshev and Cauer filters will have different output impedance from the specified input impedance. Another interesting characteristic of the

Cauer filter is that it has the same ripple in the rejection band as it has in the pass band. The Butterworth, Chebyshev and Cauer filters differ from the Bessel filter in their phase response. The phase response is very nonlinear across the pass band. This nonlinearity of the phase creates a varying group delay. The group delay introduces varying time delays to wideband signals which, in turn, can cause distortion to the signal. Group delay is simply the derivative, or slope, of the transmission phase and defined by Equation (4-34). Figure 4-46 shows the respective set of filter transmission characteristics with their corresponding group delay. Note the relative values of the group delay on the right hand axis.

$$\tau_g = -\frac{d\phi}{d\omega}$$

(4-34)

Where, ϕ is the phase shift in radians and ω is in radians per second.

From the group delay plots of Figure 4-46 it is evident that the group delay peaks near the corner frequency of the filter response. The sharper cutoff characteristic results in greater group delay at the band edge.

Filter Return Loss and Passband Ripple

The Bessel and Butterworth filters have a smooth transition between their cutoff frequency and rejection frequency. The forward transmission, S21, is very flat vs. frequency. The Chebyshev and Cauer filters have a more abrupt transition between their cutoff and rejection frequencies. This makes these filter types very popular for many filter applications encountered in RF and microwave engineering. It is clear from Figure 4-46 that a sharp-cutoff response is generally incompatible with a good phase response, or a group delay in the passband [6].

Figure 4-46 Group delay characteristic for various lowpass filter types

The Chebyshev and Cauer filter types have ripple in the forward transmission path, S21. The amount of ripple is caused by the degree of mismatch between the source and load impedance and thus the resulting return loss that is realized by these filter types. For a given Chebyshev or Cauer filter order, the roll off of the filter response is also steeper for greater values of passband ripple. The cutoff frequency of the filters that have passband ripple is then defined as the passband ripple value. For all-pole filters such as the Butterworth, the cutoff frequency is typically defined as the 3 dB rejection point. Figure 4-47 shows the passband ripple of a fifth order low pass filter for ripple values of 0.01, 0.1, 0.25, and 0.5 dB.

Note that the ripple shown is produced by ideal circuit elements. In practice the finite unloaded Q or losses in the inductors and capacitors will tend to smooth out this ripple.

Figure 4-47: Passband ripple values in lowpass Chebyshev filter

In Chapter 2 the relationship for mismatch loss between a source and load was presented. For the Chebyshev and Cauer filters this mismatch loss is the passband ripple.

vswr ( )	ReturnLoss_dB ( )	Ripple_dB ( )
1.1	26.444	0.01
1.239	19.433	0.05
1.3	17.692	0.075
1.355	16.435	0.1
1.405	15.473	0.125
1.452	14.688	0.15
1.538	13.474	0.2
1.62	12.518	0.25
1.984	9.636	0.5

Figure 4-48: Calculation of filter ripple versus VSWR

Figures 4-49 and 4.50 show the same filters from Figure 4-47 with the return loss plotted along with the insertion loss, S21. We can see that for a given filter order, there is a tradeoff between filter rejection and the amount of ripple, or return loss, that can be tolerated in the passband. In most RF and microwave filter designs the 0.01 and 0.1 dB ripple values tend to be more popular. This is due to the tradeoff between good impedance match and reasonable filter skirt slope. Figure 4-47 shows good correlation of the worst case return loss with that which is calculated in Figure 4-48. When tuning filters using modern network analyzers it is sometimes easier to see the larger changes in the return loss as opposed to the fine grain ripple as shown in Figure 4-47. For this reason it is common to tune the forward transmission of the filter by observing the level and response of the filter's return loss. Return loss is a very sensitive indicator of the filter's alignment and performance.

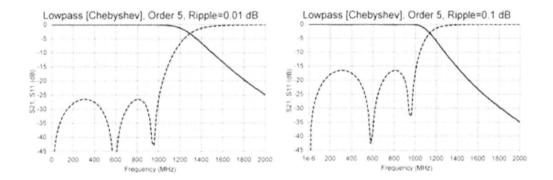

Figure 4-49: Lowpass Chebyshev filter rejection and return loss

Figure 4-50: Lowpass Chebyshev filter rejection and return loss versus passband ripple

4.8 Lumped Element Filter Design

Classical filter design is based on extracting a prototype frequency-normalized model from a myriad of tables for every filter type and order. Fortunately these tables have been built into many filter synthesis in ADS software applications that are readily available. In this section we will examine the filter synthesis tool that is built into the ADS software. We will work through two practical filter examples, one low pass and one high pass using the ADS filter synthesis tool.

Low Pass Filter Design

As a practical filter design, consider a full duplex communication link (simultaneous reception and transmission) through a satellite with the following requirements:

- The uplink signal is around 145 MHz while the downlink is at 435 MHz.

- A 20 W power amplifier is used on the uplink with 25 dB gain.

- It is necessary to provide a low pass filter on the uplink (only pass the 145 MHz uplink signal while rejecting any noise power in the 435 MHz band.

- It is necessary to provide a high pass filter on the downlink so that the 435 MHz downlink signal is received while rejecting any noise power at 145 MHz.

The transmitter and receiver antennas are on the same physical support boom so there is limited isolation between the transmitter and receiver. Even though the signals are at different frequencies, the broadband noise amplified by the power amplifier at 435 MHz will be received by the UHF antenna and sent to the sensitive receiver. Because the receiver is trying to detect very low signal levels, the received noise from the amplifier will interfere or 'de-sense' the received signals.

Example 4-10: Design a 145 MHz Low Pass filter for this satellite link system. The specifications chosen for the filter design are selected as:

- Having a Chebyshev Response with 0.1 dB pass band ripple.

- Having a passband cutoff frequency (not the -3 dB frequency) at 160 MHz

- Having at least -40 dB rejections at 435 MHz.

Solution: Create a new workspace and open a new schematic window in Cell_1. Use the Filter DesignGuide utility in ADS to design the lowpass filter. The procedure follows.

From the schematic window, click DesignGuide > Filter > Filter Control Window to open the Filter DesignGuide window.

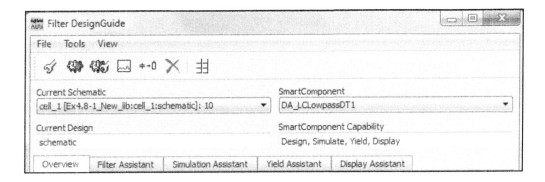

Figure 51-: Filter DesignGuide control window

In the Filter DesignGuide control window, click View > Component Palette – All. Place the filter SmartComponent Palette on the schematic window.

Figure 4-52: Smart Component Palette in the schematic window

- From the list of Filter DG-All Palettes select the lowpass filter SmartComponenet, DA_LCLowpassDT.

- Click anywhere within the schematic window to place the Smart Component.

- Double-click the SmartComponent to open a dialog box containing all parameters.

- Modify the parameters to meet the design specifications, as shown in Figure 4-53.

- In the Filter DesignGuide control window select the Filter Assistant tab and click Design to start a simulation and generate the filter sub-network, as shown in Figure 4-53.

Figure 4-53: Modified parameters of the lowpass filter

- In the Filter DesignGuide control window select the Filter Assistant tab and click Design to start a simulation and generate the filter sub-network, as shown in Figure 4-54.

Figure 4-54: Lowpass filter sub-network (N=5)

The required filter order is determined by increasing the order until the specification of -40 dBc attenuation at 435 MHz is achieved. As the filter response curve in Fig.4-56 shows, this Low Pass filter must be of fifth order to achieve the required attenuation.

After SmartComponents are designed and tested, they can be used as stand-alone components. The Filter DesignGuide is not needed to use them in new designs unless you want to modify or analyze them. In Figure 4-55 the lowpass filter SmartComponent is used in S parameter simulation circuit.

Figure 4-55: SmartComponent used in S parameter simulation circuit

Simulated Response of the low pass filter is shown in Figure 4-56.

Figure 4-56: Simulated Response of the low pass filter

Physical Model of the Low Pass Filter in ADS

It is important to realize that the synthesized filter is an ideal design in the sense that ideal (no parasitics and near infinite Q) components have been used. To obtain a good 'real-world' simulation of the filter we need to use component models that have finite Q and parasitics such as multilayer chip capacitors for shunt capacitors. For the capacitors, choose the 6003 series chip capacitors from ATC Corporation. ATC Corporation has a useful application for selection of chip capacitors called ATC Tech Select. This program is available for free download from the ATC web site: www.atceramics.com. ATC provides S-Parameter files for their capacitors that are readily available on the company website. For the physical design of the filters the ATC chip capacitor models must be installed into the ADS workspace.

Example 4-11: Convert the low pass filter to physical model and display the response from 0 to 500 MHz.

Solution: Because the filter is passing relatively high power (20 W), we cannot use small surface mount style chip inductors. Instead we will use air wound coils to realize the series inductors. The inductors will be realized with AWG#16 wire nickel-tin plated copper wire. The wire has a diameter of 0.05 inches or 50 mils. They will be wound on a 0.141 inch diameter form. Use the techniques covered in Chapter one to design the inductors using the Air Wound inductor model in ADS. The filter model is then reconstructed using the physical inductor models for the series inductors. Make sure to model the substrate and the interconnecting printed circuit board traces as microstrip lines. Also model the ground connection of the shunt capacitors as a microstrip via hole.

Although these PCB parasitic effects are normally more pronounced at frequencies above 2 GHz, it is often surprising the effect that these parasitics have at lower frequencies. The physical filter schematic is shown in Figure 4-57.

Figure 4-57: Schematic of the physical low pass filter

The physical filter response is shown in Figure 4-58.

Figure 4-58: Response of the physical lowpass filter

The response shows that the attenuation specification has been achieved.

Because the circuit has physical models replacing the ideal lumped elements, the engineer can be confident that the filter can be assembled and will achieve the designed response. Figure 4-59 is a photo of the prototype low pass filter circuit with SMA coaxial connectors attached to the circuit board.

Figure 4-59: Physical prototype of the low pass filter (courtesy of BT Microwave LLC)

High Pass Filter Design

Example 4-12: Design a high pass filter that passes frequencies in the 420 MHz to 450 MHz range. This filter could be placed in front of the preamp used in the downlink of the satellite system. This would help to keep out any of the transmit energy or noise power in the 146 MHz transmit frequency range. The High Pass Filter specifications are:

- The pass band cutoff frequency (not the -3 dB frequency) is 420 MHz.

- The filter has a Chebyshev response with 0.1 dB pass band ripple. The reject requirement is at least -60 dB rejections at 146 MHz.

Solution: Create a new workspace in ADS and open a new schematic window. From the schematic window, click DesignGuide > Filter > Filter Control Window to open the Filter DesignGuide control window. In the Filter DesignGuide control window, click View > Component Palette – All to place the filter SmartComponent Palette in the schematic window. From the list of Filter DG - All Palette select the highpass filter SmartComponenet, DA_LCHighpassDT, and click anywhere within the schematic window to place the component. Modify the component parameters to meet the highpass filter design specifications, as shown in Figure 4-60.

DA_LCHighpassDT1_cell_1
DA_LCHighpassDT1
Fs=146 MHz
Fp=420 MHz
As=60 dB
N=7
ResponseType=Chebyshev
Rg=50 Ohm
Rl=50 Ohm

Figure 4-60: Parameters of the highpass filter

The required filter order is determined by increasing N until the specification of -60 dBc attenuation at 146 MHz is achieved. It is always a good practice to design for some additional rejection (margin) that exceeds the minimum requirement, as shown in Figure 4-61. The Filter DesignGuide session recommends a filter of 7th order.

Figure 4-61: DesignGuide highpass filter response

The high pass filter sub-network is shown in Figure 4-62.

Figure 4-62: Lumped element model of the high pass filter (N=7)

Attach 50 Ohm terminations to the highpass filter SmartComponent model and simulate the schematic from 100 to 500 MHz, as shown in Figure 4-63.

Figure 4-63: Simulation of the high pass filter

The simulated response of the highpass filter is shown in Figure 4-64.

Figure 4-64: Response of the high pass filter

As Figure 4-60 shows the attenuation of -60 dBc at 146 MHz has been achieved with a good margin.

Physical Model of the High Pass Filter in ADS

Using the same techniques as described for the Low Pass Filter design we can proceed with the High Pass Filter realization. The **Filter DesignGuide** application calculated series capacitance values of 6.416 pF and 3.614 pF. Looking through the available ATC 700B series chip capacitors, the nearest values are 6.8 pF and 3.9 pF capacitors. The shunt inductors are realized using the Air Wound inductor model. Figure 4-61 shows the completed assembly of the High Pass Filter on a printed circuit board with coaxial SMA connectors.

Figure 4-65: Physical prototype of the 420 MHz highpass filter (courtesy of BT Microwave LLC)

4.9 Microstrip Stepped Impedance Low Pass Filter Design

In the microwave frequency region filters can be designed using distributed transmission lines. Series inductors and shunt capacitors can be realized with microstrip transmission lines. In the next section we will explore the conversion of a lumped element low pass filter to a design that is realized entirely in microstrip.

Example 4-13: Design a lumped element 2.2 GHz Chebyshev-response lowpass filter having 0.1 dB passband ripple and -40 dB rejection at 6 GHz.

Solution: Following the procedure discussed in Example 4-12, the SmartComponent design of the lowpass filter is show in Figure 4-66.

Figure 4-66: Lumped element design of the 2.2 GHz low pass filter

The lumped element sub-network of the filter is shown in Figure 4-67.

.

Figure 4-67: Lumped element 2.2 GHz low pass filter

The simulated response of the filter is shown in Figure 4-68.

Figure 4-68 Response of the lumped element 2.2 GHz lowpass filter

The marker m1 in Figure 4-68 shows that the 3 dB bandwidth of the lowpass filter is 2495 MHz.

Lumped Element to Distributed Element Conversion

Example 4-14: Convert all the lumped elements of the filter in Figure 4-67 to microstrip transmission lines by using the Rogers's 6010 substrate ($\varepsilon_r = 10.2$) with a 0.025 inch dielectric thickness. Display the response and notice the change in the 3 dB bandwidth.

Solution: After a Filter has been designed, the lumped inductors and capacitors can be transformed into equivalent distributed element counterparts using the ADS Transformation Assistant. The Filter Transformation Assistant helps us to quickly and easily transform an ideal filter topology to a form that is realizable for RF and microwave systems.

The Transformation Assistant is opened from the Filter DesignGuide Control window, by selecting Tools > Distributed Element Transformations. When the Transformation Assistant is opened, the SmartComponent subnetwork appears in the schematic window and a dialog box is opened. The transformations are then accomplished using the controls on the dialog.box.

After the Transformation Assistant has been selected, the graphical area displays the components that can be transformed. Black components represent elements included in the original circuit available for transformation, while gray components represent elements not included in the original circuit. Check the LC, TLine to Microstrip transformations and select the series inductors L1 and L2 to be transformed to microstrip transmission lines. Set the characteristic impedance of the microstrip line to $Z_0 = 80$ Ohm and enter the microstrip substrate parameters, as shown in Figure 4-69.

Figure 4-69: Transformation Assistance window

Click Transform and then click OK. As Figure 4-70 shows the series inductors L1 and L2 have been transformed to 80 Ω microstrip transmission lines on the microstrip substrate. Repeat the same process for the capacitors except setting Z_0 = 20 Ohms.

Figure 4-70: Transformation of shunt capacitors to 20 Ω microstrip line

Click Transform and then click OK. Now the capacitors have also been transformed to microstrip lines.

Figure 4-71 Initial schematic of the distributed low pass filter

Now the lumped element filter in Figure 4-67 has been converted to microstrip stepped impedance low pass filter of Figure 4-71. Simulate the schematic in Figure 4-72 and display the response from 0 to 10 GHz.

Figure 4-72: Initial response of the low pass filter

Note that the marker m1 in Figure 4-72 shows that the 3 dB bandwidth of the lowpass filter has slightly decreased to 2421 MHz.

The printed circuit board layout of the initial lowpass filter is shown in Figure 4-73.

PCB Layout

Figure 4-73: Initial PCB layout of the lowpass filter

Examine the printed circuit board, PCB, layout of the lowpass filter of Figure 4-73. Note the change in geometry as the impedance transitions from 50 Ω at the input to 20 Ω, representing the shunt capacitor, and then from 20 Ω to 80 Ω, representing the series inductor. These abrupt changes in geometry are known as discontinuities. Discontinuities in geometry result in fringing capacitance and parasitic inductance that will modify the frequency response of the circuit. At RF and lower microwave frequencies (up to about 2 GHz) the effects of discontinuities are minimal and sometimes neglected [4]. As the operation frequency increases, the effects of discontinuities can significantly alter the performance of a microstrip circuit. ADS software has several model elements that can help to account for the effects of discontinuities. These include: T-junctions, cross junctions, open circuit end effects, coupling gaps, and bends.

Example 4-15: Modify the filter by placing Microstrip Step, MSTEP, elements between series lines of abruptly changing geometry to account for the step discontinuities. Simulate the schematic and notice the change in the frequency response.

Solution: Figure 4-75 shows the lowpass stepped impedance filter with the step elements added between each transmission line section

Figure 4-74 Stepped impedance filter with added "step" elements

The simulated response of the modified filter is shown in Figure 4-75.

Figure 4-75: Filter frequency shift due to step discontinuities

A comparison of the initial lowpass filter response in Figure 4-72 and the modified model response in Figure 4-75 shows that there is some frequency shift in the filter response as it is evidenced, about 100 MHz, by the 3 dB bandwidth.

Electromagnetic Analysis of the Stepped Impedance Filter

Electromagnetic modeling, EM, is a useful tool in microstrip circuit design as it offers a means of potentially more accurate simulation than linear modeling. The linear microstrip component models used to model the stepped impedance filter are based on closed form expressions developed over many years. For many designs the linear model is quite acceptable. Microstrip circuits that contain several distributed components in a dense printed circuit layout will be affected by cross coupling and enclosure effects. This is because the microstrip circuitry is quasi-TEM with some portion of the EM fields in the free-space above the dielectric material. These effects are very difficult to accurately simulate with linear modeling techniques. The ADS software suite has a very useful electromagnetic simulation engine named Momentum. Momentum is based on the method-of-moments (MoM) numerical solution of Maxwell's equations [3]. Unlike some EM simulation software Momentum's solutions are presented in the S parameter format that is familiar to the microwave circuit designer. A dataset is created that can be graphed just like any linear simulation. The Momentum model is created from the circuit layout rather than the schematic. In this section we will create a Momentum model from the layout that was created by the linear schematic. However we could import an arbitrary PCB artwork from any CAD program. Right click on the Layout window to expose the Layout Properties. On the General Tab make sure to specify the correct units (mils) that represent the drawing. Also check the 'show EM Box' check box so that a proper enclosure is modeled for the circuit. The box represents a metal enclosure that will serve as the boundary conditions for the EM simulation. The simulator will identify any box resonances that may occur which could have an adverse effect on the circuit design. The box sides must be lined up perpendicular to the input and output ports. The box size (length and width) can be adjusted by entering the desired dimensions in the Box Width (X) and Box Height (Y) settings as shown in Figure 4-61. The box height is specified in the Layers tab as the air above the metal conductor or 250 mils as shown in Figure 4-72.

Figure 4-76: General properties settings

On the Layer Tab make sure that the microstrip dielectric material is defined on the Substrate line. Once all of the Layer settings have been specified add the Momentum Analysis to the Workspace as shown in Figure 4-77.

Name	#	Color	Layer Type	Hide	On Bottom (Mirrored)	Plot	Etch Factor	Use	Use Layer Mesh Density	Mesh Density	Use Layer TL Mesh	TL Mesh	E
Top Cover			Cover										
Air Above			Air					✓					
TOP MASK	1		Mask	☐	☐	☐							
TOP SILK	2		Silk	☐	☐	☐							
TOP METAL	3		Metal	☐	☐	✓	0	✓	✓	30	☐		De
SUBSTRATE	4		Substrate	☐	☐	✓		✓					
BOT METAL	5		Metal	☐	✓	✓	0	☐	☐			☐	
BOT SILK	6		Silk	✓	✓	☐							
BOT MASK	7		Mask	✓	☐	☐							
Air Below			Air					☐					
Bottom Cover			Cover										

Name	Rho	Height	Er	Tand/ Sigma	Ur	Rough	Surface Imp. Value or File	Current Direction	Thick Metal (Slow)	Element Z-Ports
Top Cover	1					0.055				
Air Above		250	1	0	1					
TOP METAL	1					0.079		Normal	Thin	Down
SUBSTRATE		25	10.2	5e-3	1.0000					
BOT METAL								Normal	Thin	Down
Air Below		196.85	1	0	1					
Bottom Cover	1					0.055				

Figure 4-77: Layer tabs of the layout properties

The Momentum filter layout is shown in Figure 4-78.

Figure 4-78: Filter layout showing box outline and conductor mesh

Figure 4-79: Momentum simulation options setup

On the General Tab, set the start and stop frequency for the simulation and select the adaptive sweep type. The adaptive sweep reduces frequency point interpolation error. On the Simulation Options Tab choose the RF simulation mode. The RF simulation mode is a much faster EM simulation and is suitable for lower microwave (RF) frequencies where there is not a significant amount of coupling among transmission lines. The Microwave simulation mode is a full wave EM analysis that includes all coupling radiation within the box. Also check the 'Calculate – All' button so that the metal mesh and the substrate are used in the solution.

Figure 4-80: Comparison of linear and momentum simulations

The comparison between the Linear and Momentum simulations shows that there is some further deviation in the filter rejection as the frequency increases above 2 GHz.

Figure 4-81 3D View of filter and prototype filter printed circuit board

Microstrip Coupled Line Filter Design

The edge coupled microstrip line is very popular in the design of bandpass filters. A cascade of half-wave resonators in which quarter wave sections are parallel edge coupled lines, are very useful for realizing narrow band, band pass filters. This type of filter can typically achieve $\leq$ 15% fractional bandwidths [4].

Example 4-16: Design a band pass filter at 10.5 GHz. The filter is designed on RO3010 substrate ($\varepsilon_r = 10.2$) with a dielectric thickness of 0.025 inches. The filter should have a pass band of 9.98 – 11.03 GHz. As a design goal the filter should achieve at least 20 dB rejection at 9.65 GHz. In other words the filter is required to have > 20 dB rejection at 330 MHz below the lower passband frequency.

Solution: The Passive Circuit DesignGuide utility in ADS is used to design the filter network. The procedure for opening and using the Passive Circuit DesignGuide utility is as follows.

1. In the schematic window, choose DesignGuide > Passive Circuit > Passive Control Window.

2. From Passive Circuit DesignGuide toolbar, choose View > Component Pallet > Microstrip

3. From Passive Circuit DG–Microstrip list, choose Filter-Bandpass

4. From Filter-Bandpass pull-down list, choose Chebyshev

5. Set the filter parameters and vary the order until the desired filter rejection is achieved.

The Passive Circuit DesignGuide program shows that a 6th order filter should meet the rejection specifications. The synthesized filter schematic and response are shown in Figures 4-82 and 4-83.

Figure 4-82: Parallel line edge coupled microstrip bandpass filter schematic

Figure 4-83: Band pass filter response

The designer must be cautious when using Linear Analysis techniques to design circuits with multiple edge coupled microstrip lines. We know that there is a large percentage of the parallel line coupling that occurs in the free space above the microstrip substrate and the conductors. This can lead to considerable error when relying on the linear simulation results. The coupled line models used by the linear simulator are based on closed form expressions derived from coupling measurements on parallel lines with loosely defined boundary conditions.

References and Further Readings

[1]   *Handbook of Filter Synthesis*, Analtol I. Zverev, Wiley 1967

[2]   *RF Circuit Design*, Second Edition, Christopher Bowick, Elsevier 2008

[3]   Keysight Technologies, Manuals for Advanced Design System, *ADS 2015.07 Documentation Set*, EEsof EDA Division, Santa Rosa, California www.keysight.com

[4]   *Foundations for Microstrip Circuit Design*, T.C. Edwards, John Wiley & Sons, New York, 1981

[5]   *Q Factor*, Darko Kajfez, Vector Fields, Oxford Mississippi, 1994

[6]   David M. Pozar, *Microwave Engineering*, Third Edition, John Wiley and Sons, Inc. 2005

[7]   *Q Factor Measurement with Network Analyzer*, Darko Kajfez and Eugene Hwan, IEEE Transactions on Microwave Theory and Techniques, Vol. MTT-32, No. 7, July 1984.

[8]   *High Frequency Techniques*, Joseph F. White, John Wiley & Sons, Inc., 2005

[9]   *Soft Substrates Conquer Hard Designs*, James D. Woermbke, Microwaves, January 1982.

[10]   *Principles of Microstrip Design*, Alam Tam, RF Design, June 1988.

[11]   Ali A. Behagi and Stephen D. Turner, *Microwave and RF Engineering, A Simulation Approach with Keysight Genesys Software*, BT Microwave LLC, State College, PA , March 2015

Problems

4-1.   Consider the one port resonator that is represented as a series RLC circuit as shown. Analyze the circuit, with R = 5 Ω, L = 5 nH, and C = 5 pF. Plot the magnitude of the resonator input impedance and measure the resonance frequency.

4-2.   Consider the one port resonator that is represented as a parallel RLC circuit as shown. Analyze the circuit, with R = 500 Ω, L = 50 nH, and C = 50 pF. Plot the magnitude of the resonator input impedance and measure the resonance frequency.

4-3.   Design a Butterworth lowpass filter having a passband of 2 GHz with an attenuation 20 dB at 4 GHz. Plot the insertion loss versus frequency from 0 to 5 GHz. The system impedance is 50 Ω.

4-4.   Design a 5th order Chebyshev highpass filter having 0.2 dB equal ripples in the passband and cutoff frequency of 2 GHz. The system impedance is 75 Ω. Plot the insertion loss versus frequency from 0 to 5 GHz.

4-5.   In a full duplex communication link, the uplink signal is around 200 MHz while the downlink is at 500 MHz. A 25 Watt power amplifier is used on the uplink with 20 dB gain.

(a) Design a low pass filter on the uplink to pass the 200 MHz uplink signal while rejecting any noise power in the 500 MHz band. Design the passband cutoff frequency is at 220 MHz, therefore, the filter should have a Chebyshev Response with 0.1 dB pass band ripple. The reject requirement is at least -40 dB rejections at 500 MHz.

(b) Design a High Pass Filter that passes frequencies in the 480 MHz to 520 MHz range. The High Pass Filter specifications are: The passband cutoff frequency is 480 MHz, therefore, the filter should have a Chebyshev response with 0.1 dB pass band ripple. The reject requirement is at least -60 dB losses at 190 MHz.

Chapter 5

Power Transfer and Impedance Matching

5.1 Introduction

Impedance matching is an integral part of RF and microwave circuit and system design. It is necessary for the efficient transfer of power from a source to the load. For example, in microwave amplifier design, the need for impedance matching arises when the amplifier must be properly terminated at both terminals in order to deliver maximum power from the source to the load. In narrowband applications impedance matching can be achieved, at a single frequency, with a lossless two-element network, known as L-network or L-section. In this chapter the basics of power transfer and the conditions for maximum power transfer are presented. The mathematical equations for the design of discrete L-networks are derived using MATLAB compatible expressions. This builds a solid foundation for the engineer to handle more complicated matching problems including broadband matching applications. In this chapter both analytical and graphical techniques are used to design narrowband and broadband matching networks. An introduction to the Impedance Matching Utility program, which is integrated into the ADS software, is also presented. The VBScript capability is also used to create a simple L-network matching utility that solves the impedance matching equations for arbitrary source and load impedances. Engineers can use VBScript programming techniques to generate their own synthesis applications within the ADS software.

5.2 Power Transfer Basics

At low frequencies, where the electrical wavelengths of the signals are much longer than the physical dimensions of the wires and lumped components, the phase of the voltage and current waveforms do not change significantly along the length of wires or components. Therefore, power is transmitted from the source to the load with little loss. At RF and microwave frequencies, where the signal wavelengths are equal to or shorter than the physical dimension of the network components, the amplitude and phase of the voltage and current waveforms change significantly as they travel from source to the load. In this case power is reflected at discontinuities and the maximum power will not reach the load. To achieve maximum power transfer we need to eliminate reflections at discontinuities by inserting proper impedance matching networks.

Maximum Power Transfer Conditions

For the network of Figure 5-1 a voltage source, V_S, and the series impedance $Z_S = R_S + jX_S$ are connected to a network, having the input impedance $Z_{IN} = R_{IN} + jX_{IN}$, the power transferred to the network is given by Equation (5-1).

$$P_{Network} = \frac{\text{Re}\left[V_{IN} I_{IN}^*\right]}{2} \tag{5-1}$$

In Equation (5-1) Re denotes the real part and the symbol * denotes the conjugate value.

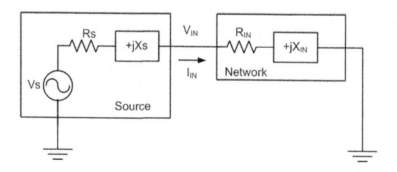

Figure 5-1 Voltage source connected to complex load impedance

In Figure 5-1, we assume V_S is sinusoidal steady state voltage source, R_S and R_{IN} are positive, and X_S and X_{IN} are real numbers. The input voltage and current to the network can be related to the source voltage as:

$$V_{IN} = \frac{V_S(R_{IN} + jX_{IN})}{(R_{IN} + R_S) + j(X_{IN} + X_S)}$$

$$I_{IN}^* = \frac{V_S}{(R_{IN} + R_S) - j(X_{IN} + X_S)}$$

Therefore, multiplying V_{IN} by I_{IN}^*, Equation (5-1) can be written as:

$$P = \frac{\left(\dfrac{V_S^2 R_{IN}}{2}\right)}{(R_{IN} + R_S)^2 + (X_{IN} + X_S)^2} \tag{5-2}$$

To maximize the power transfer, we differentiate Equation (5-2) with respect to R_{IN} and X_{IN} and set them equal to zero,

$$\frac{V_S^2}{2}\left[(R_{IN} + R_S)^2 + (X_{IN} + X_S)^2\right] - \frac{V_S^2 R_{IN}}{2}\left[2R_{IN} + 2R_S\right] = 0$$

$$-\frac{V_S^2 R_{IN}}{2}(2X_{IN} + 2X_S) = 0$$

A simultaneous solution of these two equations for R_{IN} and X_{IN}, leads to:

$$R_{IN} = R_S \tag{5-3}$$

$$X_{IN} = -X_S \tag{5-4}$$

Therefore, the maximum power transfer condition is that the load impedance be equal to the conjugate of the source impedance.

$$Z_{IN} = Z_S^* \tag{5-5}$$

This maximum power transfer condition between the source and load impedance can be divided into three cases.

Case 1:
If the source impedance is purely resistive the load impedance must also be purely resistive and equal to source resistance.

$$Z_{IN} = R_{IN} = R_S$$

Case 2:
If the source impedance is a resistor in series with a capacitor, $Z_S = R_S - jX_S$, the load impedance must be a resistor in series with an inductor such that:

$$Z_{IN} = R_S + jX_S$$

Case 3:
If the source impedance is a resistor in series with an inductor, $Z_S = R_S + jX_S$, the load impedance must be a resistor in series with a capacitor such that:

$$Z_{IN} = R_S - jX_S$$

Maximum Power Transfer with Purely Resistive Source and Load Impedance

This section explores in detail the three cases for maximum power transfer along with solutions using the ADS software.

Prove the maximum power transfer condition when the source and load impedance is purely resistive, as shown in Figure 5-2.

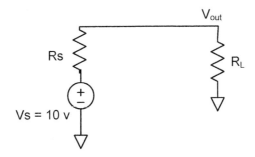

Figure 5-2 Network with purely resistive source and load impedance

When the source impedance is purely resistive and the load resistance is R_L, the maximum power is transferred to the load when $R_L = R_S$. Using the resistor voltage-divider principle we can determine the output voltage, V_{out} for the following three possible cases:

$$\text{Case I:} \qquad R_L = R_S$$

$$\text{Case II:} \qquad R_L < R_S$$

$$\text{Case III:} \qquad R_L > R_S$$

Case I: If the input voltage is 10 VDC and $R_L = R_S = 50\ \Omega$, the output voltage is 5 Volts and the output power is 0.5 Watts. This is the maximum power that can be transferred.

$$V_{out} = V_S \frac{R_L}{(R_S + R_L)} = 10 \frac{50}{(50 + 50)} = 5\ volts$$

$$P_L = \frac{V_{out}^{\ 2}}{R_L} = \frac{5^2}{50} = 0.5\ Watts$$

Case II: If $R_L = 25\ \Omega$ and $R_S = 50\ \Omega$, the output voltage is 3.333 Volts and the output power is 0.444 Watts.

$$V_{out} = V_S \frac{R_L}{(R_S + R_L)} = 10 \frac{25}{(50 + 25)} = 3.333 \ volts$$

$$P_L = \frac{V_{out}^2}{R_L} = \frac{3.333^2}{25} = 0.444 \ Watts$$

Case III: If $R_L = 100 \ \Omega$ and $R_S = 50 \ \Omega$, the output voltage is 6.666 Volts and the output power is 0.444 Watts.

$$V_{out} = V_S \frac{R_L}{(R_S + R_L)} = 10 \frac{100}{(50 + 100)} = 6.666 \ volts$$

$$P_L = \frac{V_{out}^2}{R_L} = \frac{6.666^2}{100} = 0.444 \ Watts$$

Notice that the power output in Case I is greater than either Cases II or III. Therefore, the maximum power transfer is achieved only when $R_L = R_S$.

Maximum Power Transfer Validation in ADS

The electronic design automation techniques, EDA, used in this book are based solely on the linear simulation capabilities of the ADS software which in turn is based on the matrix manipulation of S parameters

Example 5-1: Prove the maximum power transfer condition when the source and load impedances are purely resistive.

Solution: This is a very simple ADS schematic with only input and output ports, as shown in Figure 5-3. The input port represents an RF signal source with 50 Ω source impedance and the output port is simply a 50 Ω resistive load. Simulate the schematic from 450 to 550 MHz and add a rectangular graph with the insertion loss, S21, in dB. Figure 5-3 shows the schematic and plot indicating that S21 = 0 dB. Because there is zero insertion loss between the source and load, there is maximum power transfer.

Figure 5-3 Case I power transfer with $R_L = R_S$

Simulate the schematic and display the insertion loss, S21, in a rectangular plot as shown in Figure 5-4.

Figure 5-4 Insertion Loss with $R_L = R_S$

Notice that when the load impedance is equal to the source impedance the insertion loss is 0 dB indicating maximum power transfer.

Change the load impedance in Figure 5-3 from 50 Ohm to 25 Ω as shown in Figure 5-5.

Figure 5-5 Power transfer with $R_L < R_S$

Simulate the schematic and display the insertion loss, S21, in a rectangular plot as shown in Figure 5-6.

Figure 5-6 Insertion Loss with $R_L < R_S$

Notice that S21 = -0.512 dB indicating insertion loss. To calculate the amount of power loss, we know that the maximum power transfer is 0.5 Watts. To determine the amount of 0.512 dB power loss we first convert the 0.5 Watts to dBm which is the power in dB relative to 1 mW. Utilizing the conversion equation,

$$10 \log (\text{power in mW}) = \text{power in dBm}.$$

$$10 \log (500 mW) = 26.98 \ dBm$$

The loss of 0.512 dB is subtracted from the 26.98 dBm to result in (26.98 dBm – 0.512 dB) = 26.47 dBm. Then converting from dBm back to mW we get 444 mW as calculated in Example 5.2-1.

$$10^{\left(\frac{26.47}{10} \right)} = 444 \ mW \quad or \quad 0.444 \ Watts$$

Maximum Power Transfer with Complex Load Impedance

According to Equation 5-5 maximum power transfer occurs when $Z_S = Z_L{}^*$. Therefore, if $Z_L = R_L - jX_L$, then for maximum power transfer we must have $Z_S = R_L + jX_L$.

Example 5-2: If the load is 50 Ω in series with 15 pF capacitor, find the source impedance to achieve maximum power transfer at 500 MHz.

Solution: We can find a source inductance that cancels the reactance of the load at this frequency. The reactance of the 15 pF capacitor is:

$$X_C = \frac{1}{2 \pi f C} = 21.231 \ \Omega$$

Therefore,

$$Z_L = 50 - j21.231 \ \Omega$$

For maximum power transfer the source impedance must be:

$$Z_S = 50 + j21.231 \quad \Omega$$

At 500 MHz the value of the source series inductor is:

$$L = \frac{21.231}{2\pi f} = 6.76 \quad nH$$

To demonstrate the maximum power transfer, create a schematic in ADS as shown in Figure 5-7. Place the specified 15 pF capacitance in series with the load and the 6.76 nH inductance in series with the source. Plot the insertion loss and VSWR on a rectangular graph as shown in Figure 5-8. Note that unlike the purely resistive source and load case, a complex conjugate match occurs at a single frequency. A perfect 1:1 VSWR is achieved at the conjugate match frequency of 500 MHz.

Figure 5-7 Maximum power transfer with complex impedance

Simulate the schematic to see the maximum power transfer at 500 MHz.

Figure 5-8 VSWR and insertion loss with complex source and load

5.3 Analytical Design of Impedance Matching Networks

One of the important tasks in RF and microwave engineering is the determination of how an arbitrary complex load impedance, $Z_L = R_L + jX_L$, is analytically matched to any complex source impedance, $Z_S = R_S + jX_S$, as shown in Figure 5-9. This problem arises mainly in the design of inter-stage matching networks between active devices or between antenna transmitters.

Figure 5-9 Complex impedance matching

In Figure 5-9 the complex load impedance, $Z_L = R_L + j\ X_L$, is to be matched to the source impedance $Z_S = R_S + jX_S$. The only condition for impedance matching is that both R_S and R_L must be nonnegative while X_S and X_L could take any real value. In section 5.2 it was shown that maximum power would be transferred from the source to the load when the load impedance is the conjugate of the source impedance. For L-network matching there are two configurations that can match arbitrary load impedances to arbitrary source impedances. In the first configuration the first element adjacent to the load is a series element as shown in Figure 5-10.

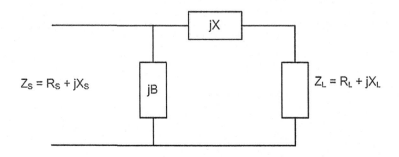

Figure 5-10 First impedance matching configuration

In the second configuration the first element adjacent to the load is a shunt element as shown in Figure 5-11.

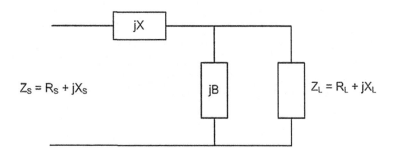

Figure 5-11 Second impedance matching configuration

Matching a Complex Load to Complex Source Impedance

To match a complex load to any complex source impedance with a single L-network, either the first or the second configuration may be used. The choice of configurations depends on the conditions that source and load impedances dictate. Applying Equation $Z_S{}^* = Z_{IN}$ to the first matching configuration in Figure 5-10 we get:

$$R_S - jX_S = \cfrac{1}{jB + \left(\cfrac{1}{jX + R_L + jX_L}\right)} \tag{5-6}$$

By separating the real and imaginary parts of Equation (5-6) we obtain two solutions for B and X as follows:

$$B_1 = \frac{R_L X_S + \sqrt{R_L R_S (R_S{}^2 + X_S{}^2 - R_L R_S)}}{R_L (R_S{}^2 + X_S{}^2)} \tag{5-7}$$

$$X_1 = \frac{R_L X_S - R_S X_L}{R_S} + \frac{R_S - R_L}{B_1 R_S} \tag{5-8}$$

And,

$$B_2 = \frac{R_L X_S - \sqrt{R_L R_S (R_S{}^2 + X_S{}^2 - R_L R_S)}}{R_L (R_S{}^2 + X_S{}^2)} \tag{5-9}$$

$$X_2 = \frac{R_L X_S - R_S X_L}{R_S} + \frac{R_S - R_L}{B_2 R_S} \tag{5-10}$$

Similarly, applying the same procedure we have:

$$R_S - jX_S = jX + \cfrac{1}{jB + \left(\cfrac{1}{R_L + jX_L}\right)} \tag{5-11}$$

Separating the real and imaginary parts of Equation (5-11), we also get two sets of solutions for B and X:

$$B_3 = \frac{R_S X_L + \sqrt{R_L R_S (R_L^2 + X_L^2 - R_L R_S)}}{R_S (R_L^2 + X_L^2)} \qquad (5\text{-}12)$$

$$X_3 = \frac{R_S X_L - R_L X_S}{R_L} + \frac{R_L - R_S}{B_3 R_L} \qquad (5\text{-}13)$$

And,

$$B_4 = \frac{R_S X_L - \sqrt{R_L R_S (R_L^2 + X_L^2 - R_L R_S)}}{R_S (R_L^2 + X_L^2)} \qquad (5\text{-}14)$$

$$X_4 = \frac{R_S X_L - R_L X_S}{R_L} + \frac{R_L - R_S}{B_4 R_L} \qquad (5\text{-}15)$$

Conditions for the validity of solutions are that the arguments of the square roots in Equations (5-7), (5-9), (5-12) and (5-14) be positive or zero.

- If $R_S^2 + X_S^2 - R_L R_S > 0$ and $R_L^2 + X_L^2 - R_L R_S < 0$, the two solutions obtained from Equations (5-7) through (5-10) are the only valid solutions.

- If $R_S^2 + X_S^2 - R_L R_S < 0$ and $R_L^2 + X_L^2 - R_L R_S > 0$, the two solutions obtained from Equations (5-12) through (5-15) are the only valid solutions.

- If $R_S^2 + X_S^2 - R_L R_S > 0$ and $R_L^2 + X_L^2 - R_L R_S > 0$, all four solutions obtained from Equations (5-7) through (5-10) and Equations (5-12) through (5-15) are valid.

Once the real values for B and X are calculated, the values of the matching elements are obtained from the following equations:

1. If B is positive, the matching element is a capacitor given by:

$$C = \frac{B}{2\pi f} \tag{5-16}$$

2. If B is negative, the matching element is an inductor given by:

$$L = -\frac{1}{2\pi f B} \tag{5-17}$$

3. If X is positive, the matching element is an inductor given by:

$$L = \frac{X}{2\pi f} \tag{5-18}$$

4. If X is negative, the matching element is a capacitor given by:

$$C = -\frac{1}{2\pi f X} \tag{5-19}$$

In the above equations, if the frequency is in Hz, capacitors and inductors are in Farads and Henrys, respectively.

Now we utilize Equations (5-7) through (5-15) to design the matching L-networks.

Example 5-3: Design a two element L-network to match the complex load, $Z_L = 10 - j15\ \Omega$ to a complex source impedance, $Z_S = 15 - j20\ \Omega$, at 2 GHz.

Since $R_S^2 + X_S^2 - R_L R_S = 475 > 0$, and $R_L^2 + X_L^2 - R_L R_S = 175 > 0$, the Example 5=3 has four solutions. Each solution is found separately.

First solution: We utilize Equations (5-7) and (5-8) in MATLAB script to calculate the element values of the matching L-network. The procedure follows.

1. Enter design parameters

RS = 15; XS = -20; RL = 10; XL = -15; f = 2e9

2. Use Equations (5-7) and (5-8) to calculate the matching element values

B1 = ((RL*XS)+sqrt(RS*RL*(RS^2+XS^2-RS*RL)))/(RL*(RS^2+XS^2))

X1 = (RL*XS-RS*XL)/RS+(RS-RL)/(B1*RS)

L1 = X1/(2*pi*f)

C2 = B1/(2*pi*f)

The calculation results show that B1 = 0.011 and X1 = 32.795, therefore, the series element is an inductor, L1 = 2.61 nH, and the shunt element is a capacitor, C2 = 0.852 pF.

To verify the solution, create a new workspace in ADS and open a new schematic window. Insert the S_Params Template and add capacitor and inductor from the Lumped-Components palette. Connect the matching elements as shown in Figure 5-12.

Figure 5-12 Schematic of the first matching L-network

Simulate the schematic and display S11 and S21 in a rectangular plot.

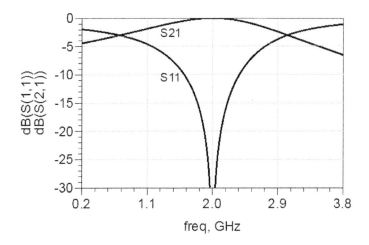

Figure 5-13 Response of the first matching L-network

Figure 5-13 shows that the matching L-network perfectly matches the load impedance to the source impedance at 2 GHz.

Example 5-4: Find the second Solution to Example 5-3.

Second Solution: Use Equations (5-9) and (5-10) in MATLAB script to calculate the second solution. The procedure follows.
1. Enter Design Parameters
RS = 15; XS = -20; RL = 10; XL = -15; f = 2e9

2. Use Equations (5-9) and (5-10) in MATLAB script to calculate the matching element values

B2 = ((RL*XS)-sqrt(RS*RL*(RS^2 + XS^2-RS*RL)))/(RL*(RS^2+XS^2))

X2 = (RL*XS-RS*XL)/RS+(RS-RL)/(B2*RS)

C1 = -1/(2*pi*f*X2)

L2 = -1/(2*pi*f*B2)

The calculation results show that B2 = -0.075 and X2 = -2.795, therefore, the series element is a capacitor, C1 = 28.47 pF and the shunt element is an inductor, L2 = 1.065 nH.

To plot the response of the matching network, create a new workspace in ADS and open a new schematic window. Insert the S_Params Template and add capacitor and inductor from the Lumped-Components palette. Connect the matching elements as shown in Figure 5-14.

Figure 5-14 Schematic of the second matching L-network

Simulate the schematic from 0 to 4 GHz and display the return loss, S11, and insertion loss, S21, in dB in a rectangular plot, as shown in Figure 5-15.

Figure 5-15 Response of the second matching L-network

Figure 5-15 shows that the matching L-network perfectly matches the load impedance to the source impedance at 2 GHz.

Example 5-5: Find the third Solution to Example 5-3.

Third Solution: Use Equations (5-12) and (5-13) to calculate *B3* and *X3* for the third solution. The procedure follows.

1. Enter design parameters
RS=15; XS=-20; RL=10; XL=-15; f=2e9

2. Use Equations (5-12) and (5-13) in MATLAB script to calculate the matching element values

B3 = ((RS*XL)+sqrt(RS*RL*(RL^2+XL^2-RS*RL)))/(RS*(RL^2+XL^2))

X3 = (RS*XL - RL*XS)/RL + (RL - RS)/(B3*RL)

L1 = -1/(2*pi*f*B3)

L2 = X3/(2*pi*f)

The calculation results show that B3 = -0.013 and X3 = 36.202, therefore, the shunt element is an inductor L1= 6.16 nH and the series element is another inductor L2=2.881 nH, as shown in Figure 5-16.

To plot the response of the matching network, create a new workspace in ADS and open a new schematic window. Insert the S_Params Template and add capacitor and inductor from the Lumped-Components palette. Connect the matching elements as shown in Figure 5-16.

Figure 5-16 Schematic of the third matching L-network

Simulate the schematic and display S11 and S21 in a rectangular plot.

Figure 5-17 Response of the third matching L-network

Figure 5-17 shows that the matching L-network perfectly matches the load impedance to the source impedance at 2 GHz.

Example 5-6: Find the fourth Solution of the Example 5-3.
Fourth Solution: Use Equations (5-14) and (5-15) to calculate *B4* and *X4*.

1. Enter design parameters:
RS=15; XS=-20; RL=10; XL=-15; f=2e9

2. Use Equations (5-14) and (5-15) in MATLAB script to calculate the matching element values

B4 = ((RS*XL) -sqrt(RS*RL*(RL^2+XL^2-RS*RL)))/(RS*(RL^2+XL^2))

X4 = (RS*XL-RL*XS)/RL + (RL - RS)/(B4*RL)

L1 = -1/(2*pi*f*B4)

L2 = X4/(2*pi*f)

The calculation results show that B4 = -0.079 and X4 = 3.798, therefore, the shunt element is an inductor L1=1.002 nH and the series element is another inductor L2=0.302 nH.

To plot the response of the matching network, create a new workspace in ADS and open a new schematic window. Insert the S_Params Template and add capacitor and inductor from the Lumped-Components palette. Connect the matching elements as shown in Figure 5-18.

Figure 5-18 Schematic of the fourth matching L-network

Simulate the schematic and display S11 and S21 in a rectangular plot.

Figure 5-19 Response of the fourth matching L-network

Figure 5-19 shows that the matching L-network perfectly matches the load impedance to the source impedance at 2 GHz.

Matching a Complex Load to Real Source Impedance

In amplifier design a common matching problem is the matching of a complex load impedance, $Z_L = R_L + jX_L$ to a real source impedance, $Z_S = R_S$. The complex impedance is usually the load and the real impedance is the characteristic impedance of transmission line connected to the source. In order to design the impedance matching networks we use both configurations of Figures 5-10 and 5-11. For the real source impedance the matching configuration of Figure 5-10 is redrawn in Figure 5-20.

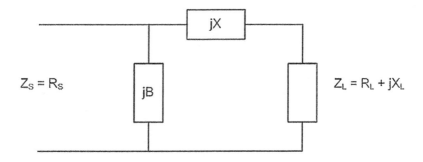

Figure 5-20 Matching complex load to resistive source (first configuration)
To derive the analytical expressions for B and X we utilize the maximum power transfer condition and set the conjugate of the source impedance equal to input impedance of the matching network followed by the load impedance, as given in Equation (5-20).

$$R_S = \frac{1}{jB + \left(\dfrac{1}{jX + R_L + jX_L} \right)} \qquad (5\text{-}20)$$

Note that for the real source resistor its conjugate is equal to itself. The solutions for B and X in Equation (5-20) can be obtained by substituting $X_S = 0$ in Equations (5-7) through (5-10).

$$B_1 = \frac{+\sqrt{R_S - R_L}}{R_S\sqrt{R_L}}$$

(5-21)

$$X_1 = +\sqrt{R_L(R_S - R_L)} - X_L$$

(5-22)

$$B_2 = \frac{-\sqrt{R_S - R_L}}{R_S\sqrt{R_L}}$$

(5-23)

$$X_2 = -\sqrt{R_L(R_S - R_L)} - X_L$$

(5-24)

Note that the solutions given in Equations (5-21) through (5-24) are only valid if $R_L < R_S$. To calculate B and X, when $R_L > R_S$, we use the second matching configuration shown in Figure 5-21,

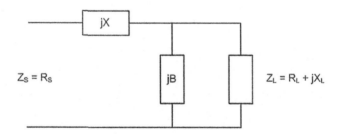

Figure 5-21 Matching complex load to resistive source (2nd configuration)

Applying the maximum power condition to the matching network in Figure 5-21, we have:

$$R_S = jX + \frac{1}{jB + \left(\dfrac{1}{R_L + jX_L}\right)}$$

(5-25)

The solutions for B and X in Equation (5-25) can be obtained by reusing Equations (5-12) and (5-14) and substituting $X_S = 0$ in Equations (5-13) and (5-15).

$$B_3 = \frac{R_S X_L + \sqrt{R_L R_S (R_L^2 + X_L^2 - R_L R_S)}}{R_S (R_L^2 + X_L^2)} \tag{5-26}$$

$$X_3 = \frac{R_S X_L}{R_L} + \frac{R_L - R_S}{B_3 R_L} \tag{5-27}$$

And,

$$B_4 = \frac{R_S X_L - \sqrt{R_L R_S (R_L^2 + X_L^2 - R_L R_S)}}{R_S (R_L^2 + X_L^2)} \tag{5-28}$$

$$X_4 = \frac{R_S X_L}{R_L} + \frac{R_L - R_S}{B_4 R_L} \tag{5-29}$$

The conditions for the valid solutions are that the arguments of the square roots in Equations (5-26) through (5-29) be non-negative. Therefore, the two solutions obtained from Equations (5-26) through (5-29) are valid only if $R_L > R_S$. Combined conditions for valid solutions are summarized in Table 5-1.

Case #	First Condition	Second Condition	# of Solutions	Equations Used
1	$R_L < R_S$	$R_L^2 + X_L^2 - R_L R_S > 0$	4	(5-21) to (5-24) (5-26) to (5-29)
2	$R_L < R_S$	$R_L^2 + X_L^2 - R_L R_S < 0$	2	(5-21) to (5-24)
3	$R_L > R_S$	N/A	2	(5-26) to (5-29)

Table 5-1 Impedance matching conditions and the number of solutions

The solutions in Equations (5-26) through (5-29) can be simplified by normalizing the load impedance with respect to the source resistor.

Therefore, if we let the source resistor be equal to Z_0, the normalized load resistance and reactance become,

$$r = \frac{R_L}{Z_0} \tag{5-30}$$

$$x = \frac{X_L}{Z_0} \tag{5-31}$$

The simplified equations for the first solution are:

$$B_1 = \frac{\sqrt{\frac{(1-r)}{r}}}{Z_0} \tag{5-32}$$

$$X_1 = Z_0 \left[\sqrt{r(1-r)} - x \right] \tag{5-33}$$

The simplified equations for the second solution are:

$$B_2 = -\frac{\sqrt{(1-r)}}{Z_0} \tag{5-34}$$

$$X_2 = -Z_0 \left[\sqrt{r(1-r)} + x \right] \tag{5-35}$$

The simplified equations for the third solution are:

$$B_3 = \frac{x + \sqrt{r(r^2 + x^2 - r)}}{Z_0(r^2 + x^2)} \tag{5-36}$$

$$X_3 = Z_0 \sqrt{\frac{(r^2 + x^2 - r)}{r}} \tag{5-37}$$

Finally the simplified equations for the fourth solution are:

$$B_4 = \frac{x - \sqrt{r\left(r^2 + x^2 - r\right)}}{Z_0\left(r^2 + x^2\right)} \tag{5-38}$$

$$X_4 = -Z_0 \sqrt{\frac{\left(r^2 + x^2 - r\right)}{r}} \tag{5-39}$$

Example 5-7: Design a single L-network that will match a real source impedance $Z_0 = 50\ \Omega$ to a complex load impedance, $Z_L = 7 - j22\ \Omega$, at a frequency of 1 GHz.

For this example $R_L < Z_0$ but $R_L^2 + X_L^2 - R_L Z_0 = 183 > 0$, therefore, Example 4-5 has four solutions.

First Solution: We use Equations (5-32) and (5-33) in MATLAB script to calculate the element values of the matching network.

1. Enter design parameters and normalized load impedance

Z0=50; RL=7; XL=-22; f=1000e6; r=RL/Z0; x=XL/Z0

2. Use Equations (5-32) and (5-33) in MATLAB script to calculate the matching element values

B1 = sqrt((1-r)/r)/Z0

X1 = Z0*sqrt(r*(1-r))-x*Z0

LS1 = X1/(2*pi*f)

CP2 = B1/(2*pi*f)

The calculation results show that B1 = 0.05 and X1 = 39.349, therefore, the series element is an inductor L1= 6.263 nH and the shunt element is a capacitor C2=7.889 pF, as shown in Figure 5-22.

To plot the response of the matching network, create a new workspace in ADS and open a new schematic window. Insert the S_Params Template and add capacitor and inductor from the Lumped-Components palette. Connect the matching elements as shown in Figure 5-22.

Figure 5-22 Schematic of the first matching L-network

Simulate the schematic and display S11 and S21 in a rectangular plot.

Figure 5-23 Response of the first matching L-network

Figure 5-23 shows that the matching L-network perfectly matches the load impedance at 1 GHz.

Example 5-8: Find the second solution of the Example 5-7.
Second Solution: Use Equations (5-34) and (5-35) to calculate the element values of the second matching network. The procedure follows.

1. Enter design parameters and the normalized load impedance

Z0=50; RL=7; XL=-22; f=1000e6; r=RL/Z0; x=XL/Z0

2. Use Equations (5-34) and (5-35) in MATLAB script to calculate the matching element values

B2 = -sqrt((1-r)/r)/Z0

X2 = -Z0*sqrt(r*(1-r))-x*Z0

L1 = X2/(2*pi*f)

L2 = -1/(2*pi*f*B2)

The calculation results show that B2 = -0.05 and X2 = 4.651, therefore, the series element is an inductor L1= 0.74 nH and the shunt element is another inductor L2= 3.211 nH, as shown in Figure 5-24.

To plot the response of the matching network, create a new workspace in ADS and open a new schematic window. Insert the S_Params Template and add capacitor and inductor from the Lumped-Components palette. Connect the matching elements as shown in Figure 5-24.

Figure 5-24 Schematic of the second matching L-network

Simulate the schematic and display S11 and S21 in a rectangular plot.

Figure 5-25 Response of the second matching L-network

Figure 5-25 shows that the matching L-network perfectly matches the load impedance to the source impedance at 1 GHz.

Example 5-9: Find the third solution to Example 5-7.

Third Solution: We use Equations (5-36) and (5-37) to calculate the element values of the matching network. The procedure follows.

1. Enter design parameters and normalized load impedance
Z0=50; RL=7; XL=-22; f=1000e6; r=RL/Z0; x=XL/Z0

2. Use Equations (5-36) and (5-37) in MATLAB script to calculate the matching element values

B3 = (x + sqrt(r*(r^2+x^2-r)))/(Z0*(r^2+x^2))

X3 = Z0*sqrt((r^2+x^2-r)/r)

L2 = X3/(2*pi*f)

L1 = -1/(2*pi*f*B3)

The calculation results show that B3 = -0.032 and X3 = 36.154, therefore, the shunt element is an inductor L1= 5.008 nH and the series element is another inductor L2=5.754 nH, as shown in Figure 5-26.

To plot the response of the matching network, create a new workspace in ADS and open a new schematic window. Insert the S_Params Template and add capacitor and inductor from the Lumped-Components palette. Connect the matching elements as shown in Figure 5-26.

Figure 5-26 Schematic of the third matching L-network

Simulate the schematic from 0.5 to 1.5 GHz and display the input return loss, S11, and the insertion loss, S21, in dB.

Figure 5-27 Response of the third matching L-network

Figure 5-27 shows that the matching L-network perfectly matches the load impedance to the source impedance at 1 GHz.

Example 5-10: Find the fourth solution to Example 5-7.

For the fourth solution use Equations (5-38) and (5-39) to calculate the element values of the matching network. The procedure follows.

1. Enter design parameters and normalize the load impedance

Z0=50; RL=7; XL=-22; f=1000e6; r=RL/Z0; x=XL/Z0

2. Use Equations (5-38) and (5-39) to calculate the matching element values

B4 = (x - sqrt(r*(r^2+x^2 - r)))/(Z0*(r^2 + x^2))

X4 = -Z0*sqrt((r^2+x^2 - r)/r)

C2 = -1/(2*pi*f*X4)

L1 = -1/(2*pi*f*B4)

The solution in the second configuration shows that B4 = -0.051 and X1 = -36.154, therefore, the shunt element is an inductor L1= 3.135 nH and the series element is a capacitor C2=4.402 pF.

To plot the response of the matching network, create a new workspace in ADS and open a new schematic window. Insert the S_Params Template and add capacitor and inductor from the Lumped-Components palette. Connect the matching elements as shown in Figure 5-28

.

Figure 5-28 Schematic of the fourth matching L-network

Simulate the schematic and display S11 and S21 in a rectangular plot.

Figure 5-29 Response of the fourth matching L-network

Figure 5-29 shows that the matching L-network perfectly matches the load impedance to the source impedance at 1 GHz.

Matching a Real Load to Real Source Impedance

When source and load impedances are both real the first matching configuration of Figure 5-10 is redrawn in Figure 5-30.

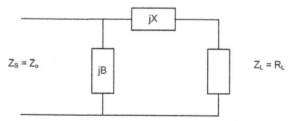

Figure 5-30 First matching configuration with $X_L = X_S = 0$

To design the matching network, apply the maximum power transfer condition and require that $Z_0^* = Z_{IN}$. Therefore,

$$Z_0 = \cfrac{1}{jB + \left(\cfrac{1}{jX + R_L}\right)}$$

(5-40)

Substituting $r = \dfrac{R_L}{Z_0}$ in Equation (5-40), we get:

$$Z_0 = \cfrac{1}{jB + \left(\cfrac{1}{jX + rZ_0}\right)}$$

(5-41)

The solutions for B and X in Equation (5-41) can be obtained by reusing Equations (5-32) and (5-34) and substituting x = 0 in Equations (5-33) and (5-35).

$$B_1 = \frac{\sqrt{(1-r)/r}}{Z_0}$$

(5-42)

$$X_1 = Z_0\sqrt{r(1-r)}$$

(5-43)

$$B_2 = -\frac{\sqrt{(1-r)/r}}{Z_0}$$

(5-44)

$$X_2 = -Z_0\sqrt{r(1-r)}$$

(5-45)

Note that the two solutions given by Equations (5-42) through (5-45) are only valid if r is less than 1 or $R_L < Z_0$. If r > 1, the second matching network configuration is used.

Figure 5-31 Second matching configuration with resistive load and source

To calculate the B and X values, we require that, $Z_0^* = Z_{IN}$, therefore,

$$Z_0 = jX + \frac{1}{jB + \left(\dfrac{1}{Z_0 r}\right)}$$

(5-46)

The solutions for B and X in Equation (5-46) can be obtained by substituting x = 0 in Equations (5-36) through (5-39).

$$B_3 = \frac{\sqrt{r-1}}{Z_0 r}$$

(5-47)

$$X_3 = Z_0\sqrt{r-1}$$

(5-48)

$$B_4 = \frac{-\sqrt{r-1}}{Z_0 r}$$

(5-49)

$$X_4 = -Z_0\sqrt{r-1}$$

(5-50)

Note that the two solutions given by Equations (5-47) through (5-50) are only valid if *r* is greater than 1 or $R_L > Z_0$. The combined conditions for the validity of solutions are given below and summarized in Table 5-2.

Case 1 If *r* is less than 1 there are two L-networks that match the two impedances. The two solutions are given by Equations (5-42) through (5-45).

Case 2 If *r* is greater than 1 there are two L-networks that match the two impedances. The two solutions are given by Equations (5-47) through (5-50).

Case No	Condition	Solutions	Equations
1	$r < 1$	2	(5-42) to (5-45)
2	$r > 1$	2	(5-47) to (5-50)

Table 5-2 Impedance matching conditions and the number of solutions

Example 5-11: Design an L-network to match a 10 Ω load to a 50 Ω source resistor at 500 MHz

Since the load resistor is smaller than the source resistor, the example has two solutions given in Equations (5-42) through (5-45).

First Solution: For the first solution use Equations (5-42) and (5-43) to calculate the element values of the matching L-network. The procedure follows.

1. Enter design parameters and normalized load impedance
Z0=50; RL=10; f=500e6; r=RL/Z0

2. Use Equations (5-42) and (5-43) in MATLAB script to calculate the matching element values

B1 = sqrt((1 - r)/r)/Z0

X1 = Z0*sqrt(r*(1 - r))

L1 = X1/(2*pi*f)

C2 = B1/(2*pi*f)

The calculation results show that B1 = 0.04 and X1 = 20, therefore, L1=6.366 nH and C2=12.73 pF.

To generate the schematic and plot the response of the matching network, create a workspace in ADS and open a new schematic window. Insert the S_Params Template and add capacitor and inductor from the Lumped-Components palette. Connect the matching elements shown in Figure 5-32.

Figure 5-32 Schematic of the first matching L-network

Simulate the schematic and display S11 and S21 in a rectangular plot.

Figure 5-33 Response of the first matching L-network

The simulated response in Figure 5-33 shows that the matching L-network perfectly matches the load impedance to the source impedance at 0.5 GHz.

Example 5-12: Find the second solution to Example 5-11.

Second Solution: To design the second matching L-network, use Equations (5-44) and (5-45) and calculate the matching element values.

1. Enter design parameters and normalize the load impedance

Z0=50; RL=10; f=500e6; r=RL/Z0

2. Calculate the matching element values

B2 = - sqrt((1 - r)/r)/Z0
X2 = -Z0*sqrt(r*(1 - r))
C1 = -1/(2*pi*f*X2)
L2 = -1/(2*pi*f*B2)

The calculation results show that B2 = -0.04 and X2 = -20, therefore, the series element is a capacitor, C=15.92 pF, and the shun element is an inductor, L= 7.958 nH.

To generate the schematic and plot the response, create a new workspace in ADS and open a new schematic window. Insert the S_Params Template and add capacitor and inductor from the Lumped-Components palette. Connect the matching elements as shown in Figure 5-34.

Figure 5-34 Schematic of the second matching L-network

Simulate the schematic and display S11 and S21.

Figure 5-35 Response of the second matching L-network

The simulated response in Figure 5-35 shows that the matching L-network perfectly matches the load impedance to the source impedance at 0.5 GHz.

5.4 Introduction to Broadband Matching Networks

In the previous sections, the L-section matching networks achieved an impedance match at a fixed frequency capable of producing a 20 dB return loss over a narrow fractional bandwidth of less than 20%. Broadband networks are generally considered to have greater than 20% fractional bandwidths. In this section it is demonstrated that the bandwidth of a matching network can be increased by cascading L-networks. It is demonstrated that by cascading L-networks of equal Q factor, the bandwidth of a network can be increased. The design of equal-Q matching networks is based on the selection of intermediate, or virtual, resistors not necessarily 50 Ω, and then matching the load and source impedance to the virtual resistors. Successively adding additional L-networks of equal Q will continue to extend the bandwidth of the overall circuit.

Design of the Broadband Matching Networks

This section demonstrates the importance of the selection of the proper intermediate network resistance that will result in the best broadband return loss. In example 5.4-1 the complex source and load impedance are matched to one specific intermediate resistor thus creating two, equal-Q, L-networks. The purpose is to show that this method provides a broader matching bandwidth at 20 dB return loss compared to the case when we chose a different resistor value. The Q of each L-network is the loaded Q factor defined by the source and load resistance ratio.

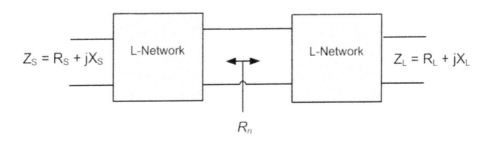

Figure 5-36 Cascaded L-networks with intermediate resistance, R_n

Example 5-13: A transmitter with the source impedance $55 + j10\ \Omega$ is to be connected to an antenna with the input impedance $20 + j15\ \Omega$. Design a cascade of two L-networks that match the transmitter to the antenna at 1 GHz.

Solution: The first step in the solution is to calculate the intermediate resistor, R_n. The optimum intermediate resistor value is equal to square root of the product of the real part of the source and load impedance.

$$R_n = \sqrt{(55)(20)} = 33.166 \; \Omega$$

Use the Equation Editor to solve Equations (5-32) and (5-33) to calculate the element values of the load matching network. The calculation results show that the series element is an inductor, *LS1* = 0.195 nH and the shunt element is a capacitor, *CP2* = 3.893 pF.

1. Enter design parameters and normalized load impedance
Z0=33.166; RL=20; XL=15; f=1000e6; r=RL/Z0; x=XL/Z0

2. Calculate matching element values

B1 = sqrt((1 - r)/r)/Z0

X1 = Z0*sqrt(r*(1 - r))-x*Z0

LS1 = X1/(2*pi*f)

CP2 = B1/(2*pi*f)

The calculation results show that the series element is an inductor, L1 = 0.195 nH, and the shunt element is a capacitor, C1 = 3.893 pF.

To plot the response of the matching network, create a new workspace in ADS and open a new schematic window. Insert the S_Params Template and add capacitor and inductor from the Lumped-Components palette. Connect the matching elements as shown in Figure 5-37.

Figure 5-37 Schematic of the matching L-network

Simulate the schematic and display S11 and S21 in a rectangular plot.

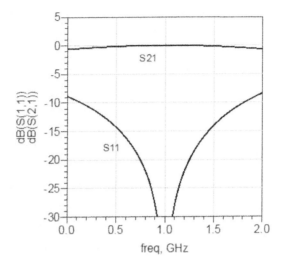

Figure 5-38 Response of the matching L-network

To match the source impedance to the intermediate resistor, we use Equations (5-36) and (5-37) and calculate the element values of the second matching network, as follows.

1. Enter design parameters and normalized load impedance
Z0=33.166; RL=55; XL=10; f=1000e6; r=RL/Z0; x=XL/Z0

2. Calculate matching element values
B3 = (x + sqrt(r*(r^2 + x^2 - r)))/(Z0*(r^2 + x^2))

X3 = Z0*sqrt((r^2 + x^2 - r)/r)

LS1 = X3/(2*pi*f)

CP2 = B3/(2*pi*f)

The calculation results show that the shunt element is a capacitor, C1= 2.875 pF, and the series element is an inductor, L1=4.458 nH.

To plot the response of the matching network, create a new workspace in ADS and open a new schematic window. Insert the S_Params Template and add capacitor and inductor from the Lumped-Components palette. Connect the matching elements as shown in Figure 5-39.

Figure 5-39 Schematic of the matching L-network

Simulate the schematic and display S11 and S21 in a rectangular plot.

Figure 5-40 Response of the matching L-network

Finally, we cascade the two matching L-networks as shown in Figure 5-41.

Figure 5-41 Schematic of the Cascaded L-networks

Simulate the schematic and display S11 and S21 in a rectangular plot.

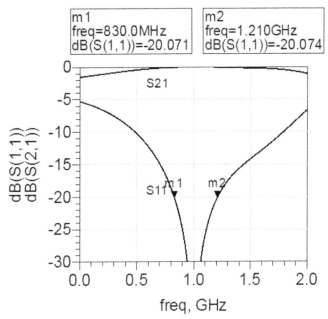

Figure 5-42 Response of the Cascaded L-networks

The simulated response in Figure 5-42 perfectly matches the complex load impedance to the source impedance at 1 GHz. Notice that the matching bandwidth at 20 dB return loss is about 380 MHz.

$$BW_{20\,dB\ return\ loss} = 1210 - 830 = 380 \quad MHz$$

Therefore, the corresponding fractional bandwidths at 20dB return loss is.

$$FBW_{20\,dB\,return\,loss} = \frac{380}{\sqrt{(1210)(830)}} = 0.379 = 37.9\,\%$$

The Q factor of the each L-network is calculated by the following equation.

$$Q = \frac{1}{2}\sqrt{\frac{R_2}{R_1} - 1} \qquad\qquad R_2 > R_1$$

Where R_2 and R_1 are the input and output resistors of the L-network.

For Example 5.13 the Q of the source and load matching networks are:

$$Q_{source} = Q_{load} = \frac{1}{2}\sqrt{\frac{33.166}{20} - 1} = \frac{1}{2}\sqrt{\frac{55}{33.166} - 1} = 0.405$$

Example 5-14: Redesign the Example 5.13 by matching the source and load impedances to an intermediate resistance of 50 Ω instead of 33.166 Ω. Compare the fractional bandwidth and Q factors of the two examples.

Solution: To redesign the matching network, change the intermediate resistor in the Matlab Equations to 50 Ω and recalculate the matching element values as shown in Figure 5-43.

Figure 5-43 Matching networks

Notice that the matching element values in both schematics have changed due to the change in the intermediate resistor. The cascaded schematic and simulated response are shown in Figure 5-44.

Figure 5-44 Schematic of the cascaded matching L-networks

Figure 5-45 Response of the cascaded matching L-networks

The simulated response in Figure 5-45 shows that the matching L-network perfectly matches the load impedance to the source impedance at 0.5 GHz.

The marker frequencies at 20 dB return loss shows that the bandwidth is:

$$BW_{20\,dB\ return\ loss} = 1126 - 874 = 252\ MHz$$

Therefore, the corresponding fractional bandwidths at 20dB return loss is:

$$FBW_{20dB\,return\,loss} = \frac{252}{\sqrt{(1126)(874)}} = 0.253 = 25.4\ \%$$

A comparison of the fractional bandwidths for the two examples show that the matching network in Figure 5-41 provides over 50 % more matching bandwidth, at 20 dB return loss, than the matching network in Figure 5-44. We can show that the lesser bandwidth is due to the fact that the source and load matching networks in the second example do not have the same Q factors, as shown by the following calculations:

$$Q_{source} = \frac{1}{2}\sqrt{\frac{55}{50} - 1} = 0.158$$

$$Q_{load} = \frac{1}{2}\sqrt{\frac{50}{20} - 1} = 0.612$$

The equal Q factors in Example 5.4-1 cause the cascaded matching network to transfer more power to the load while the unequal Q factors in example 5.4-2 cause the matching network to have less power transferred.

Cascaded Broadband Impedance Matching Networks

In Example 5.13 we showed that cascading two equal-Q L-networks convert a narrowband matching L-network into a broadband matching network. Because the Q factor is related to the ratio of the source and load resistance on each L-network, the Q can be further reduced by applying multiple equal Q L-networks in cascade. In practice as the number of L-networks becomes greater than five, the element values become difficult to physically realize. In this section we show that by using a network of four equal-Q L-networks in cascade, we can lower the individual Q factor and provide an even greater matching bandwidth for the Example of 5.13.

Example 5-15: Redesign the matching network of Example 5.13 with four equal-Q L-networks. Compare the Q and bandwidth of this example with Example 5.13.

Solution: This example uses the same steps developed for Example 5.13. The general equation for the calculation of any number of intermediate resistors is given by Equation (5-51).

$$R_n = R_S(r)^{n/N} \qquad\qquad n = 1, 2, 3, to\ N - 1 \qquad (5\text{-}51)$$

Where:

R_n is the intermediate resistor values

R_S is the source resistor value

r is the normalized load resistor, $r = R_L/R_S$

N is the number of cascading networks

First we use Equation (5-51) to calculate intermediate resistors for $N = 4$.

1. Enter design parameters and normalize the load impedance
RS = 55; RL = 20; r = RL/RS; N = 4

2. Use MATLAB script to calculate intermediate resistor values

R1 = RS*r^(1/N)

R2 = RS*r^(2/N)

R3 = RS*r^(3/N)

The calculation results show that R1=42.71 Ω, R2=33.166 Ω, and R3=25.755 Ω.

Use the following steps to design the matching networks.

1. Enter design parameters and the normalized load impedance

R3 = 25.755; RL = 20; XL=15; f =1000e6; r = RL/R3; x=XL/R3

2. Use MATLAB script to calculate the matching element values

B1 = sqrt((1 - r)/r)/R3

X1 = R3*sqrt(r*(1 - r)) - x*R3

CS1 = -1/(2*pi*f*X1)

CP2 = B1/(2*pi*f)

The calculation results show that C1 = 37.26 pF and C2 = 3.315 pF, as shown in Figure 5-46.

Figure 5-46 Schematic of the first matching L-network

Similarly the calculation of the matching L-network, between R3 and R2, are shown here.

1. Enter design parameters and normalized load impedance

R2=33.166; RL=25.755; f=1000e6; r=RL/R2

2. Calculate matching element values

B1 = sqrt((1 - r)/r)/R2

X1 = R2*sqrt(r*(1 - r))

LS1 = X1/(2*pi*f)

CP2 = B1/(2*pi*f)

The calculation results show that L= 2.199 nH and C1= 2.574 pF, as shown in Figure 5-47.

Figure 5-47 Schematic of the second matching L-network

Next, the calculation of the matching L-network, between R2 and R1, is shown here.

1. Enter design parameters and normalized load impedance

R1=42.71; RL=33.166; f=1000e6; r=RL/R1

2. Calculate matching element values

B1=sqrt((1-r)/r)/R1

X1=R1*sqrt(r*(1-r))

LS1=X1/(2*pi*f)

CP2=B1/(2*pi*f)

The calculation results show that L1= 832 nH and C1=1.999 pF, as shown
in Figure 5-48.

Figure 5-48 Schematic of the third matching L-network

Finally, the calculation of the matching L-network between R1 and the
source impedance is:

1. Enter design parameters and normalized load impedance

R1=42.71; RL=55; XL=10; f=1000e6; r = RL/Z0; x=XL/Z0

2. Calculate matching element values

B3 = (x + sqrt(r*(r^2+x^2-r)))/(R1*(r^2+x^2))

X3 = R1*sqrt((r^2+x^2-r)/r)

LS1 = X3/(2*pi*f)

CP2 = B3/(2*pi*f)

The calculation results show that L1=3.907 nH and C1= 2.119 pF.

Figure 5-49 Schematic of the fourth matching L-network

Finally cascade the four L-networks in Figure 5-50

Figure 5-50 Schematic of the four cascaded matching L-networks

The response of the cascaded 4 L-networks is shown in Figure 5-51.

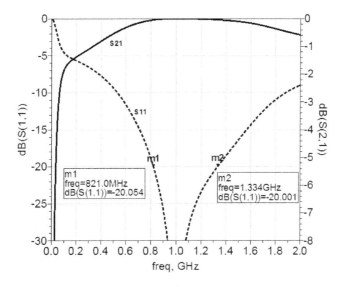

Figure 5-51 Response of the cascaded matching L-networks

Figure 5-51 shows that the matching bandwidth at 20 dB return loss is:

$$BW_{20\,dB} = 1334 - 821 = 513 \ MHz$$

Therefore, the fractional bandwidth at 20 dB return loss is:

$$FBW_{20\,dB} = \frac{513}{\sqrt{(1334)(821)}} = 0.490 = 49.0\%$$

The comparison between the fractional bandwidth of this example with the fractional bandwidth of Example 5-13 shows that cascading four equal-Q L-networks increases the fractional bandwidth by more than 93 % over the network with only two equal-Q L-networks.

As we stated earlier, the reason for wider matching bandwidth is that all four individual L-networks have the same Q factor as calculated here.

$$Q_{4L} = \frac{1}{2}\sqrt{\frac{55}{42.71}-1} = \frac{1}{2}\sqrt{\frac{42.71}{33.166}-1} = \frac{1}{2}\sqrt{\frac{33.166}{25.755}-1} = \frac{1}{2}\sqrt{\frac{25.755}{20}-1} = 0.268$$

Derivation of Equations for Q and the Number of L-Networks

The loaded Q factor of a single L-network matching two real resistors R_1 and R_2 was given by:

$$Q_1 = \frac{1}{2}\sqrt{\frac{R_2}{R_1}-1} \qquad\qquad R_2 > R_1$$

For a cascade of N equal-Q L-networks, the individual Q factor is given by:

$$Q_N = \frac{1}{2}\sqrt{\left(\frac{R_2}{R_1}\right)^{1/N}-1} \qquad N = 1,2,3 \qquad\qquad (5\text{-}52)$$

Notice that by increasing the number of L-networks the individual Q factor is decreased and, as a result, the matching bandwidth will be increased. Equation (5-52) can be used to calculate the number of L-networks needed for a given resistor ratio and Q factor. Equation (5-52) can be written as:

$$1 + 4Q_N{}^2 = \left(\frac{R_2}{R_1} \right)^{1/N}$$

Or,

$$\left[1 + 4Q_N^2 \right]^N = \left(\frac{R_2}{R_1} \right)$$

Taking logarithm of both sides, the required number of cascaded L-networks, N, can be obtained from Equation (5-53).

$$N \geq \frac{\log \left(\dfrac{R_2}{R_1} \right)}{\log \left[1 + 4Q_N^2 \right]} \tag{5-53}$$

Note that in Equation (5-53) the resistor R_2 must be greater than R_1 so that the number of L-networks, N, become a positive integer.

As an example, calculate the minimum number of cascaded L-networks that achieves a loaded Q factor of 0.3.

To calculate N, substitute the resistor ratio of 3 and Q = 0.3 into Equation (5-53).

$$N \geq \frac{\log (3)}{\log \left[1 + 4(0.3)^2 \right]} = \frac{0.477}{0.133} = 3.58$$

Therefore, a minimum of four L-networks is needed to achieve a Q of 0.3 or less.

To verify this we substitute the resistor ratio and N into Equation (5-52) and calculate the Q factor.

$$Q_4 = \frac{1}{2}\sqrt{\left(\frac{R_2}{R_1}\right)^{1/4} - 1} = 0.28$$

As you can see the Q factor of 4 cascaded L-Networks is less than 0.3.

5.5 Designing with Q-Curves on the Smith Chart

We have seen that increasing the number of matching L-networks increases the bandwidth of the matching networks. Each successive section is matched to an intermediate resistance, R_n. The overall Q of the network is determined by the ratio of the source to load resistor, as given by Equation (5-52). The Q factor is reduced as the number of L-networks is increased.

We have also shown that the bandwidth of such a cascade is optimized when the Q factor of all sections are the same. The cascade of successive L-networks of constant Q can also be accomplished on the Smith chart. Curves of constant Q can be drawn on the Smith chart at every point at which $Q = X / R$. Such a plot of Q curves is shown in Figure 5-52 for Q factor values of 1, 2, and 3.

A given Q curve is actually the external Q of a given L-network section. As such it does not account for loading on both ports of the network and is therefore two times the value of the Q as defined by Equation (5-52). The matching sequence progresses between the source impedance and the conjugate of the load impedance using the reactive element movements on the Smith chart. Each L-network should intersect a point on the real axis of the Smith chart.

The points on the real axis represent the intermediate resistance, R_n. The inductor and capacitor values must be chosen to stay within the boundary of the Q curve. Keeping each section equal distant to the Q curve results in a network in which each L-network has the same external Q factor. This is not to be confused with the overall loaded Q of the matching network.

The Q Curve selection can be visualized as a compromise between the desired bandwidth and the number of L-networks that may be required for a given impedance match. Using the smallest Q curve will result in the widest possible bandwidth. It can also be noted that for very high Q load impedances, it may not be possible to achieve a broadband match with reactive L-networks. For these types of loads it may be necessary to use transmission line transformer techniques [8]. Even in narrowband applications, engineers prefer to keep the matching network Q as low as possible in circuits that involve high power levels. High Q matching networks can create very high voltage or current peaks when excited with high RF power levels. The Q curve technique will be demonstrated by revisiting Example 5.13

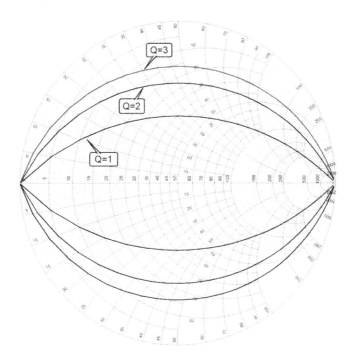

Figure 5-52 Smith chart display of constant Q-curves

Q-Curve Impedance Matching Example

Example 5-16: A transmitter operates over a frequency range of 835 MHz to 1200 MHz. At 1 GHz the source impedance is $Z_S = 55 + j10$ Ω while the antenna input impedance is $Z_L = 20 + j15$ Ω. Use the constant Q curve method in ADS to implement the cascaded matching L-networks.

Solution: A separate schematic and analysis is created in the ADS Workspace to generate the Q curve. Create a schematic that consists of a one port impedance element. Make the resistance and reactance values tunable variables. The S parameter simulation should be set at a fixed frequency in which any frequency can be used. Add a Parameter Sweep to the Workspace so that the resistance of the one port impedance can be swept over a range of 0.1 Ω to 4000 Ω in 5 Ω steps. Then write equations to calculate the impedance array that result in points of constant Q. These points can then be plotted on the Smith chart to create the Q curve. The desired value of the Q Curve can be entered in the equations or in the Tune Window. The procedure follows.

- Q=2(0.268) = 0.536

- R1=X1./Q

- Ztop=complex(R1,X1)

- Ztopn=(Ztop-50)/(Ztop+50)

- setindep("Ztopn","X1")

- Zbottom=complex(R1,-X1)

- Zbottomn=(Zbottom-50)/(Zbottom+50)

- setindep("Zbottomn","X1")

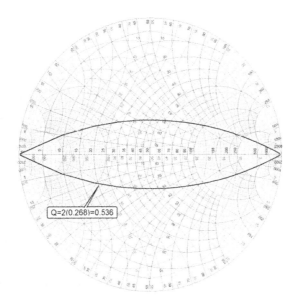

Figure 5-53 Q curve plot for Q=0.536

The Q curve for a Q value of 0.536 is shown in Figure 5-53. Because Q-curve plots do not consider loading on both ports of the network, we need to double the individual Q factor in order to obtain the external Q used in plotting the Q curve. For the network in Figure 5-50 the individual Q factor was 0.268, therefore, for plotting the Q curve on the Smith chart we must use Q = 2 (0.268) = 0.536 on the Smith chart and in the equations.

Impedance Matching Progression: Using the lumped element movement techniques learned in Chapter 3 the matching network can be designed on the Smith chart. On the Smith chart we are matching from the load at Z_A to the conjugate of the source at Z_I. The Smith chart of Figure 5-54 shows the lumped element movements on the constant conductance and resistance circles that maintain equal distant arcs within the specified Q curve. This ensures that each L-network maintains equal Q. The matching sequence between the source and load impedance progresses by using a series inductor from Z_A to intersect the Q curve at Z_B. Then add a shunt capacitor to move from the Q curve to the real axis at point Z_C. This process is continued until the last shunt capacitor intersects the impedance at Z_I.

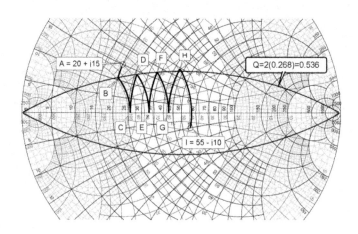

Figure 5-54 Q curve output for Example 5-15 (Q=0.536)

The Q curve plot of Figure 5-54 shows that all the node impedances fall on the same Q curve. To see the change in impedance as we move from the load impedance at 20 + j15 to the source impedance at 55 + j10 we have connected the points together indicating the addition of capacitors and inductors on the Smith chart. The displayed node impedances on the Smith chart show that three of the impedances fall on the real axis. These are the intermediate resistors. The intermediate virtual resistance values on the real axis are found to be:

$$Z_C = 25.777 \; \Omega \quad Z_E = 33.167 \, \Omega \quad Z_G = 42.715 \, \Omega$$

The impedances on the Q = 0.536 curve is measured as:

$$Z_B = 20 + j10.729 \; \Omega \qquad Z_D = 25.777 + j13.816 \, \Omega$$

$$Z_F = 33.167 + j17.797 \; \Omega \qquad Z_H = 42.715 + j24.55 \, \Omega$$

5.6 Limitations of the Broadband Matching Networks

From the previous examples we can deduce that the Q of the complex source and load impedance has an impact on the maximum bandwidth over which a good impedance match, low return loss, can be achieved. There is a finite limit on the achievable return loss for a given load impedance and circuit bandwidth known as Fano's limit [1]. Fano's Limit is the optimum reflection coefficient that can be achieved with a given load impedance. It is a theoretical limit that considers an infinite number of lossless matching elements. Fano's limit is defined as:

$$| \Gamma | = e^{\frac{-\pi Q_L}{Q_{UL}}}$$ (5-54)

Where:

Q_{UL} = the ratio of the reactance to resistance of the load

Q_L = the loaded Q of the network or the ratio of the center frequency of the network divided by the 3 dB bandwidth as defined by Equation (4-11).

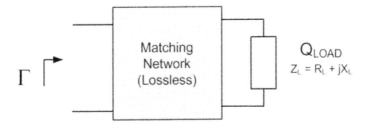

Figure 5-55 General configuration of impedance matching network

Fano's Limit Calculation

In the following example we apply the Fano's limit to calculate the optimum reflection coefficient for a given network.

Apply Fano's Limit to find the lowest reflection coefficient that can be achieved in the 3 dB range of the network shown in Figure 5-22.

From the network response in Figure 5-23 we notice that f_a=659 MHz and f_b=1228 MHz, therefore, the center frequency is $f_0 = \sqrt{(1228)(659)} = 899.5$ MHz. The matching network loaded Q_L is:

$$Q_L = \frac{f_o}{f_b - f_a} = \frac{899.5\,MHz}{1228\,MHz - 659\,MHz} = 1.580$$

For the load impedance, $Z_L = 7 - j22$, the unloaded Q_{UL} is defined as:

$$Q_{UL} = \frac{X_L}{R_L} = \frac{22}{7} = 3.14$$

Fano's limit states that the best achievable Γ is given by:

$$|\Gamma| = e^{\frac{-\pi Q_L}{Q_{UL}}} = e^{\frac{-\pi(1.580)}{3.14}} = 0.20$$

From Table 2-1 we know that a reflection coefficient of 0.20 is equivalent to a return loss of 13.98 dB or VSWR = 1.5. We must remember that Fano's limit gives a strictly theoretical result for return loss assuming lossless components and an infinite number of elements. The reflection coefficient defined by Fano's limit is essentially a rectangular return loss characteristic which is not possible to achieve in practice. It can be used however to give a quick estimate of the difficulty of a particular matching network, particularly for high Q load impedances.

5.7 Matching Network Synthesis

Filter Characteristics of the L-networks

The matching L-networks designed so far take the form of either a low pass or high pass characteristic. Based on the location of the inductor and capacitor, the network, acts as a low pass or a high pass filter. The low pass network consists of a series inductor and a shunt capacitor while the high pass network consists of a series capacitor and shunt inductor. Figures 5-56 and 5-57 show two low pass configurations that are used to match a source and load impedance together. With the low pass configuration at very low frequencies the inductive reactance is very small (short circuit) and the output is close to input. At very high frequencies the inductor has a high reactance and the output is near zero.

Figure 5-56 Low pass matching L-network

Figure 5-57 Low pass matching L-network

The high pass network consists of a shunt inductor and a series capacitor. Figures 5-58 and 5-59 show two high pass configurations that are used to match a source and load impedance based on the ratio of the real component the source and load impedance. At very low frequencies the inductor has a very small reactance, (short circuit), and the output is close to zero. At high frequencies the inductor has a high reactance, (like an open), and the output is nearly equal to input. At very low frequencies the capacitor has a very high reactance, (open circuit), and the output is close to zero while at high frequencies the capacitor has a small reactance, (short circuit), and the output is nearly equal to the input.

Figure 5-58 High pass matching L-network

Figure 5-59 High pass matching L-network

Impedance Matching Utility in ADS

The ADS software also has a powerful Impedance Matching Utility integrated into the software. In an ADS schematic select the Impedance Matching Utility by first clicking Tools > Impedance Matching to open the Impedance Matching Utility Control window, and then from the Control window, place the Impedance Matching SmartComponent palette on the schematic. The detail procedure in the following example shows the use of the ADS Impedance Matching Utility.

Example 5-17. Design a matching network between a source of 100 Ω and a load of 500 Ω resistor in parallel with a 2 pF capacitance, as shown in Figure 5-60. It is required that a 20 dB return loss and greater than -1 dB insertion loss be achieved over a frequency range of 60 MHz to 160 MHz.

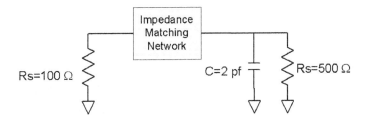

Figure 5-60 Matching load to 100 Ω source resistor

Solution: The Impedance Matching Utility in ADS provides SmartComponents and Matching Assistant for the design and simulation of impedance matching networks. Use the following procedure to design the required matching network.

1. Create a new workspace in ADS and open a new schematic window.

2. From the schematic window, click Tools > Impedance Matching to open the Impedance Matching Utility.

3. From the list of Impedance Match smart components select the bandpass MATCH component and place it on the schematic window

4. Click DA_LCBandpassMatch on the component palette to select the component as shown in Figure 5-61.

Figure 5-61 Bandpass filter SmartComponent

5. In the Control window. Select the DA_LCBandpassMatch component from the SmartComponent drop-down list.

6. Select the Matching Assistant tab and start editing the filter parameters

7. From the Source Impedance drop-down list box, select Resistive and set R=100 Ohm

8. From the Load Impedance drop-down list box, select Parallel RC and set R=500 Ohm and C=2 pF

9. For a center frequency of 100 MHz select the lower passband corner frequency Fp1= 61 MHz and the upper passband corner frequency Fp2=164 MHz, as shown in Figure 5-62.

Figure 5-62 Impedance Matching Utility Control window

10. Increase the order of the bandpass matching network until the design requirements are met. Figure 5-65 shows the matching network for N=9.

Figure 5-63 Schematic of the impedance matching network

The Impedance Matching SmartComponent with design parameters is shown in Figures 5-64.

Figure 5-64 Bandpass impedance matching design

Simulating the schematic in Figure 5-65 we get the following response.

Figure 5-65 Response of the matching network (N = 9)

Figure 5-65 shows that the design requirements at 61 and 164 MHz are fully met.

Effect of Finite Q on the Matching Networks

To complete the matching circuit design, the components need to be converted to their physical equivalents by accounting for the finite Q factor of the capacitors and inductors. This can be accomplished by using either S parameter or Modelithic models for the elements. A quick approach is to model each element with a Q factor that closely approximates the physical components. In this design we'll demonstrate a technique to assign a common variable name representing the Q factor of each component. This allows the evaluation of the necessary Q factor of the components required to meet the specifications of the matching network. The variable name, Qcap, is assigned to all capacitors in the matching network. Similarly the variable name, Qind, is assigned to all of the inductors. The frequency at which the Q factor is defined is also defined as a variable, Qf. This allows the Q factor of all inductors and all capacitors to be tuned simultaneously.

Example 5-18: Assign Qcap and Qind values to capacitors and inductors in the cascaded matching network of Figure 5-63. Show that the required 20 dB return loss and greater than -1dB insertion loss is achieved over a frequency range of 60 MHz to 160 MHz.

Solution: The subnetwork in Figure 5-66 is the same as Figure 5-63 except with the added Q factors for capacitors and inductors.

Figure 5-66 Schematic of the cascaded matching L-networks
(Qcap=150 and Qind=100)

Simulate the schematic in Figure 5-64 with the subnetwork in Figure 5-66 and display S11 and S21 in a rectangular window.

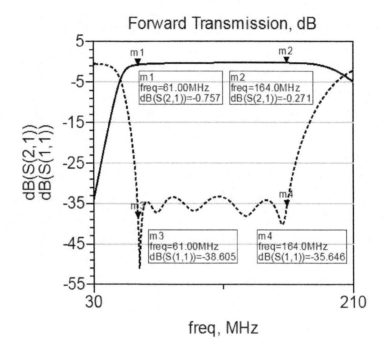

Figure 5-67 Response with Qcap=150 and Qind=100

The markers in Figure 5-67 show that the required 20 dB return loss and greater than -1dB insertion loss is achieved over a frequency range of 60 MHz to 160 MHz.

Change Q_C to 50 and Q_L to 40 I Figure 5-66 and display the response.

Figure 5-68 Schematic of the cascaded matching L-networks (Qcap=50 and Qind=40)

The response with Qcap=50 and Qind=40 is shown in Figure 5-69.

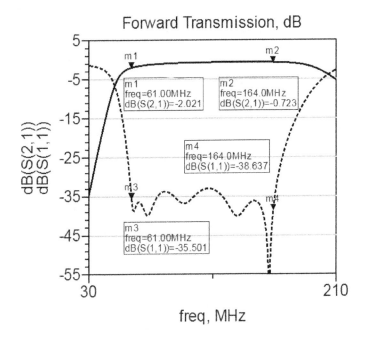

Figure 5-69 Response with Qcap=50 and Qind=40

As Figure 5-69 shows, a capacitor Q of 50 and an inductor Q of 40 results in an insertion loss that falls short of meeting the insertion loss specification.

References and Further Readings

[1]   R. K. Feeney and D. R. Hertling, *RF/Wireless Principles & Practice*, Georgia Institute of Technology, 1998.

[2]   Keysight Technologies, Manuals for Advanced Design System, *ADS 2015.07 Documentation Set*, EEsof EDA Division, Santa Rosa, k California www.keysight.com

[3]   Guillermo Gonzales, *Microwave Transistor Amplifiers – Analysis and Design*, Second Edition, Prentice Hall Inc., Upper Saddle River, NJ.

[4]   Randy Rhea, *The Yin-Yang of Matching: Part 2 – Practical Matching Techniques*, High Frequency Electronics, March 2006

[5]   Steve C. Cripps, *RF Power Amplifiers for Wireless Communications*, Artech House Publishers, Norwood, MA. 1999.

[6]   David M. Pozar, *Microwave Engineering*, Third Edition, John Wiley & Sons, New York, 2005

[7]   R. Ludwig, P. Bretchko, *RF Circuit Design*, Theory and Applications, Prentice Hall, Upper Saddle River, NJ, 2000

[8]   Jerry Sevick, *Transmission Line Transformers*, The American Radio Relay League, Newington, CT., 1990.

[9]   Ali A. Behagi and Stephen D. Turner, Microwave and RF Engineering, A Simulation Approach with Keysight Genesys Software, BT Microwave LLC, State College, PA , March 2015

Problems

5-1.   For a load of 75 Ω with a 10 pF series capacitance we want to have maximum power transfer at 1 GHz. Find a source inductance that cancels the reactance of the load at this frequency.

5-2.   Analytically design all the L-networks that will match a complex load impedance, $Z_L = 15 - j10\ \Omega$, to a complex source impedance, $Z_S = 25 + j20\ \Omega$, at a frequency of 1 GHz. Verify all the solutions by plotting the response of the matching networks.

5-3.   Analytically design all the L-networks that will match a source impedance, $Z_S = 30\ \Omega$, to a complex load impedance, $Z_L = 25 + j20\ \Omega$, at a frequency of 1 GHz. Verify all the solutions by plotting the response of the matching networks.

5-4. Analytically design all the L-networks that will match a load impedance, $Z_L = 15$ Ω, to a source impedance, $Z_S = 75$ Ω, at a frequency of 1.5 GHz. Verify all the solutions by plotting the response of the matching networks.

5-5. The output impedance of a transmitter operating at a frequency of 2 GHz is: $Z_S = 30 + j10$ Ω. Analytically design all the matching L-networks such that the maximum power is delivered to the antenna whose input impedance is $Z_L = 10 + j15$ Ω. Compare the matching bandwidth at 20 dB return loss with the method of using 50 Ω interconnecting line.

5-6. Redesign the network of Problem 5-5 by matching the source and load impedances to a 50 Ω line. Compare fractional bandwidth and Q factors for examples 5.5 and 5.6.

5-7. Redesign the matching network in Example 5.5 with four equal-Q L-networks. Compare the Q and bandwidth of the two networks.

5-8 For a load and source resistor ratio of 5, find the minimum number of cascaded L sections needed to achieve a loaded Q of 0.5.

5-9. Use the Impedance Matching Utility in ADS to solve a complex load matching example with $R_L = 1000$ Ω in parallel with a 3 pF capacitance. For the source select $R_S = 50$ Ω, and for the load select the parallel RC with R = 1000 Ω and C = 3 pF. Compare the Pi and Tee Matching Network response. Plot the insertion loss of both networks on the same plot.

Chapter 6

Distributed Impedance Matching Networks

6.1 Introduction

Distributed networks are comprised of transmission line elements rather than discrete resistors, inductors, and capacitors. Transmission lines elements can take various forms as they were covered in chapter 2. At RF and microwave frequencies, where the wavelengths of the signals become comparable to the physical dimensions of the components, even lumped elements behave like distributed components. At microwave frequencies distributed matching networks are more realizable form of matching than the lumped element versions discussed in the previous chapter. As a general rule, any electrical part larger than one tenth of the signal wavelength should be analyzed as distributed element. In an impedance matching network, operating at RF and microwave frequencies, reflections from short lengths of wire can create effects that are not predictable by the lumped element analysis. In this chapter both narrowband and broadband distributed matching networks are analyzed. Several examples are given to show how the matching networks are, analytically and graphically, designed. Distributed matching networks, discussed in this chapter, include quarter-wave and single-stub matching networks. For the quarter-wave matching networks the matching bandwidth, power loss and Q factor are analytically calculated.

6.2 Quarter-Wave impedance Matching Networks

The quarter-wave transformer is a useful network for impedance matching between two resistors. At RF and microwave frequencies impedance matching between a resistive source and load impedance can easily be achieved by a 90 degree transmission line known as a Quarter-Wave Transformer or Quarter-Wave Network. In this section the quarter-wave matching network is defined and its properties are investigated.

Analysis of Quarter-Wave Matching Networks

Equation (2-41) in chapter 2 showed that the input impedance of a quarter-wave network with characteristic impedance Z_0, terminated in a resistive load R_L, is given by:

$$Z_{IN} = \frac{Z_0^{\,2}}{R_L}$$

This equation can be written as:

$$Z_O = \sqrt{R_L Z_{IN}} \qquad (6\text{-}1)$$

In chapter 5 it was shown that maximum power transfer from a source with resistance R_S to a network terminated in a resistive load R_L is achieved only if the input impedance of the network is equal to the source resistance:

$$Z_{IN} = R_S$$

Therefore, the characteristic impedance of quarter-wave matching network, as shown in Figure 6-1, must satisfy the following equation.

$$Z_O = \sqrt{R_S R_L} \qquad (6\text{-}2)$$

Figure 6-1 Quarter-wave network terminated in resistor R_L

Equation (6-2) states that the characteristic impedance of the quarter-wave network, matching R_L to R_S, must be equal to the square root of the product of source and load resistors.

If we normalize the load resistor R_L with respect to R_S,

$$r = \frac{R_L}{R_S} \qquad (6\text{-}3)$$

The characteristic impedance of the quarter-wave network becomes a function of R_S and r.

$$Z_O = R_S \sqrt{r} \qquad (6\text{-}4)$$

Notice that for $R_L > R_S$, the characteristic impedance Z_0 is greater than R_S while for $R_L < R_S$, the characteristic impedance Z_0 is less than R_S. The fractional bandwidth of a network, *FBW*, is defined in Equation (6-5) where f_H and f_L are the upper and lower frequencies of the bandwidth and the center frequency f_0 is equal to $\sqrt{f_H f_L}$, respectively.

$$FBW = \frac{f_H - f_L}{\sqrt{f_H f_L}} \qquad (6\text{-}5)$$

The fractional bandwidth of a quarter-wave matching network is given in Equation (6-6) [5]:

$$FBW = 2 - \frac{4}{\pi} \cdot \cos^{-1}\left(\frac{2\Gamma_m \sqrt{r}}{\sqrt{1 - \Gamma_m^{\,2}} \, |1 - r|} \right) \qquad (6\text{-}6)$$

Where Γ_m is the magnitude of the reflection coefficient?

Equation (6-6) shows that the fractional bandwidth of a quarter-wave matching network depends upon the magnitude of the input reflection coefficient, Γ_m, and the mismatch ratio, r. The solutions to Equation (6-6) are only valid if,

$$\frac{2\Gamma_m \sqrt{r}}{\sqrt{1-\Gamma_m^2}\,|1-r|} \leq 1$$

At 3 dB return loss the reflection coefficient is $\Gamma_m = 0.707$, therefore, Equation (6-6) reduces to:

$$FBW_{3dB} = 2 - \frac{4}{\pi} \cdot \cos^{-1}\left(\frac{2\sqrt{r}}{|1-r|}\right) \qquad (6\text{-}7)$$

At 3 dB return loss Equation (6-7) has valid solutions only if,

$$\frac{2\sqrt{r}}{|1-r|} \leq 1 \quad or \quad r^2 - 6r + 1 \geq 0 \qquad (6\text{-}8)$$

Similarly, if we define the bandwidth at $\Gamma_m = 0.1$, corresponding to 20 dB return loss, as a good matching bandwidth it is insightful to evaluate the fractional bandwidth associated with this 20 dB return loss. From Equation (6-6) the fractional bandwidth at $\Gamma_{in} = 0.1$, is:

$$FBW_{20dB} = 2 - \frac{4}{\pi} \cdot \cos^{-1}\left(\frac{0.2\sqrt{r}}{\sqrt{0.99}\,|1-r|}\right) \qquad (6\text{-}9)$$

At 20 dB return loss Equation (6-9) has valid solutions only if,

$$\frac{0.2\sqrt{r}}{\sqrt{0.99}\,|1-r|} \leq 1 \quad or \quad 99r^2 - 202r + 99 \geq 0 \qquad (6\text{-}10)$$

The loaded quality factor, Q_L, of the quarter-wave matching network is defined as the inverse of the fractional bandwidth at 3 dB return loss; therefore, the loaded Q factor can be calculated from Equation (6-11).

$$Q_L = \frac{1}{FBW_{3dB}} = \frac{1}{2 - \dfrac{4}{\pi} \cdot \cos^{-1}\left(\dfrac{2\sqrt{r}}{|1-r|}\right)} \qquad (6\text{-}11)$$

Equation (6-11) shows that the validity condition in Equation (6-8) for the 3 dB fractional bandwidth is the same for the Q factor except that whenever the 3 dB fractional bandwidth tends towards infinity the Q factor tends towards zero. The Q factor given in Equation (6-11) is not to be confused with the unloaded transmission line Q factor as covered in chapter 4. This is actually an external Q factor as it relates to the loaded Q of the overall network. If f is the center (design) frequency, the bandwidth of the circuit is then calculated from Equation (6-12).

$$BW = (f) \cdot (FBW) \qquad (6\text{-}12)$$

Design of the Quarter-Wave Matching Networks

In this subsection, based on the equations developed in section 6.2.1, two quarter-wave matching networks for $R_L = 2\ \Omega$ and $R_L = 150\ \Omega$ are designed. For each case the loaded Q factor and bandwidth is calculated at 3 and 20 dB return loss.

Example 6-1 Design a quarter-wave network to match a 50 Ω source to a 2 Ω load at 100 MHz. Calculate the Q factor and the fractional bandwidths at

3 and 20 dB return loss. Compare the calculations with the simulation results in ADS.

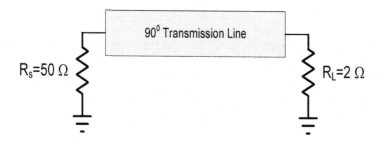

Figure 6-2 Matching quarter-wave transformer ($R_L < R_s$)

Solution: First we solve the problem analytically. Using the equations developed in section 6.2.1, the characteristic impedance, loaded Q factor, and the bandwidths of the matching network are calculated as follows.

1. Enter design parameters and normalize the load impedance

RS=50; RL=2; f=100e6; r=RL/RS

2. Calculate Z1, BW, FBW, and Q

Z1 = RS*sqrt(r)

FBW20dB = 2-(4/PI)*acos((0.2*sqrt(r))/(sqrt(0.99)*(abs(1-r))))

BW20dB = (f*FBW20dB)

FBW3dB = 2-(4/PI)*acos((2*sqrt(r))/(abs(1-r)))

BW3dB = (f*FBW3dB)

Q = 1/FBW3dB

The calculation results show that the Z1 is 10 Ω, Q factor is 1.827, and the bandwidths at 3 dB and 20dB return loss are 54.72 MHz and 5.333 MHz, respectively.

The fractional bandwidth at 3 dB return loss is 54.7 % and at 20 dB return loss is only 5.333 % indicating a narrowband matching network. This is characteristic of a narrowband matching network with a load resistor that is much smaller than the source resistor.

To measure the same parameters in ADS, create a new workspace and open a new schematic window. Insert the S_Params Template and place the TLIN component on the schematic. Set the component values as shown in Figure 6-3.

Figure 6-3 Schematic of the quarter-wave matching network

Simulate the schematic and display the input reflection coefficient, S11, and forward transmission, S21 in a rectangular plot. In data display window, to measure the 3 dB bandwidth automatically, use the built-in function in ADS as shown in Figure 6-4.

Figure 6-4 Network Response and 3 dB bandwidth

Figure 6-4 shows that the 3 dB bandwidth is 54.58 MHz. To measure the bandwidths manually, place markers at 3 and 20 dB return loss as shown in Figure 6-5.

Figure 6-5 Bandwidth Measurement at 3 and 20 dB return loss

Reading marker frequencies at 3 and 20 dB return loss, the corresponding bandwidths are:

$$BW_{-3dB} = 127.3 - 72.7 = 54.6 \qquad \text{MHz}$$

$$BW_{-20dB} = 102.7 - 97.3 = 5.4 \qquad \text{MHz}$$

The Q factor of the matching network is measured by using Equation (6-9),

$$Q = \frac{1}{FBW_{-3dB}} = \frac{\sqrt{(127.3)(72.7)}}{127.3 - 72.7} = 1.76$$

Note that the measured Q factor and bandwidths are in close agreement with the calculated values.

Example 6-2 Design a quarter-wave network to match a 50 Ω source to a 150 Ω load at 100 MHz. Compare the calculated Q factor and the fractional bandwidths, at 3 and 20 dB return loss, with the measurements.

Solution: The schematic of the matching network is shown in Figure 6-6.

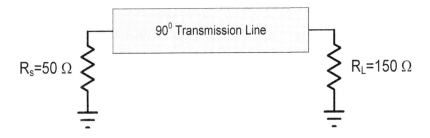

Figure 6-6 Quarter-wave matching network (R_L > R_S)

Using Equation (6-2) the characteristic impedance of the quarter-wave matching network is:

$$Z_1 = \sqrt{(50)(150)} = 86.6 \ \Omega$$

The ADS schematic of the matching network is shown in Figure 6-7.

Figure 6-7 Schematic of the matching quarter-wave network

Using Equations developed in section 6.2.1, calculate the characteristic impedance, the Q factor, and the bandwidths of the matching network at 3 and 20 dB return loss. The procedure follows.

1. Enter design parameters and normalized load impedance

RS=50; RL=150; f=100e6; r=RL/RS

2. Calculate Z1, FBW, BW and Q factor

Z1 = RS*sqrt(r)

FBW20dB = 2 - (4/PI)*acos((0.2*sqrt(r))/(sqrt(0.99)*(abs(1 - r))))

BW20dB = (f*FBW20dB)

FBW3dB = 2-(4/PI)*acos((2*sqrt(r))/(abs(1 - r)))

BW3dB = (f*FBW3dB)

Qe = 1/FBW3dB

The calculation results show that the bandwidth at 20 dB return loss is 22.28 MHz. This is over four times the bandwidth that was achieved with 2 Ω load impedance.

Next simulate the matching network in Figure 6-7 from 50 MHz to 150 MHz and display the input reflection coefficient, S11, and forward transmission, S21 in a rectangular plot. Place markers to measure the bandwidths at 3 and 20 dB return loss as shown in Figure 6-8.

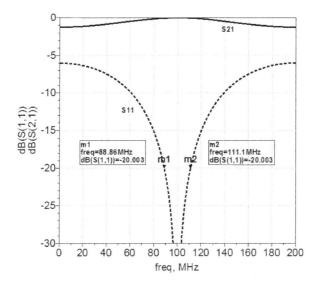

Figure 6-8 Response of the quarter-wave matching network

As Figure 6-8 shows the measured bandwidth at 20 dB return loss is:

$$111.1 - 88.86 = 22.24 \text{ MHz}$$

This agrees well with the calculated bandwidth.

6.3 Quarter-Wave Impedance Matching Bandwidth

Equation (6-6) shows that the achievable bandwidth in a quarter-wave matching network is related to the ratio of the load to the source impedance (mismatch ratio) as well as the value of the input reflection coefficient. It is insightful to examine the relationship between these quantities when one of the parameters is swept in value.

Quarter-Wave Matching Bandwidth and Power Loss

The fractional bandwidth and power loss of a quarter-wave matching network can be calculated as a function of the input reflection coefficient, Γ_{IN}, and the normalized load resistor r. The procedure is listed here.

1. Enter equations for input reflection coefficient, power loss, and the conversion of reflection coefficient to return loss in dB.
2. Enter the desired values for the source and load resistors
3. Normalize the load resistor with respect to source resistor
4. Use Equation (6-6) to calculate the fractional bandwidth.

Example 6-3: For a 50 Ω source and 2 Ω load resistors, calculate the fractional bandwidth and power loss from $\Gamma = 0.1$ to $\Gamma = 0.707$.

Solution: Follow the above procedure to calculate the fractional bandwidth and power loss when $R_S = 50$ Ω and $R_L = 2$ Ω.

1. Enter reflection coefficient, power loss, and return loss Equations.

Vswr = Sweep1_Data.VSWR1

ReflCoef = (Vswr - 1)/(Vswr1 + 1)

Powerloss = (1-(1- (abs(ReflCoef)^2)))*100

RLdB = -20*log(abs(ReflCoef))

2. Enter the source and load resistor values

RS = 50; RL = 2; r = RL/RS

3. Calculate the Fractional Bandwidth

FBW = (2-(4/PI)*acos((2*(ReflCoef)*sqrt(r))/(sqrt((1-(ReflCoef)^2))*abs(1-r))))

The ADS schematic is shown in Figure 6-9.

Figure 6-9: Calculation of fractional bandwidth and power loss

Sweep the parameters to display the fractional bandwidth and power loss for reflection coefficients from 0.1 to 0.707, as shown in Table 6-1.

	ReflCoef	FBW ...	RLdB	Powerloss
1	0.1	0.053	20	1
2	0.11	0.059	19.172	1.21
3	0.12	0.064	18.417	1.44
4	0.13	0.07	17.721	1.69
5	0.14	0.075	17.077	1.96
6	0.15	0.081	16.478	2.25
7	0.16	0.086	15.917	2.56
8	0.17	0.092	15.391	2.89
9	0.18	0.097	14.895	3.24
10	0.19	0.103	14.425	3.61
11	0.2	0.108	13.979	4
12	0.3	0.167	10.458	9
13	0.4	0.233	7.959	16
14	0.5	0.309	6.021	25
15	0.6	0.405	4.437	36
16	0.707	0.547	3.012	49.985

Table 6-1 Fractional bandwidth and power loss for $R_L = 2\ \Omega$

Table 6-1 shows that the fractional bandwidths at 0.1 reflection coefficient, corresponding to 20 dB return loss, is 5.3 % with 1% power loss while at 0.707 reflection coefficient, corresponding to 3 dB return loss, the fractional bandwidth is 54.7 % with 49.985 % power loss. Notice that the fractional bandwidths, at 3 and 20 dB return loss, are very close to the calculated values in Example 6-1.

Example 6-4: For a 50 Ω source and 150 Ω load resistors, calculate the fractional bandwidth and power loss from $\Gamma = 0.1$ to $\Gamma = 0.707$.

Solution: Following the procedure listed in Example 6-3, the calculations are shown here. Sweep the parameters and display the result, as shown in Table 6-3.

1. Enter reflection coefficient, power loss, and return loss Equations

Vswr = Sweep1_Data.VSWR1

ReflCoef = (Vswr - 1)/(Vswr + 1)

Powerloss = (1 - (1 - (abs(ReflCoef)^2)))*100

RLdB = -20*log(abs(ReflCoef))

2. Enter the source and load resistor values and normalized load

RS=50; RL=150; r=RL/RS

3. Calculate the Fractional Bandwidth

FBW = (2-(4/PI)*acos((2*(ReflCoef)*sqrt(r))/(sqrt((1-(ReflCoef)^2))*abs(1-r))))

The ADS schematic is shown in Figure 6-10.

Figure 6-10: Calculation of fractional bandwidth and power loss

	ReflCoef	FBW (rad)	RLdB	Powerloss
1	0.1	0.223	20	1
2	0.11	0.246	19.172	1.21
3	0.12	0.269	18.417	1.44
4	0.13	0.292	17.721	1.69
5	0.14	0.315	17.077	1.96
6	0.15	0.339	16.478	2.25
7	0.16	0.362	15.917	2.56
8	0.17	0.386	15.391	2.89
9	0.18	0.411	14.895	3.24
10	0.19	0.435	14.425	3.61
11	0.2	0.46	13.979	4
12	0.3	0.733	10.458	9
13	0.4	1.091	7.959	16
14	0.5	2	6.021	25
15	0.6	1.#QO	4.437	36
16	0.707	1.#QO	3.012	49.985

Table 6-2 Fractional bandwidth and power loss for R_s=50 Ω and R_L=150 Ω

Table 6-2 shows that the fractional bandwidth at $\Gamma = 0.1$, corresponding to 20 dB return loss, is 22.3 % with a 1% power loss.

Notice that the fractional bandwidth is the same as calculated in the previous example. The higher fractional bandwidth in this example, compared to its value in the previous example, is due to the lower ratio of the load to source resistance.

6.4 Single-Stub Impedance Matching Networks

The single-stub, also known as line and stub, matching network is a popular narrowband transmission line technique used to match real or complex load impedance to real source impedance. This technique is frequently used in distributed matching circuit designs using microstrip or stripline. The single-stub matching network, shown in Figure 6-11, consists of a series transmission line connected directly to the load impedance and a shunt stub (short-circuited or open-circuited transmission line) attached to the source impedance. The characteristic impedance of both matching elements has the same value as the source impedance, R_s. This section demonstrates both analytical and graphical techniques to design fixed frequency single-stub matching networks.

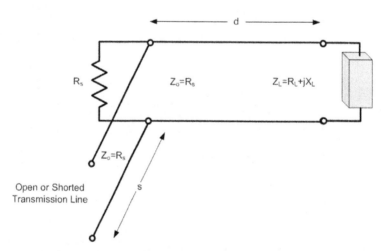

Figure 6-11: Single-stub matching network

To start the design of the single-stub matching network, attach a transmission line section, with characteristic impedance equal to R_S to the load and determine its electrical length in such a way that the normalized admittance at a distance d from the load falls on the unit conductance circle of the Smith chart. Calculation of the electrical lengths for the series transmission line and the shunt stub are given separately.

Analytical Design of the Series Transmission Line

The input impedance of a lossless transmission line of length d and characteristic impedance Z_0 terminated in an arbitrary load Z_L, was given in chapter 2 in Equation (2-46) and repeated here for convenience.

$$Z_{IN} = Z_o \frac{Z_L + jZ_o \tan \beta d}{Z_o + jZ_L \tan \beta d}$$

Setting $Z_0 = R_S$ and $\tan \beta d = t$, the input admittance of the network in Figure 6-9 can be written as:

$$Y_{IN} = \frac{1}{Z_{IN}} = \frac{R_S + jZ_L t}{R_S(Z_L + jR_S t)} = G_{IN} + jB_{IN} \qquad (6\text{-}13)$$

Substituting the normalized load impedance, $Z_L/R_s = r + jx$ into Equation (6-13) and separating its real and imaginary parts we get:

$$G_{IN} = \frac{r(1+t^2)}{R_S(r^2 + x^2 + t^2 + 2xt)} \qquad (6\text{-}14)$$

$$B_{IN} = \frac{xt^2 + (r^2 + x^2 - 1)t + x}{R_S(r^2 + x^2 + t^2 + 2xt)} \qquad (6\text{-}15)$$

The value of d, which implies t, can be obtained by setting the input conductance, G_{IN}, equal to source conductance:

$$\frac{r(1+t^2)}{R_S(r^2 + x^2 + t^2 + 2xt)} = \frac{1}{R_S} \qquad (6\text{-}16)$$

Equation (6-16) can be rearranged as:

$$(r-1)\cdot t^2 - 2xt - \left(r^2 + x^2 - r\right) = 0 \qquad (6\text{-}17)$$

Notice that the quadratic Equation (6-17) has two solutions for t. For a wider bandwidth and lower loss usually the smaller value of t is selected. The two solutions for t are:

$$t_1 = \frac{x + \sqrt{r(r^2 + x^2 - 2r + 1)}}{r - 1} \qquad (6\text{-}18)$$

$$t_2 = \frac{x - \sqrt{r(r^2 + x^2 - 2r + 1)}}{r - 1} \qquad (6\text{-}19)$$

With $\tan \beta d = t$, and $\beta \lambda = 2\pi$, we have $d = \dfrac{\lambda}{2\pi} \tan^{-1} t$ and the two solutions for d are:

$$d_1 = \frac{\lambda}{2\pi} \tan^{-1} t_1 \qquad t_1 \geq 0 \qquad (6\text{-}20)$$

$$d_2 = \frac{\lambda}{2\pi} \tan^{-1} t_2 \qquad t_2 \geq 0 \qquad (6\text{-}21)$$

To specify the lengths of d_1 and d_2 in electrical degrees, we have:

$$d_1 = \frac{360}{2\pi} \tan^{-1} t_1 \qquad t_1 \geq 0 \qquad (6\text{-}22)$$

$$d_2 = \frac{360}{2\pi} \tan^{-1} t_2 \qquad t_2 \geq 0 \qquad (6\text{-}23)$$

Because at every half wavelength the input impedance of a transmission line repeats, there are an infinite number of transmission line lengths that matches the load to source impedance. Usually the shorter length is selected to improve the matching bandwidth. If t_1 or t_2 is negative, we add half a wavelength to each line to get positive d_1 and d_2.

$$d_1 = \frac{360(\pi + \tan^{-1} t_1)}{2\pi} \quad \text{If } t_1 < 0 \qquad (6\text{-}24)$$

$$d_2 = \frac{360(\pi + \tan^{-1} t_2)}{2\pi} \quad \text{If } t_2 < 0 \qquad (6\text{-}25)$$

Analytical Design of the Open-Circuited Stub

To calculate the electrical length of the open-circuited stub, substitute t_1 and t_2 in Equation (6-15) to determine B_1 and B_2.

$$B_1 = \frac{xt_1{}^2 + (r^2 + x^2 - 1)t_1 + x}{R_S(r^2 + x^2 + t_1{}^2 + 2xt_1)} \qquad (6\text{-}26)$$

$$B_2 = \frac{xt_2{}^2 + (r^2 + x^2 - 1)t_2 + x}{R_S(r^2 + x^2 + t_2{}^2 + 2xt_2)} \qquad (6\text{-}27)$$

The electrical lengths of the open-circuited stubs are found by setting the susceptance of the stubs equal to the negative of the input susceptance.

$$so_1 = \frac{-\lambda\left(\tan^{-1}(R_S B_1)\right)}{2\pi} \qquad (6\text{-}28)$$

$$so_2 = \frac{-\lambda\left(\tan^{-1}(R_S B_2)\right)}{2\pi} \qquad (6\text{-}29)$$

If either stub lengths in Equation (6-28) or (6-29) is negative, add one half wavelength to obtain a positive stub length. For short-circuited stubs, the two solutions are:

$$ss_1 = \frac{\lambda\left(tan^{-1}\left(\frac{1}{R_S B_1}\right)\right)}{2\pi} \qquad (6\text{-}30)$$

$$ss_2 = \frac{\lambda\left(tan^{-1}\left(\frac{1}{R_S B_2}\right)\right)}{2\pi} \qquad (6\text{-}31)$$

Design of the Single-Stub Matching Network

Example 6-5: Design an open-circuited single-stub network to match a load resistance $Z_L = 2 - j5\ \Omega$ to a resistive source $R_S = 50\ \Omega$ at 100 MHz. Display the response and measure the bandwidths at 3 and 20 dB return loss.

Solution: The design example is shown in Figure 6-12.

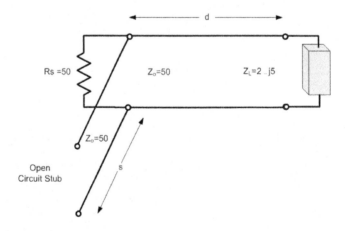

Figure 6-12 Complex load to resistive source matching network

Using equations developed earlier, calculate the electrical lengths of the matching line and stubs. The calculation in MATLAB follows.

1. Enter design parameters and normalized load impedance

RS = 50; RL = 2; XL = -5; f = 100e6; r = RL/RS; x = XL/RS

2. Calculate t1, t2, d1 and d2, B1, B2, so1, and so2.

t1 = (x + sqrt(r*(r^2+x^2-2*r + 1)))/(r - 1)

t2 = (x - sqrt(r*(r^2+x^2-2*r + 1)))/(r - 1)

d1 = 360*(atan(t1))/(2*pi)

d2 = 360*(atan(t2))/(2*pi)

B1 = (x*t1^2 + (r^2+x^2-1)*t1-x)/(RS*(r^2+x^2+t1^2 + 2*x*t1))

B2 = (x*t2^2 + (r^2+x^2-1)*t2-x)/(RS*(r^2+x^2+t2^2 + 2*x*t2))

so1 = 360*(pi - atan(RS*B1))/(2*pi)

so2 = -360*atan(RS*B2)/(2*pi)

The calculation results show that the problem has two solutions. Either solution can be used in the design of the single-stub matching network. However, for both line and stub, usually the shorter line lengths are chosen. For this example we select the shorter electrical lengths in the second solution; E=d2=16.975 degree for the line and E=so2=78.293 degree for the open-circuited stub. The schematic is shown in Figure 6-13.

Figure 6-13: Schematic of the single-stub matching network

Simulate the schematic and display S11 and S21 in a rectangular plot.

Figure 6-14: Response of the single-stub matching network

Notice that the fractional bandwidth at 3 dB return loss is about 11% while at 20dB return loss is only 1%. This suggests a very narrow matching bandwidth.

6.5 Design of the Single-Stub Matching Networks

Building on the techniques covered in chapter 3 this section demonstrates the ease in which the single-stub matching network can be graphically designed using the Smith chart. The Smith chart combined with tunable elements in an ADS schematic is a very powerful tool in which matching networks can be approximately designed without the need to solve the exact Equations of section 6.4.

Graphical Design of the Single-Stub Matching Network

In this section a 50 Ω source will be matched to a 5-25j Ω load at a frequency of 1000 MHz. Both open-circuited and short-circuited shunt stubs will be considered.

Example 6-6: Design a single-stub network to match the 5 - j25 Ω load impedance to 50 Ω source resistor. Use an open-circuited stub.

Solution: Create a new workspace in ADS and open a new schematic window. Insert the S_Params Template and add a series transmission line (TLIN) between the source and load terminations. Wire up the components and set the component values as shown in Figure 6-15.

To place a shunt element after the series transmission line, enable the admittance circles on the Smith chart. Make the length of the line tunable and tune it to move the load impedance (point A) to intersect the unit conductance circle on the top half of the Smith chart (point B. As the schematic shows, an electrical length of 42.5° places the impedance on the unit conductance circle at point B.

Figure 6-15: Adding series transmission line (electrical length=42.5°)

The impedance movement from point A to point B is shown in Figure 6-16.

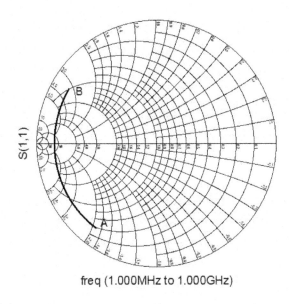

freq (1.000MHz to 1.000GHz)

Figure 6-16: Point B on the unit conductance circle (electrical length=42.5°)

At point B the normalized impedance is z = 0.088 + 0.28j Ω. To move point B to the center of Smith chart, add an open-circuited shunt transmission line and tune the length of the line until the impedance moves to the center of the chart (50Ω). As the schematic of Figure 6-17 shows, a 73° length of transmission line would be required.

Figure 6-17: Adding open-circuited shunt transmission line (73°) to network

The movement of point B to the center of the Smith chart is shown in Figure 6-18.

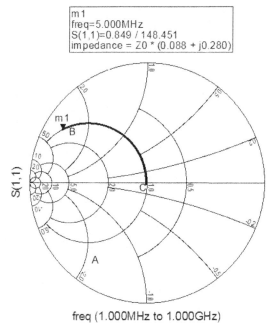

freq (1.000MHz to 1.000GHz)

Figure 6-18: Moving point B to the center of Smith chart (73°)

Graphical Design Using Short-Circuited Stubs

In this Section a short-circuited shunt stub will be used.

Example 6-7: Design a single-stub network to match the 5-j25 Ω load impedance to 50 Ω source resistor. Use a short-circuited stub.

Solution: A short-circuited shunt transmission line can be used to perform the function of the shunt stub. Using a short-circuited shunt transmission line, the series transmission line should intersect the unit conductance circle on the bottom half of the Smith chart. Add a series transmission line of 11° electrical length to move the impedance at point A to intersect the unit conductance circle at point B as shown in Figure 6-18. Then add the short-circuited shunt transmission line as shown in Figure 6-19. Tune the length to 17° to move the impedance to the center of the Smith chart.

Figure 6-19 Adding series transmission line (11°) to 5-j25 Ω

Simulate the schematic and notice the movement of the impedance from point A to point B.

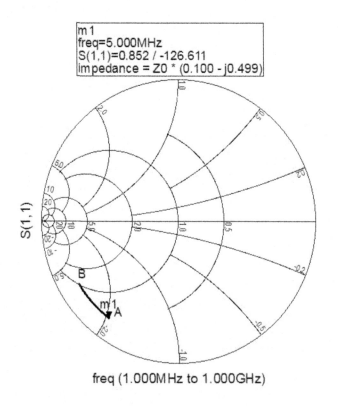

Figure 6-20: Adding series transmission line (11°) to 5-j25 Ω

To move point B to the center of Smith chart, add a short-circuited shunt transmission line and tune the length of the line until the impedance moves to the center of the chart (50Ω). As the schematic and display of Figures 6-21 and 6-22 show, a 17° length of transmission line would be required.

Figure 6-21: Adding short-circuited shunt transmission line (17°)

Simulate the schematic and notice the movement of the impedance from point B to the center of Smith chart.

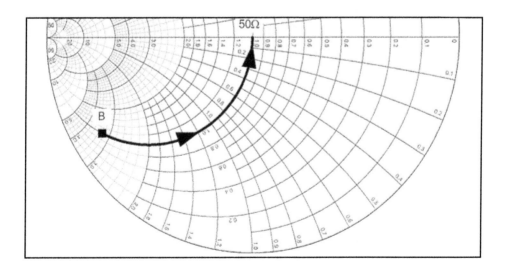

Figure 6-22: Adding short-circuited shunt transmission line (17°)

6.6 Cascaded Single-Stub Matching Networks

When the impedance of the load and the source are both complex functions, we can define a virtual resistor and design single-stub networks to match the complex impedances to the virtual resistor. The final matching network is obtained by cascading the single-stub matching networks. The procedure is demonstrated in the following example.

Example 6-8: Design single-stub networks to match a complex load $Z_L = 10 - j5\ \Omega$ to a complex source $Z_S = 50 - j15\ \Omega$ at 100 MHz.

First Solution: The matching procedure follows:

1. Find the intermediate resistor, $R_1 = \sqrt{R_L R_S} = \sqrt{(10)\,(50)} = 22.36\ \Omega$

2. Design a single-stub matching network between R1 and the source

3. Design a second single-stub matching network between R1 and the load

4. Cascade the two matching networks.

Follow the above procedure to match the complex source to the intermediate resistor. Make sure to consider the source as a load.

1. Enter design parameters and normalized source impedance

RS = 22.36; RL = 50; XL = -15; f = 100e6; r = RL/RS; x = XL/RS

2. Use MATLAB script to calculate t1, t2, d1, d2, B1, B2, so1, and so2

t1 = (x + sqrt(r*(r^2 + x^2-2*r + 1)))/(r - 1)

t2 = (x - sqrt(r*(r^2 + x^2 - 2*r + 1)))/(r - 1)

d1 = 360*(atan(t1))/(2*pi)

d2 = 360*(pi + atan(t2))/(2*pi)

B1 = (x*t1^2 + (r^2 + x^2 - 1)*t1 - x)/(RS*(r^2 + x^2 + t1^2 + 2*x*t1))

B2 = (x*t2^2 + (r^2 + x^2 - 1)*t2 - x)/(RS*(r^2 + x^2 + t2^2 + 2*x*t2))

so1 = 360*(pi-atan(RS*B1))/(2*pi)

so2 = -360*atan(RS*B2)/(2*pi)

From calculation results we select d2 = 114.019 degrees for the line and so2 = 43.245 degrees for the stub. The schematic is shown in Figure 6-23.

Figure 6-23: Schematic of the first matching network

Next we match the complex load to the intermediate resistor.

1. Enter design parameters and normalize the load impedance

RS=22.36; RL=10; XL=-5; f=100e6; r=RL/RS; x=XL/RS

2. Calculate t1 and t2, d1 and d2, B1 and B2, so1 and so2,

t1 = (x + sqrt(r*(r^2 + x^2 - 2*r + 1)))/(r - 1)

t2 = (x - sqrt(r*(r^2 + x^2 - 2*r + 1)))/(r - 1)

d1 = 360*(pi+atan(t1))/(2*pi)

d2 = 360*(atan(t2))/(2*pi)

B1 = (x*t1^2 + (r^2 + x^2 - 1)*t1 - x)/(RS*(r^2 + x^2 + t1^2 + 2*x*t1))

B2 = (x*t2^2 + (r^2 + x^2 - 1)*t2 - x)/(RS*(r^2 + x^2 + t2^2 + 2*x*t2))

so1 = 360*(pi-atan(RS*B1))/(2*pi)

so2 = -360*atan(RS*B2)/(2*pi)

From calculation results we select d2 = 48.39 degrees for the line and so2 = 41.722 degrees for the stub. The schematic of the second matching network is shown in Figure 6-24.

Figure 6-24: Schematic of the second matching network

Now cascade both matching networks to obtain the complete matching network.

Figure 6-25: Cascading single-stub matching networks

Example 6-9: Simulate the matching network in Figure 6-25 and calculate the matching bandwidths at 3 dB and 20 dB return loss. Display the response and verify the calculations with simulation results.

Solution: The simulated response of the matching network in Figure 6-25 is shown in Figure 6-26.

Figure 6-26 Response of the cascaded matching network

Notice that the bandwidth of the matching network at -3dB is,

$$BW_{-3dB} = 121.0 - 18.27 = 102.73 \quad MHz$$

Which agrees well with the measurements shown in Figure 6-26. Therefore, the fractional bandwidth at -3 dB is 102.7 per cent.

Similarly, the matching bandwidth at -20 dB is,

$$BW_{-20dB} = 103.2 - 95.92 = 7.28 \quad MHz$$

6.7 Broadband Design with Quarter-Wave Matching Network

In Examples 6-1 and 6-2, the bandwidth of a single quarter-wave transformer matching network is less than 10 % which is considered to be a narrowband matching network. We can increase the bandwidth by cascading two or more quarter-wave transformers to achieve a broader matching network.

To design a broadband matching network with N quarter-wave transformers first use Equation (6-32) to calculate the characteristic impedance of each quarter-wave transformer then cascade all the sections into one matching network. Let Rs and R_L be the source and load impedances to be matched by the N quarter-wave transformation network. The characteristic impedance of each section is calculated from Equation (6-32).

$$Z_n = R_S(r)^{(2n-1)/2N} \quad n = 1, 2, \dots, N \tag{6-32}$$

Where $r = R_L/R_S$ is the normalized load resistance and N is the number of quarter-wave transformers.

Example 6-10: Design a three-section quarter-wave transformer network to match a load resistance $R_L = 2\ \Omega$ to a source $R_S = 50\ \Omega$ at 100 MHz.

(a) Calculate the characteristic impedance of the quarter-wave transformers, the Q factor and the fractional bandwidths of the matching network at 3 and 20 dB return loss.

(b) Display the simulated response and compare the measurements with the measurements of single quarter-wave transformer matching network.

Solution: (a) Using Equation (6-32) the characteristic impedances of the 3-section quarter-wave transformers are:

$Z1 = R_S(r)^{1/2N} = 50(0.04)^{1/6} = 29.24$ Ohm

$Z2 = R_S(r)^{3/2N} = 50(0.04)^{3/6} = 10.00$ Ohm

$Z3 = R_S(r)^{5/2N} = 50(0.04)^{5/6} = 3.42$ Ohm

The intermediate resistors, R_n, can be obtained from Equation (6-33).

$$R_n = R_S (r)^{\frac{n}{N}} \quad n = 1, 2, 3, ..., N-1 \tag{6-33}$$

Therefore, the two intermediate resistors are:

$$R_1 = 50 (0.04)^{\frac{1}{3}} = 17.1 \ \Omega, \text{ and } R_2 = 50 (0.04)^{\frac{2}{3}} = 5.848 \ \Omega$$

The schematic of the three-section quarter-wave matching network is shown in Figure 6-27.

Figure 6-27 Three-section quarter-wave matching network

The simulated response of the matching network is shown in Figure 6-28.

Figure 6-28: Response of the cascaded matching network

Figure 6-28 shows that the bandwidth simulated at the 3 dB return loss is:

$$BW_{3dB} = 157.7 - 42.3 = 115.4 \text{ MHz}$$

$$\text{FBW}_{3dB} = \frac{115.4 x 100}{\sqrt{(157.7).(42.3)}} = 140.8\,\%$$

Similarly the simulated bandwidth at the 20 dB return loss is:

$$\text{BW}_{20dB} = 133.8 - 66.2 = 67.6 \text{ MHz}$$

$$\text{FBW}_{20dB} = \frac{67.6 x 100}{\sqrt{(133.8).(66.2)}} = 71.8\,\%$$

The measured Q factor for the matching network is,

$$Q = \frac{1}{1.408} = 0.71$$

The wide bandwidth and lower Q factor is an indication that, by adding two more quarter-wave sections, the Q factor has reduced to less than one half and the 3-dB bandwidth has more than doubled compared to a single quarter-wave matching network.

Example 6-11: Design a broadband quarter-wave network to match a complex load, $Z_L = 10 - j5\ \Omega$ to $50\ \Omega$ source impedance at 100 MHz. Calculate the bandwidth at 20 dB return loss and compare with the bandwidth of a single-stub matching network.

Solution: To design a broadband matching network between a resistive source and complex load impedance; first design a 5 section matching network between the real source and the real part of the load impedance. Then replace the quarter-wave transformer adjacent to the load with a single-stub that matches the complex load to the real resistor. Calculation of intermediate resistors follow.

1. Enter design parameters and normalize the load impedance

RS=50; RL=10;f=100e6; r=RL/RS; N=5

2. Calculate characteristic impedances and intermediate resistors

$Z1 = RS*r^{(1/(2*N))} = 42.567$

$Z2 = RS*r^{(3/(2*N))} = 30.852$

$Z3 = RS*r^{(5/(2*N))} = 22.361$

$Z4 = RS*r^{(7/(2*N))} = 16.207$

$Z5 = RS*r^{(9/(2*N))} = 11.746$

$R1 = RS*r^{(1/N)} = 36.239$

$R2 = RS*r^{(2/N)} = 26.265$

$R3 = RS*r^{(3/N)} = 19.037$

$R4 = RS*r^{(4/N)} = 13.797$

And the matching network is:

Figure 6-29 Five-section quarter-wave transformer matching network

Next replace the quarter-wave section adjacent to the load with a single-stub matching network. The design of the single-stub matching network is shown in the following Equation Editor. Note that the source resistor, R4 = 13.797 Ω, was calculated in the Equations.. The single-stub matching network is shown in Figure 6-30.

1. Enter design parameters and normalize the load impedance

RS=13.797; RL=10; XL=-5; f=100e6; r=RL/RS; x=XL/RS

2. Calculate t1, t2, d1, d2, B1, B2, so1, and so2,

$t1 = (x + sqrt(r*(r^2 + x^2 - 2*r + 1)))/(r - 1)$

$t2 = (x - sqrt(r*(r^2 + x^2 - 2*r + 1)))/(r - 1)$

$d1 = 360*(pi+atan(t1))/(2*pi)$

$d2 = 360*(atan(t2))/(2*pi)$

$B1 = (x*t1^2 + (r^2 + x^2 - 1)*t1 - x)/(RS*(r^2 + x^2 + t1^2 + 2*x*t1))$

$B2 = (x*t2^2 + (r^2 + x^2 - 1)*t2 - x)/(RS*(r^2 + x^2 + t2^2 + 2*x*t2))$

$so1 = 360*(pi-atan(RS*B1))/(2*pi)$

$so2 = -360*atan(RS*B2)/(2*pi)$

From calculation results we select d2 = 69.845 degrees for the line and so2 = 28.125 degrees for the stub. The schematic is shown in Figure 6-30.

Figure 6-30: Schematic of the single-stub matching network

Now cascade the line and stub network with the remaining four quarter-wave networks to form the final design of the matching network.

Figure 6-31: Schematic of the broadband matching network

The simulated response of the matching network is shown in Figure 6-32.

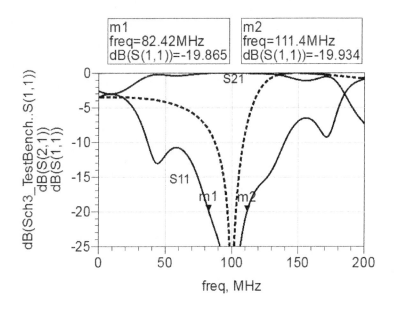

Figure 6-32: Response of the broadband matching network

Figure 6-30 shows that the bandwidth at 20 dB return loss is:

$$BW_{20dB} = 110 - 83 = 27 \text{ MHz}$$

And the fractional matching bandwidth at 20 dB return loss is:

$$FBW_{20dB} = \frac{27}{\sqrt{(110).(83)}} = 28.2 \%$$

The same bandwidths for the single-stub matching network are:

$$BW_{20dB} = 102.8 - 96.8 = 6 \qquad \text{MHz}$$

$$FBW_{20dB} = \frac{6x100}{\sqrt{(102.8).(96.8)}} = 6 \%$$

Notice that fractional bandwidth for the broadband at 20 dB return loss is 28.2 % as opposed to only 6 % for the narrowband single-stub matching network. Therefore, we have increased the matching bandwidth at 20 dB return loss by more than four times over the single-stub matching network.

Example 6-12: Design a broadband network to match a complex load, $Z_L = 150 - j30$ to 50 Ω source impedance at 100 MHz. Display the simulated response and measure the bandwidth at 20 dB return loss. Compare the results with the singe-stub matching network.

Solution: Use the same method as in Example 6.6.1 to design the broadband matching network. The design of the broadband quarter-wave transformer matching network with five quarter-wave sections is shown in Figure 6-31.

1. Enter design parameters and normalize the load impedance

RS=50; RL=150; f=100e6; r=RL/RS; N=5

2. Calculate characteristic impedances and intermediate resistors

Z1 = RS*r^(1/(2*N)) = 55.806

Z2 = RS*r^(3/(2*N)) = 69.519

Z3 = RS*r^(5/(2*N)) = 86.603

Z4 = RS*r^(7/(2*N)) = 107.883

Z5 = RS*r^(9/(2*N)) = 134.394

R1 = RS*r^(1/N) = 62.287

R2 = RS*r^(2/N) = 77.592

R3 = RS*r^(3/N) = 96.659

R4 = RS*r^(4/N) = 120.411

The ADS schematic of the five-section quarter-wave matching network is shown in Figure 6-33.

Figure 6-33: Five-section quarter-wave matching network

The simulated response of the quarter-wave matching network is shown in Figure 6-34.

Figure 6-34: Response of the matching network

Next replace the quarter-wave transformer adjacent to the load with a single-stub matching network. The design of the single-stub matching network is shown in the following Equation Editor. Note that the source resistor, R4 = 13.797 Ω, was previously calculated.

1. Enter design parameters and normalize the load impedance

RS=120.411; RL=150; XL=-30; f=100e6; r=RL/RS; x=XL/RS

2. Calculate t1 and t2, d1 and d2, B1 and B2, so1 and so2,

$t1 = (x + sqrt(r*(r^2 + x^2-2*r + 1)))/(r - 1)$

$t2 = (x - sqrt(r*(r^2 + x^2 - 2*r + 1)))/(r - 1)$

$d1 = 360*(atan(t1))/(2*pi)$

$d2 = 360*(pi + atan(t2))/(2*pi)$

$B1 = (x*t1^2 + (r^2 + x^2 - 1)*t1 - x)/(RS*(r^2 + x^2 + t1^2 + 2*x*t1))$

$B2 = (x*t2^2 + (r^2 + x^2 - 1)*t2 - x)/(RS*(r^2 + x^2 + t2^2 + 2*x*t2))$

$so1d = 360*(pi-atan(RS*B1))/(2*pi)$

$so2d = -360*atan(RS*B2)/(2*pi)$

From the solutions we select d2 = 111.013 degrees for the line and so2 = 17.408 degrees for the stub. Cascade the two matching networks to form the final design of broadband matching network as shown in Figure 6-35.

Figure 6-35: Schematic of the broadband matching network

The simulated response of the quarter-wave matching network is shown in Figure 6-36.

Figure 6-36: Response of the broadband matching network

Figure 6-36 shows that the bandwidth of the broadband matching network at 20 dB return loss is:

$$BW_{20dB} = 114.2 - 85.5 = 28.7 \text{ MHz}$$

And the fractional matching bandwidth at 20 dB return loss is:

$$FBW_{20dB} = \frac{28.7 x 100}{\sqrt{(114.2).(85.5)}} = 29.04 \text{ %}$$

The same bandwidths for the single-stub matching network are:

$$BW_{20dB} = 102.8 - 97.1 = 5.7 \text{ MHz}$$

And,

$$FBW_{20dB} = \frac{5.7 x 100}{\sqrt{(102.8).(97.1)}} = 5.7 \text{ %}$$

Notice that the fractional bandwidth at 20 dB return loss is over 29 % as opposed to only 5.7 % for the narrowband matching network. This is an indication that, by adding four quarter-wave sections to the single-stub matching network, we have increased the matching bandwidth at 20 dB return loss nearly five times over a single-stub matching network.

References and Further Readings

[1]   Keysight Technologies, Manuals for Advanced Design System, *ADS 2015.07 Documentation Set*, EEsof EDA Division, Santa Rosa, California www.keysight.com

[2]   Guillermo Gonzales, *Microwave Transistor Amplifiers – Analysis and Design*, Second Edition, Prentice Hall Inc., Upper Saddle River, NJ.

[3]   Randy Rhea, *The Yin-Yang of Matching: Part 1 – Basic Matching Concepts*, High Frequency Electronics, March 2006

[4]   Steve C. Cripps, *RF Power Amplifiers for Wireless Communications*, Artech House Publishers, Norwood, MA. 1999.

[5]   David M. Pozar, *Microwave Engineering*, Third Edition, John Wiley & Sons, New York, 2005

[6]   R. Ludwig, P. Bretchko, *RF Circuit Design*, Theory and Applications, Prentice Hall, Upper Saddle River, NJ, 2000

[7]   Ali A. Behagi and Stephen D. Turner, Microwave and RF Engineering, A Simulation Approach with Keysight Genesys Software, BT Microwave LLC, State College, PA , March 2015

Problems

6-1.   Design a quarter-wave transmission line to match a load resistance $R_L = 5\ \Omega$ to a resistive source $R_S = 75\ \Omega$ at 500 MHz. Calculate the characteristic impedance of the quarter-wave line, the Q factor and the fractional bandwidths of the matching network at 3 and 20 dB return loss. Display the simulated response and compare the calculations with measurements. For the quarter-wave matching network, calculate the fractional bandwidth and power loss from $\Gamma = 0.1$ to $\Gamma = 0.707$.

6-2.   Design a quarter-wave transmission line to match a load resistance $R_L = 100\ \Omega$ to a resistive source $R_S = 25\ \Omega$ at 600 MHz. Calculate the characteristic impedance of the quarter-wave line, the Q factor and the fractional bandwidths of the matching network at 3 dB and 20 dB return loss. Display the simulated response and compare the calculations with measurements. For the quarter-wave matching network, calculate the fractional bandwidth and power loss from $\Gamma = 0.1$ to $\Gamma = 0.707$.

6-3.   Design a single-stub network to match a load resistance $Z_L = 5 - j5\ \Omega$ to a resistive source $R_S = 75\ \Omega$ at 700 MHz. Calculate the electrical lengths of the matching line and stub and the fractional bandwidths of the matching network at 3 and 20 dB return loss. Display the simulated response and compare the calculations with measurements.

6-4.   Design a single-stub network to match a load resistance $Z_L = 100 + j20\ \Omega$ to a resistive source $R_S = 40\ \Omega$ at 800 MHz. Calculate the electrical lengths of the matching line and stub and the fractional bandwidths of the matching network at 3 dB and 20 dB return loss. Display the simulated response and compare the calculations with measurements.

6-5.   Design a single-stub network to match a complex load $Z_L = 20 + j5\ \Omega$ to a complex source $Z_S = 50 + j20\ \Omega$ at 1000 MHz. Calculate the electrical lengths of the matching line and stub and the fractional bandwidths of the matching network at 3 and 20 dB return loss. Display the simulated response and verify the calculations with measurements.

6-6.   Design a three-section quarter-wave network to match a load resistance $R_L = 5\ \Omega$ to a resistive source $R_S = 50\ \Omega$ at 100 MHz. Calculate the characteristic impedance of the quarter-wave line, the Q factor and the fractional bandwidths of the matching network at 3 and 20 dB return loss. Display the simulated response and compare the measurements with the singe quarter-wave matching network.

6-7.   Design a three-section quarter-wave network to match a load resistance R_L = 100 Ω to a resistive source R_S = 25 Ω at 900 MHz. Calculate the fractional bandwidths of the matching network at 3 and 20 dB return loss. Display the simulated response and compare the measurements with the singe quarter-wave matching network.

6-8.   Design a broadband network to match a complex load, Z_L = 25 + j10 Ω   to 75 Ω source impedance at 300 MHz. Measure the bandwidth at 20 dB return loss and compare it with the results of singe-stub matching network.

6-9.   Design a broadband network to match a complex load, Z_L = 100 + j20 to 40 Ω source impedance at 1200 MHz. Display the simulated response and measure the bandwidth at 20 dB return loss. Compare the results with the singe-stub matching network.

6.10   Design a broadband network to match a complex load, Z_L = 15 – j20 to 50 Ω source impedance at 100 MHz. Display the simulated response and measure the bandwidth at 20 dB return loss. Compare the matching bandwidth results with the singe-stub matching network.

6.11   Design a broadband matching L-network to match a complex load, Z_L = 50 – j20 to Z_S = 15 +j 55 Ω source impedance at 300 MHz. Display the simulated response and measure the matching bandwidth at 20 dB return loss. Compare the matching bandwidth results with the singe-stub matching network.

Chapter 7

Single Stage Amplifier Design

7.1 Introduction

Modern amplifier design involves the use of high frequency transistors to control and amplify RF energy. These transistors are fundamentally of the bipolar and field effect transistor (FET) variety. There are many subtypes of bipolar and FET devices that the reader is encouraged to explore [6]. The impedance matching techniques covered in chapters 5 and 6 are very useful for the design of linear transistor amplifiers. There are many different ways in which transistor amplifiers are impedance matched depending on the function or purpose of the amplifier circuit. For example, in the design of cascaded amplifier networks the output of each stage must be matched to the input of the next stage. In this chapter we design four single stage amplifiers that require four different impedance matching techniques.

1. Maximum Gain Amplifier Design
2. Specific Gain Amplifier Design
3. Low Noise Amplifier Design
4. Power Amplifier Design

Most amplifier designs involve selective mismatching of the transistor to its source and load impedance to accomplish its intended purpose. Only the maximum gain amplifier requires a conjugate matching network design. The specific matching techniques for each type of amplifiers are listed as:

1. **Maximum Gain Amplifier:**
   In a maximum gain amplifier the input and the output are conjugate matched to achieve maximum gain.

2. **Specific Gain Amplifier:**

A specific gain amplifier is mismatched at either the input or output to achieve a specified value of gain less than its maximum.

3.   Low Noise Figure Amplifier:
In a low noise amplifier the transistor's input is mismatched from 50 Ω to achieve a specific Noise Figure.

4.   Power Amplifier:
In a power amplifier the transistor's output is mismatched from 50 Ω for a specific amount of output power.

7.2 Maximum Gain Amplifier Design

This section covers the design of the maximum gain amplifier at 2.35 GHz using the SHF-0189 transistor. The SHF-0189 is a high performance Hetrostructure FET (HFET) housed in a surface-mount plastic package (SOT-89) as shown in Figure 7-1. The maximum gain amplifier is conjugate matched at the input and output resulting in very good return loss. A device can only be conjugate matched if it is unconditionally stable [1]. If the device is potentially unstable, a conjugate impedance match cannot be realized unless we add additional circuitry to stabilize the device.

Figure 7-1 GaAs HFET specifications (courtesy of RF Micro Devices)

Transistor Stability Considerations

Most Microwave transistors are potentially unstable at some frequency. This does not necessarily make them undesirable for use as an amplifier. A potentially unstable transistor does not mean that it will definitely oscillate in a circuit. Referring to the device in Figure 7-2 there may exist some combination of input or output reflection coefficient, Γ_S or Γ_L, that, when presented to the transistor, may indeed make the device oscillate. An oscillation condition is indicated by $|\Gamma_{IN}| > 1$ or $|\Gamma_{OUT}| > 1$. This can also be viewed as a positive value for the Return Loss, S11 or S22, in dB. This is referred to as negative resistance and is actually a design goal in the design of microwave oscillators. The conditions for unconditional stability for an RF transistor are given by equations (7-1) through (7-4) [2].

$$|\Gamma_S| < 1 \qquad (7\text{-}1)$$

$$|\Gamma_L| < 1 \qquad (7\text{-}2)$$

And,

$$|\Gamma_{IN}| = \left| S_{11} + \frac{S_{12}S_{21}\Gamma_L}{1 - S_{22}\Gamma_L} \right| < 1 \qquad (7\text{-}3)$$

$$|\Gamma_{OUT}| = \left| S_{22} + \frac{S_{12}S_{21}\Gamma_S}{1 - S_{11}\Gamma_S} \right| < 1 \qquad (7\text{-}4)$$

Typically there exists a select set of reflection coefficient values for Γ_S and Γ_L that will give the device this negative resistance characteristic. One method of dealing with this problem is to select values for Γ_S and Γ_L that avoid these unstable regions of impedance. This technique is demonstrated in Section 7.3. Another technique is to introduce a network that forces the device to be unconditionally stable for any values of Γ_S and Γ_L. This technique is often preferable as it will be shown that a transistor can be made unconditionally stable over a very wide frequency range. This is important because even though a device may be stable in its desired frequency band, it may become unstable at some frequency outside of the band of operation. A simultaneous numerical solution of Equations (7-1) through (7-4) for all values of Γ_S and Γ_L can prove that there are two conditions for unconditional stability. These entities are the stability factor, K, and stability measure, B1, and are given by the following Equations [3].

$$K = \frac{1 - |S_{11}|^2 - |S_{22}|^2 + |\Delta|^2}{2|S_{12} \cdot S_{21}|} \;>\; 1 \qquad (7\text{-}5)$$

$$B_1 = 1 + |S_{11}|^2 - |S_{22}|^2 - |\Delta|^2 \;>\; 0 \qquad (7\text{-}6)$$

$$|\Delta| \;=\; |S_{11} \cdot S_{22} - S_{12} \cdot S_{21}| \qquad (7\text{-}7)$$

Figure 7-2 Transistor input and output reflection coefficients

When the transistor is unconditionally stable a simultaneous conjugate match can be defined. The simultaneous conjugate match exists when $\Gamma_{IN} = \Gamma_S^*$ and $\Gamma_{OUT} = \Gamma_L^*$. The simultaneous conjugate match reflection coefficients are often referred to as: Γ_{MS} and Γ_{ML}. The maximum gain that can be obtained with a simultaneous conjugate matched amplifier is determined from the transducer gain equation, G_{Tmax}.

$$G_{T\max} = \frac{\left(1 - |\Gamma_{MS}|^2\right)|S_{21}|^2 \left(1 - |\Gamma_{ML}|^2\right)}{\left|\left(1 - S_{11}\Gamma_{MS}\right)\left(1 - S_{22}\Gamma_{ML}\right) - S_{12}S_{21}\Gamma_{ML}\Gamma_{MS}\right|^2} = \frac{|S_{21}|}{|S_{12}|}\left(K - \sqrt{K^2 - 1}\right) \quad (7\text{-}8)$$

When K is exactly equal to one, G_{Tmax} becomes the Maximum Stable Gain, G_{MSG}. G_{MSG} is the maximum value that G_{Tmax} can achieve.

$$G_{MSG} = \frac{|S_{21}|}{|S_{12}|} \qquad (7\text{-}9)$$

Stabilizing the Device in ADS

As equations (7-5) through (7-7) show, the stability factors are a function of the transistor's S parameters. An amplifier design begins with the placement of the device S parameters in a schematic design workspace as shown in Figure 7-2. The ADS software has built in functions to determine the stability factor and stability measure as well as Γ_{MS} and Γ_{ML}, the conjugate match reflection coefficients.

Example 7-1: Measure and display the stability factor, K, the stability measure, B1, and the maximum gain, Gmax, of the SHF-0189 FET transistor from 100 to 8000 MHz. Design the stability network if the transistor is unstable.

Solution: Create a new workspace in ADS and open a new schematic window. Insert the S_Params Template and place a two port S parameter file, S2P, from Data Items palette on the schematic. Ground the reference port and wire up the schematic. Double click on S2P icon to open the 2-Port S-parameter File dialog window. Browse the File Name and select the SHF-0189.s2p file from any folder in your computer. Set the component values as shown in Figure 7-3.

Figure 7-3 Schematic of the SHF-0189 device

Sweep the frequency range of the device over the entire range of frequencies contained in the S parameter file. When the Data Display window opens, write 3 equations to measure the stability factor, K, the stability measure, B1, and the maximum gain, Gmax, as follows.

K=stab_fact(S), B1=stab_meas(S), and Gmax=max_gain(S)

Plot parameters K, B1, and Gmax for the transistor as shown in Figure 7-4.

Figure 7-4 Plot of stability parameters and GMAX for the SHF-0189 device

Note that stability factor K is less than 1 from 100 MHz up to about 4500 MHz indicating that the transistor is potentially unstable over most of its frequency range including the design frequency of 2350 MHz. An effective stabilization network for medium and high power transistors employs a parallel RC circuit on the input of the device. Make both the R and C values tunable with a starting value of 10 Ω and 10 pF respectively. Tune the resistance and capacitance values until K > 1 for frequencies above 500 MHz. The values shown in Figure 7-5 provide sufficient stability above 500 MHz.

Figure 7-5 Added parallel RC stability network

Plot the parameters K, B1, and Gmax for the SHF-0189 device as shown in Figure 7-6.

Figure 7-6 Stability parameters and GMAX with parallel RC network

As seen in Figure 7-6, the stability measure, B1, is greater than zero throughout the entire frequency range. However the stability factor, K, goes below one at frequencies from less than 427 MHz. We want to make sure that the device is stable at all frequencies so that there is no possibility of any value of Γ_{ML} or Γ_{MS} that could make the device unstable at these out-of-band frequencies. Therefore add an R-L network in shunt with the input of the transistor for additional low frequency stability. This R-L network can be absorbed into the bias feed for the gate voltage of the transistor. Choose a fixed value of 50 Ω for the resistor. Select a starting value of 100 nH for the inductor and make this value tunable. This R-L network will load the previous R-C network so its values will need to be changed. The inductor's value can be reduced which in turn reduces the low frequency gain while not significantly reducing the in band gain at 2.35 GHz. Figure 7-7 shows the final stabilization network for the device.

Figure 7-7 Stabilization network for the SHF-0189 transistor

Simulate the schematic and display K, B1, and Gmax in a rectangular plot. Put a marker at 2350 MHz and notice in Figure 7-8 that, GMAX = 15.791 dB and K = 1.271 at the design frequency of 2.35 GHz. The device is now unconditionally stable for all frequencies from 50 MHz to 8 GHz.

Now that the device is unconditionally stable, we can determine the simultaneous conjugate match source and load impedance, Γ_{MS} and Γ_{ML}.

Figure 7-8 Stability parameters and G_{MAX} of the stabilized device

Finding Simultaneous Match Reflection Coefficients and Impedances

ADS has built in functions for the calculation of the $G1_{sm}$ and $G2_{sm}$ simultaneous match reflection coefficients as well as the corresponding simultaneous match impedance $Z1_{sm}$ and $Z2_{sm}$. Using the schematic of Figure 7-7 create a tabular output of the simultaneous conjugate source and load parameters at 2350 MHz, as shown in Figure 7-9.

Eqn Gmax=max_gain(S) Eqn Z1sm=sm_z1(S) Eqn Z2sm=sm_z2(S) Eqn G1sm=sm_gamma1(S) Eqn G2sm=sm_gamma2(S)

freq	Gmax	Z1sm	Z2sm	G1sm	G2sm
2.350 GHz	15.791	6.918 + j22.023	13.720 + j16.471	0.793 / 131.771	0.605 / 141.090

Figure 7-9 Table showing G_{MAX}, Z1sm, Z2sm, G1sm, and G2sm

Note the equivalence between the ADS function notation and the respective reflection coefficient and impedance. The following numbers are used in the design of the impedance matching networks.

$$Z1sm = Z_{MS} = 6.92 + 22.02 \ \Omega \qquad\qquad G1sm = \Gamma_{MS} = 0.793 \angle 131.7$$

$$Z2sm = Z_{ML} = 13.72 + 16.47 \ \Omega \qquad\qquad G2sm = \Gamma_{ML} = 0.605 \angle 141.1$$

7.3 Impedance Matching Network Design

There are different methods to complete the task of matching the 50 Ω source or load impedance to the Γ_{ML} or Γ_{MS}. These techniques are summarized as graphical (using the Smith chart), or analytical (by numerical computation). Because we are given a reflection coefficient that represents the conjugate of the impedance that the device represents, it is recommended to progress through the input and output match by moving from the 50 Ω point on the Smith chart to the Γ_{ML} or Γ_{MS} point on the same Smith chart. Theoretically this impedance match can be realized with any number of reactive elements. For single frequency applications or narrow bandwidths, < 10%, the impedance match is often realized with only two elements. Sometimes the engineer may prefer to use three or more elements for single frequency matching because it will make the design less sensitive to variation in the individual inductance or capacitance value. This becomes an important concern in manufacturing as practical lumped element components typically have a tolerance placed on their nominal value of 5 % to 20 %. In addition to the nominal tolerance, all components have a temperature coefficient of their nominal value. That is to say that the component's inductance or capacitance value may change with its temperature.

Design of the Input Matching Network

In the design of the SHF-0189 amplifier, we will use the analytical impedance matching techniques developed in chapter 5 and the L-Network Synthesis Utility to generate the matching networks.

When performing the analytical match we are matching the 50 Ω source impedance to the impedance looking into the device (Z_{IN} or Z_{OUT} of Figure 7-9; not the Z_{MS} or Z_{ML}. $Z1 = Z_{IN}$ and $Z2 = Z_{OUT}$ is the impedance looking into the input and output of the device. Z_{MS} and Z_{ML} are the source and load impedances that the device is looking into. Therefore the complex impedances that we are matching are given as the conjugate of Z_{MS} and Z_{ML}.

$$Z1 = Z1^* sm = 6.92 - j22.02 \ \Omega$$

$$Z2 = Z2^* sm = 13.72 - j16.47 \ \Omega$$

To match the complex load impedance to a resistive source first calculate r and x by normalizing the load impedance with respect to the source resistor, and then determine the matching networks on the basis of the conditions summarized in Table 5-1. The conditions are repeated here.

- If $r < 1$ and $r^2 + x^2 - r < 0$ there exists only two matching networks obtained from Equations (5-21) through (5-24).

- If $r < 1$ and $r^2 + x^2 - r > 0$ there exists four matching networks obtainable from Equations (5-21) through (5-24) and Equations (5-26) through (5-29).
- If $r > 1$ there exists only two matching networks obtained from Equations (5-26) through (5-29).

Example 7-2: Design the maximum gain amplifier input matching network.

Solution: For the stabilized SHF-0189 input matching network, $r = 0.1384$ and $x = -0.44$, therefore, $r < 1$ and $r^2 + x^2 - r = 0.074 > 0$. According to the above conditions, there exists four L-networks that can be used for the input matching network. The following procedure shows how to use MATLAB script to calculate the element values of the second matching network.

- Enter the source and load impedance and design frequency
- Normalize the load impedance

- Write the appropriate equations to calculate B and X
- Based on the positive or negative values of B and X, calculate the element values of the matching network.

1. Enter design parameters and normalize the load impedance

Z0=50; RL=6.918; XL=-22.03; f=2.35e9; r=RL/Z0; x=XL/Z0

2. Calculate matching element values from Equations (5-34) and (5-35).

B2 = -sqrt(1 - r)/Z0

X2 = -Z0*(sqrt(r*(1 - r)) + x)

L1 = X2/(2*pi*f)

L2 = -1/(2*pi*f*B2)

The calculation results show that the series element is an inductor L1= 0.322 nH and the shunt element is another inductor L2=1.357 nH.

To display the response of the matching network, create a new workspace in ADS and open a new schematic window. Insert the S_Params Template and connect the two inductors as shown in Figure 7-10.

Figure 7-10 Impedance matching network for the input match

Simulate from 1350 MHz to 3350 MHz and display S11 and S21, in dB, in a rectangular plot, as shown in Figure 7-11.

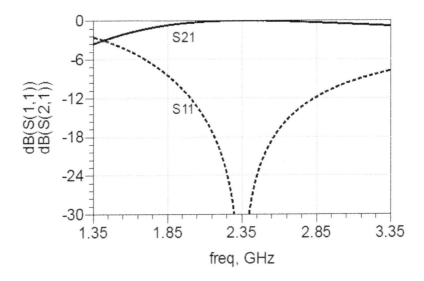

Figure 7-11 Response of the Impedance matching network

Design of the Output Matching Network

Example 7-3: Design the output matching network for the SHF-0189 amplifier at 2350 MHz.

Solution: Use the above procedure to calculate the output matching network, as shown in Figure 7-12.

Figure 7-12 Output matching L-network

The simulated response is show in 7-13

Figure 7-13 Response of the output matching L-network

Smart Simulation of the Amplifier in ADS

Example 7-4: **(a)** Assemble and simulate the amplifier to measure the maximum gain at 2.35 GHz and the fractional bandwidth at 20 dB return loss. **(b)** Create a component hierarchy and use the ADS Smart Simulation to measure the amplifier gain at 2.35 GHz and the fractional bandwidth at 20 dB return loss. **(c)** Compare the measurements in part (a) with part (b) measurements.

Solution (a): Create the ideal model of the amplifier by attaching the stabilizing components and the input-output matching networks to the device's S parameter file, as shown in Figure 7-14.

Figure 7-14 Schematic of the ideal amplifier circuit

Use a Linear Sweep from 100 MHz to 5000 MHz to analyze the response of the amplifier. The swept gain, input return loss, and output return loss is shown in Figure 7-15. As the return loss shows, an excellent match has been achieved at the input and output ports. Also the maximum gain (15.791 dB) of the amplifier at 2.35 GHz is exactly the originally calculated G_MAX indicating a successful simultaneous conjugate impedance match.

Figure 7-15 Swept response of the ideal amplifier design

The fractional bandwidth of the amplifier is calculated by sweeping the response over a narrower frequency range as shown in Figure 7-16.

Figure 7-16 Ideal amplifier response with markers at 20 dB return loss

Markers are placed on the passband response at the 0.1 dB ripple bandwidth corresponding to 20 dB return loss. As Figure 7-16 shows the 0.1 dB bandwidth is:

$$BW_{20dB} = 2396\text{-}2333 = 63 \text{ MHz}.$$

This corresponds to a fractional bandwidth of about 2.66 % consistent with a narrowband amplifier that is matched at the single frequency of 2.35 GHz.

$$FBW_{20dB} = \frac{63}{\sqrt{(2385).(2323)}} = 2.66 \text{ %}$$

Solution (b): The Simulation Wizard in ADS is provided to assist the users in setting up simulations for typical RF and microwave circuits. The

Simulation Wizard provides a number of predefined simulation setups that are application specific. For the maximum gain amplifier we usually want to run tests to compute the S-Parameters and gain among the numerous other parameters. To achieve this goal we create a component hierarchy so the Simulation Wizard can be used to test one component rather than the entire schematic. Creating a component hierarchy would represent the schematic with a symbol that we can test. Note in Figure 7-17 that we have added pins to the amplifier schematic to serve as the ports of the amplifier subnetwork. P1 is the RF input and P2 is the RF output of the amplifier.

Figure 7-17: Maximum gain amplifier subcircuit

To create a component that we can use for testing the amplifier, select the entire schematic then navigate to: Edit > Component > Create Hierarchy.

Figure 7-18: Hierarchy Cell Name

Type Amplifier for the Hierarchy Cell Name and press OK to place the top level Amplifier component on a new schematic.

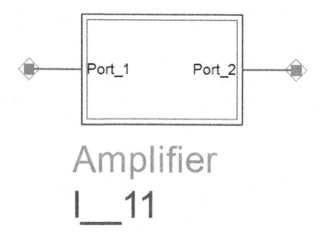

Figure 7-19: Top level Amplifier symbol

To see the subcircuit, select the Amplifier symbol and push into the toolbar button⬇. To go back to the schematic symbol click the pop out button ⬆.

We can also place the amplifier symbol on the schematic the same way we place any other component. Click on the Library icon 📚 and select the Workspace Libraries. Right click on the Amplifier and select Place Component.

We are now ready to use the Simulation Wizard. Click on the Simulation Wizard icon 🪄 to open the Smart Simulation Circuit Setup shown in Figure 7-20.

Figure 7-20: Smart simulation circuit setup

In Step 1 under Type of Application select <u>Amplifier</u> and click Next.

Figure 7-21: Select existing Amplifier design

In Step 2 under Select Amplifier select "Use an existing ADS design as the Amplifier subcircuit" and click Next to open the Library dialog box.

Figure 7-22: Library and Design selection

In Step 3 under Designs select "Amplifier" then press Next.

Figure 7-23: Pin identification

In Step 4 under pin identification select P1 for the RF Input and P2 for RF Output. Click Next to open the Smart Simulation Step 5.

Figure 7-24: Push into icpn

In Smart Simulation Step 5 press Finish to connect the Simulation Instrument to your amplifier as shown in Figure 7-25.

Figure 7-25: Smart Simulation Instrument

Double click on the Smart Simulation instrument to show the list of available simulation setups for amplifiers.

Figure 7-26: Available Simulations for Amplifiers

In the Smart Simulation Setup window select S-Pars, Noise Figure, and Stability for simulation and click Simulate. The S parameters and gain at the design frequency of 2.35 GHz are shown in Figures 7-27 and 7-28.

Figure 7-27: Available Simulations for Amplifiers

Solution (c): Note that the available power gain of 15.791 dB at 2.35 GHz matches exactly the number shown in Figures 7-15 and 7-16.

Figure 7-28: Available Simulations for Amplifiers

Notice that the maximum gain in Figure 7-28 is the same as the maximum gain of the ideal amplifier in Figure 7-15.

7.4 Physical Model of the Maximum Gain Amplifier

The ideal amplifier circuit is a good starting point to confirm the matching network design and stability of the device but is not very useful for creating the actual physical amplifier. In Chapter 4 we learned that the parasitic effects of the real lumped element components can significantly alter the expected performance of a circuit. Additionally the microstrip PCB tracks will begin to alter the performance of the circuit. As the frequency of the circuit increases, each PCB trace represents a longer portion of a wavelength and will detune the circuit. To create the physical model of the amplifier we need to select a microstrip substrate to place the PCB circuit tracks. We will also need to design bias feed networks and replace the ideal lumped element components with a physical model equivalent. Select the Roger's RO3010 material with dielectric thickness of 0.025 inches and 1 oz. copper (.00134 inch) copper thickness.

Transistor Artwork Replacement

The ADS SMT Package Layout Artwork Library contains a variety of layout footprints for various transistor packages. The selection of transistor packages is numerous but you may not always find your transistor's package outline in this library. The ADS layout tool makes it very easy to create custom artwork replacement elements for physical circuit layouts. Figure 7-29 shows the transistor package drawing of the SOT89 from the data sheet.

Figure 7-29 SOT89 package outline from data sheet

A drawing of the package can be created in any mechanical CAD program and imported into ADS as a DWG or DXF file. Normally the file should be saved in the units of mils.

Open an ADS layout cell view and select: File > Import. The following Import window open.

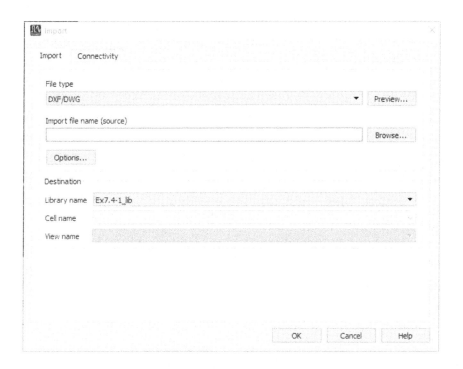

Figure 7-30 File Import dialog window

Once the Import window opens, select DXF/DWG for the File Type. Browse and select the appropriate file name and make sure the Destination/Library Name is correct. Under the Options make sure the units are correct. The SOT89 package drawing imported into ADS is shown in Figure 7-30.

Figure 7-31 SOT89 package drawing imported as the footprint

Once the package drawing is loaded into the Layout, we can add PCB solder pads and pin assignments. The source lead is to be connected directly to a ground pad. The device data sheet may give a suggested ground pad layout for optimum RF grounding and thermal conductivity. From the Layout Toolbar select Insert > Rectangle and draw a set of PCB tracks as shown in Fig. 7-32. Make the pads for the gate and drain leads 25mil x 30mil rectangles. Make sure that these pads are assigned to the correct layer. Then add the pin assignments as shown in Figure 7-29. The pin assignments should correspond to the order in which the ports are assigned on the schematic element. Because the transistor's gate and drain are the input and output respectively, these leads should be assigned pin 1 and pin 2. The source lead can then be assigned to pin 3.

Figure 7-32 PCB tracks and ports added to the metal layer

Finally save the artwork element from the menu File/Save. Choose either an existing library or create a new library to save any custom artwork that you create.

Amplifier Physical Design and Layout

Example 7-5: Design the physical amplifier bias feed and the PCB layout for the SHF-0189 maximum gain amplifier.

Solution: Start the physical design of the amplifier by placing the device S parameter file on the schematic. Use a microstrip Via Hole model for the connection of the transistor source lead to ground. Specify a Via Hole radius of 12 mils. Then assign the artwork replacement element for the SHF-0189 by opening the Properties window of the S parameter file. Select the Change Footprint button and browse to the location of the artwork replacement element created in the previous section. Proceed with the construction of the stabilization network portion of the design from Figure 7-15. This time add the Microstrip PCB tracks as shown in Figure 7-33. Use Modelithic surface mount components (30 mil x 60 mil) for the stabilization components as these will be easy to tune or optimize Use the S parameter files of the components that we do not intend to optimize. A 470 pF capacitor is added as a gate bypass capacitance. On the drain side of the transistor a 33 nH inductor is used as an RF choke to supply the drain voltage. Edit the footprint of the S parameter files and change the footprint to a 0603 surface mount component from the ADS library. The Modelithic components will automatically have the correct footprint assigned to its properties.

Figure 7-33 Construction of physical amplifier bias feed

Continue with the physical model construction by adding the matching networks. Note that on the input side of the circuit the matching network has an inductor connected to ground. Because there will be a negative voltage applied to the gate of the transistor, a DC blocking capacitor must be added to keep the inductor from shorting out the gate bias. Add an S parameter file for a 1.5 pF chip capacitor to act as a DC block. The capacitance value should be chosen such that the capacitor is operating in series resonance for minimum insertion loss. Knowing that the chip capacitor typically has some series inductance, the small series inductance of 0.323 nH can be absorbed into the DC blocking capacitor. The output matching circuit includes a series capacitance so no additional DC blocking capacitor is needed. The completed schematic of the physical amplifier model is shown in Figure 7-34. The physical PCB layout is shown in Figure 7-35.

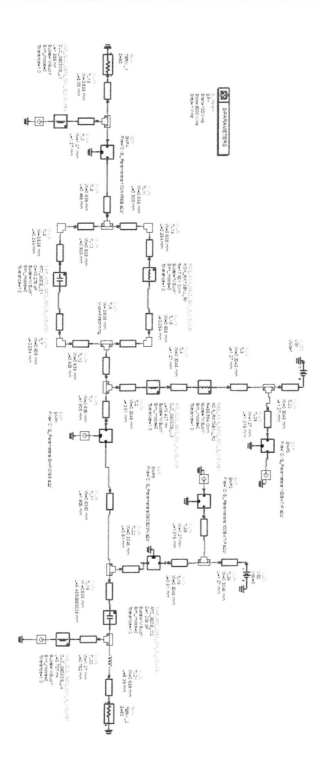

Figure 7-34 Schematic of the physical amplifier model

Figure 7-35 Physical layout of completed amplifier circuit

Optimization of the Physical Amplifier Response

After completion of the physical circuit schematic of Figure 7-34 the circuit response is swept from 100 MHz to 5000 MHz. The response of the amplifier significantly changes from the response of the ideal amplifier response of Figure 7-15. The gain and return loss have shifted in frequency. This is a typical result of replacing ideal elements with real physical models. This ability to deal with package parasitics and physical layout is a very powerful benefit of modeling the amplifier in ADS. We know that it is possible to make the component element values tunable and manually tune each element while observing the change in response. This is quite useful and encouraged so that you can see the circuit sensitivity to particular components. As the number of components and tunable elements increase in a given design, the tuning of individual elements can be cumbersome. In this section we will introduce the use of ADS Optimization to tune the amplifier's response to the desired characteristics. We can think of Optimization as an automatic circuit tuner. Selected components in the amplifier can be assigned as tunable variables. Multiple goals can then be set such as gain levels, return loss, etc. The optimization is then run and the ADS software will execute a mathematical optimization algorithm to determine the values of the variables required to achieve the specified goals [3]. In this example set all seven of the Modelithics model values as tunable.

Also make the microstrip line lengths for the series sections TL9 and TL19 variable. We will let the software optimize these variables to achieve the desired response. Make sure to set response goals for out-of-band responses as well as in band response. Initial response of the physical amplifier is shown in Figure 7-36.

Figure 7-36 Initial response of the physical amplifier circuit

Optimization Setup Procedure

We want to optimize the ideal amplifier response to achieve the desired performance without the need for manual tuning. The final specifications of the amplifier are

For the in-band frequency range from 2.30 GHz to 2.40 GHz

- 15.0 dB < Gain (S21) < 16.5 dB

- Input return loss (S11) < -10 dB

- Output return loss (S22) < -10 dB

For the out-of-band frequency range from 100 MHz to 1.5 GHz

- Gain (S21) < 5 dB

For the out-of-band Frequency Range from 4.5GHz to 5 GHz

- Gain (S21) < 5 dB

Follow the optimization setup procedure, described in part (c) of the Example 4-5, to achieve the final specifications of the amplifier. The input and output return loss is simply set to be less than -10 dB. Then set the below-band gain to be less than 5 dB from 100 MHz to 1500 MHz. Finally set the above-band gain to be less than 5 dB from 4500 MHz to 5000 MHz. These goals are close to representing the response of the ideal amplifier response. Weighting can be assigned to each Goal to aid the optimizer in obtaining a solution. For this example the in-band response is determined to be much more important than the out-of-band response so the weighting is defined as 10 and 1 respectively.

It is recommended to place a minimum and maximum component value on each element to constrain the Optimizer to stay within realistic values for the elements. For this optimization the Min-Max Gradient Search optimization was selected. The final optimized response is shown in Figure 7-37. The amplifier's response has been retuned to be very close to the response of the ideal amplifier.

Figure 7-37: Final optimized response of the physical amplifier circuit

The measured response of the prototype amplifier was found to be very close to the optimized response of Figure 7-37. This exemplifies the importance of using the ADS software to design and simulate a physical model of the amplifier. The photograph of the SHF-0189 prototype amplifier is shown in Figure 7-38.

Figure 7-38 Photograph of SHF-0189 prototype amplifier (courtesy of BT Microwave LLC)

Specific Gain Amplifier Design

In the design of RF and microwave amplifiers, it is common to design with potentially unstable transistors. The designer must know how to deal with potentially unstable devices. This section outlines the design of a 2.3 GHz amplifier using the RT243 GaN HEMT device. The RT243 has a usable frequency range of 100 MHz to 5 GHz.

Specific Gain Match

There may be situations where the maximum gain is not desired from a given amplifier stage. This could be required to reduce the power and noise from one preceding amplifier stage to another thereby not over driving the succeeding stage. We will see in following sections that there are other reasons for matching to specific impedances such as matching for low noise or maximum output power. An amplifier can be matched to achieve any level of gain below its maximum conjugate gain, Gmax. A convenient means of designing for a specific gain level is through plotting the Constant Gain Circles on the Smith chart. The Constant Gain circle is a locus of impedance values on the Smith chart in which the selection of an impedance on the circumference of the circle will result in an amplifier that will achieve that specific gain. The basic types of constant gain circle are:

1. Available Gain Circle, GA

2. Power Gain Circle, GP

The Available Gain Circle, GA, is a locus of impedance points that are referenced to the input of the active device. Selecting a point on the circumference of an Available Gain circle, GA, will selectively mismatch the input of the device to achieve the value of gain that corresponds to the Available Gain Circle. The GA value is therefore independent of the load impedance. The Available Gain can be defined as [4]:

$$GA = \frac{power\ available\ from\ the\ network}{power\ available\ from\ the\ source} \qquad (7\text{-}10)$$

Once a given source impedance has been selected on the Available Gain Circle, an output impedance can be calculated to conjugately match the output of the device to the load. The Power Gain Circle, GP, is a locus of impedance that is referenced to the output of the device. Selecting a point on the circumference of a given Power Gain Circle, GP, will selectively mismatch the output of the device to achieve a specific value of gain. The Power Gain can be defined as [4]:

$$GP = \frac{power\ delivered\ to\ the\ load}{power\ input\ to\ the\ network} \qquad (7\text{-}11)$$

Once the Power Gain Circle is plotted on the Smith chart any location on the circumference of the circle can be chosen as the load impedance for the transistor. A Specific Gain at some value below the GMAX value of the device must be selected. The Constant Power Gain Circle for a specific value of gain can be derived from the following equations [4]. The center of the Power Gain Circle is defined as:

$$r_o = \frac{GC_2{}^*}{1 + D_2 G} \qquad (7\text{-}12)$$

Where
$$G = \frac{Specific\ Gain}{|S_{21}|^2}$$

Note that the Specific Gain is the absolute gain value, not in dB.

$$C_2 = S_{22} - D_S S_{11}{}^*$$

$$D_2 = |S_{22}|^2 - |D_S|^2$$

$$D_S = S_{11}S_{22} - S_{12}S_{21}$$

The radius of the Circle is then calculated from the following equation [4].

$$\rho_o = \frac{\sqrt{1 - 2K|S_{12}S_{21}|G + |S_{12}S_{21}|^2 G^2}}{1 + D_2 G} \tag{7-13}$$

Once a given load impedance has been chosen on the circumference of a Power Gain Circle, an input impedance can be calculated that will conjugate match the input of the amplifier. The only caution in the selection of the load impedance is to make sure that the impedance is not selected in a region in which the transistor could be unstable. In the Simultaneous Conjugate match of section 7.2, the device was forced to be unconditionally stable by a RC network placed at the input of the device. This is a useful technique when designing an amplifier so that the engineer can be confident that the device will not oscillate at frequencies inside or outside of the pass band regions. There may be cases, such as Low Noise Amplifier design, in which it would not be desirable to utilize an RC stabilization network because of the degradation of noise figure. In any event it is not strictly necessary to include a stabilization network if the designer selects source and load impedances such that they do not enter unstable regions. The stability circles represent the boundaries between those values of source and load impedances that are stable and unstable [3]. Selecting a load impedance in an unstable region may cause the device to oscillate. The perimeter of the circle represents the points at which K = 1. The following equations can be used to analytically define the stability circles on the Smith chart. The center of the device input stability circle [4].

$$r_{s1} = \frac{C_1^*}{|S_{11}|^2 - |D_S|^2} \tag{7-14}$$

Where, $C_1 = S_{11} - D_S S_{22}{}^*$

The radius of the device input stability circle is defined by [4]:

$$\rho_{S1} = \left| \frac{S_{12} S_{21}}{\left| S_{11} \right|^2 - \left| D_S \right|^2} \right| \qquad (7\text{-}15)$$

The center of the device output stability circle is defined as [4]:

$$r_{s2} = \frac{C_2{}^*}{\left| S_{22} \right|^2 - \left| D_S \right|^2} \qquad (7\text{-}16)$$

The radius of the device output stability circle is defined by

$$\rho_{S2} = \left| \frac{S_{12} S_{21}}{\left| S_{22} \right|^2 - \left| D_S \right|^2} \right| \qquad (7\text{-}17)$$

Once the stability circles are plotted on the chart the stable and unstable sides of the circle must be determined. If the circle surrounds the center of the Smith chart, then the inside of the circle is the stable region of impedances for that device. If the circle does not encircle the center of the chart, then the region outside the center of the circle represents stable impedances for the device. This relationship assumes that both S11 and S22 are less than one, when measured in a 50 Ω system.

Specific Gain Amplifier Design Example

Example 7-6: Analyze the stability condition for the RT243 device.

Solution: Examine the stability circles for the RT243 by creating a new workspace and a new schematic in ADS with the small signal S parameter file as shown in Figure 7-38. Setup an S parameter simulation with both the start and stop frequencies set at 2.3 GHz.

Figure 7-38 Schematic with RT243 S parameter file

The stability parameters of the device are shown in Table 7-1.

Eqn Gmax=max_gain(S)

Eqn B1=stab_meas(S)   Eqn K=stab_fact(S)

freq	B1	K	Gmax
100.0 MHz	0.966	0.272	35.753
300.0 MHz	0.838	0.122	30.862
500.0 MHz	0.860	0.163	28.363
700.0 MHz	0.853	0.266	27.462
900.0 MHz	0.845	0.316	26.400
1.100 GHz	0.826	0.352	25.528
1.300 GHz	0.800	0.379	24.778
1.500 GHz	0.769	0.419	24.125
1.700 GHz	0.739	0.430	23.546
1.900 GHz	0.711	0.463	23.035
2.100 GHz	0.690	0.537	22.750
2.300 GHz	0.666	0.654	22.610
2.500 GHz	0.641	0.802	22.448
2.700 GHz	0.625	0.861	22.188
2.900 GHz	0.609	0.931	21.911
3.000 GHz	0.601	0.970	21.765

Table 7-1 RT243 device stability factors and GMAX

Notice that the device stability factor K is less than 1 from 100 to 3000 MHz which means the device is unstable in this range.

If the device is made stable we can generate new set of S parameters and show that the stability factor K becomes greater than 1.The schematic in the following Figure is using the stabilized transistor S parameters.

Figure 7-39 Schematic with stabilized S-parameters

Simulate the schematic and display B1, K, and Gmax in Table 7-2.

Eqn Gmax=max_gain(S)

Eqn B1=stab_meas(S)   Eqn K=stab_fact(S)

freq	B1	K	Gmax
100.0 MHz	0.740	1.068	34.165
300.0 MHz	0.648	1.972	25.214
500.0 MHz	0.738	1.692	23.509
700.0 MHz	0.747	2.157	21.368
900.0 MHz	0.770	1.983	20.723
1.100 GHz	0.769	1.796	20.359
1.300 GHz	0.758	1.636	20.110
1.500 GHz	0.735	1.502	19.936
1.700 GHz	0.713	1.366	19.933
1.900 GHz	0.691	1.294	19.782
2.100 GHz	0.675	1.286	19.539
2.300 GHz	0.652	1.332	19.164
2.500 GHz	0.630	1.444	18.493
2.700 GHz	0.616	1.424	18.320
2.900 GHz	0.600	1.451	17.928
3.000 GHz	0.594	1.457	17.755

Table 7-2 RT243 device stability factors and GMAX

Notice that K>1 throughout the simulation range.

A simulation of the circuit in Figure 7-38 will also result in a plot of the center of each stability circle displayed. To display the entire circle, click on the center trace (dot) on the Smith chart. As Figure 7-40 shows the circles are far away from the center of the chart therefore making the outside of the circles the stable region. There is only a small region of the output stability circle that represents an unstable region of impedance. These unstable regions are shaded as shown in Figure 7-40. If the device were unconditionally stable the stability circles would lie completely outside the circumference of the Smith chart. Add another simulation from 100 MHz to 3000 MHz with 100 MHz steps. Then add a Table to display K, B1, and GMAX. Note that stability factor k is less than 1 indicating that the transistor is potentially unstable over its entire frequency range. G_{max} for the device without a stabilization network is 22.6 dB at 2.3 GHz. We want to design the amplifier to have a gain of 16 dB with a 50 Ω source and load impedance.

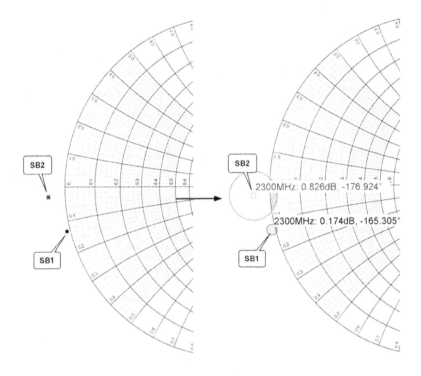

Figure 7-40 Stability circle centers and full circles at 2.3 GHz

This enables the plot of the circles on the Smith chart without the need to solve the Equations (7-12) and (7-13). Selecting the GP function (power gain circles) in the output graph plots a series of seven gain circles. When K < 1 the smallest circle represents the maximum gain, GMAX, and the inside of the circle is shaded [3]. This means that impedances inside this circle can be unstable. The successive Power Gain circles represent gain values of GMAX -1dB, GMAX-2dB, GMAX-3 dB, GMAX-4 dB, GMAX-5 dB, and GMAX-6 dB. Thus the circles represent the gain values of: 22.6 dB, 21.6 dB, 20.6 dB, 19.6 dB, 18.6 dB, 17.6 dB and 16.6 dB respectively. Figure 7-29 shows that the last or largest circle is the 16.6 dB power gain circle. An examination of the power gain and stability circles reveals another reason why we may not want to use the maximum gain from the device. The highest gain circle is very close to the region of instability on the output stability circle, SB2.

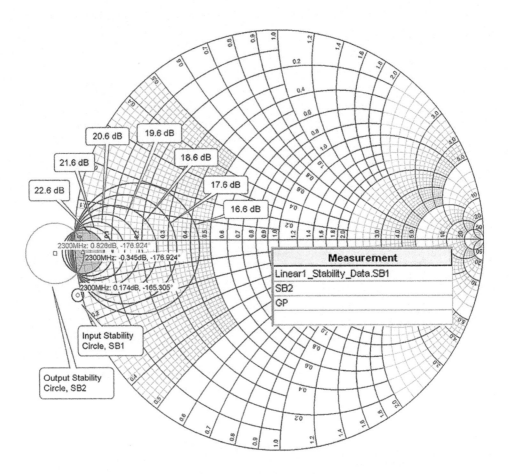

Figure 7-41 Constant power gain circles for the RT243 at 2.3 GHz

We'll choose the 16.6 dB circle because it is the closest to the design goal of 16 dB. The load impedance can be any point on the circumference of the 16.6 dB circle that does not enter the shaded, unstable, region. It is a good practice to choose locations that are not close to the unstable regions of the stability circles. The load impedance can be visually read from the Smith chart. The load impedance selected on the 16.6 dB Power Gain Circle is shown in Figure 7-41. The impedance at this point is $22 + j0\ \Omega$.

Once the load impedance has been selected it is necessary to calculate the resulting source reflection coefficient that will achieve a conjugate match on the input. Equation (7-18) is used to calculate this source reflection coefficient [4]. The source reflection coefficient is therefore defined as a function of the chosen load reflection coefficient, Γ_L. Note that the input match is then a conjugate match of the calculated source reflection coefficient, Γ_S.

$$\Gamma_S = \left[S_{11} + \frac{S_{12}S_{21}\Gamma_L}{1-\left(\Gamma_L S_{22}\right)} \right]^*$$

(7-18)

The chosen load impedance must first be converted to a reflection coefficient, Γ_L. This is easily handled by Matlab equations. Simply define the Load variable as the reflection coefficient S[1,1]. Once the load impedance is defined as a polar formatted variable, Equation (7-18) can be solved. Because two frequency step points were needed to display the circles, the equations are entered as swept array variables. The source impedance is calculated as $Z_S = 0.943\text{-}j6.594$ Ohms. Location of the source and load impedance for power gain match is shown in Figure 7-28.

Solution of Equation (7-18) is given here.

1. Enter design parameters

RL = 22; XL = 0

Load = Linear2_Data.S[1,1]

Num = Linear1_Data.S[2,1].*Linear1_Data.S[1,2].*Load

Denom = 1 - (Load.*Linear1_Data.S[2,2])

Source = Linear1_Data.S[1,1].+(Num/Denom)

2. Calculate the conjugate of the Source Impedance

Zsource = gammatoz(50,Source)

Zsource_real = real(Zsource[1])

Zsource_imag = -imag(Zsource[1])

Enter the values of Zsource_real and Zsource_imag to perform the Input Matching Circuit Design

Design of the Impedance Matching Networks

In this section we use the equations derived in Chapter 5 to design the input and output matching networks. The simple two-element LC matching circuit can be synthesized for both the input and output matching circuits.

Example 7-7: Design the output matching network for the RT243 transistor at 2300 MHz.

Solution: For the output matching circuit use the following steps.

1. Enter design parameters and normalize the load impedance

Z0=50; RL=22; f=2.3e9; r=RL/Z0

2. Calculate matching element values

B1 = sqrt((1 − r)/r)/Z0

X1 = Z0*sqrt(r*(1 - r))

L1 = X1/(2*pi*f)

C2 = B1/(2*pi*f)

The calculation results show that L1 = 1.717 nH and C2 = 1.561 pF, as shown in Figure 7-43.

Figure 7-43 Schematic used to design the output matching circuit

Example 7-8: Design the input matching network for RT243 transistor at 2300 MHz.

Solution: To design the input matching network, we use the input impedance of the RT243 transistor.

1. Enter design parameters and normalize the load impedance

Z0=50; RL=0.943; XL=6.594; f=2.3e9; r=RL/Z0; x=XL/Z0

2. Calculate the matching element values

B1 = sqrt((1 - r)/r)/Z0

X1 = Z0*sqrt(r*(1 - r))-x*Z0

L1 = X1/(2*pi*f)

C2 = B1/(2*pi*f)

The calculation results show that L1 = 0.014 nH and C1 = 9.982 pF, as shown in Figure 7-44.

Figure 7-44 Schematic used to design the input matching circuit

Assembly and Simulation of the Specific Gain Amplifier

Example 7-9: Assemble, simulate, and display the response of the specific gain Amplifier.

Solution: Create a new schematic and attach the input and output matching circuits to the device S parameter file. Create a linear analysis and sweep the amplifier from 1.3 GHz to 3.3 GHz. The resulting response is shown in Figure 7-46. Note that the gain at 2300 MHz is 16.62 dB verifying that the Power Gain circle match has been successful. Also note a major difference in return loss compared to the simultaneous conjugate match case. Here we see that the output return loss is rather poor, -1.39 dB. This is a result of the selective mismatching process to achieve a much lower value of gain than the GMAX of the device. The input return loss is very good because a conjugate match of the resulting device and load impedance combination was performed.

Figure 7-45 Ideal design of the specific gain amplifier

The simulated response of the specific gain amplifier is shown in Figure 7-46.

Figure 7-46 Response of the power gain matched amplifier

At this point the designer should begin construction of the physical design for the power gain matched amplifier. Begin with the package outline drawing of the transistor as was done in Section 7.3. Then progress with the microstrip PCB tracks and physical models for the inductors and capacitors. Clearly the 0.014 nH series inductor and possibly the 1.727 nH inductor will be absorbed into the physical design of the circuit. Finally optimize the amplifier to meet the original design goals.

7.6 Low Noise Amplifier Design

One important case of selectively mismatched amplifier design is the Low Noise Amplifier, LNA. In LNA design the input is not matched to the reflection coefficient that results in maximum gain but rather to a reflection coefficient that gives the desired noise figure. Low noise amplifiers are frequently used as the input stage in a radio receiver or satellite down converter to minimize the noise that is added to the amplified signal. Figure 7-47 depicts a signal with noise at the input and output of an LNA.

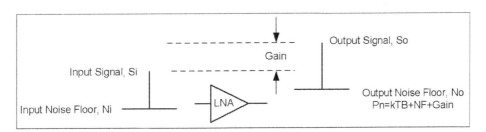

Figure 7-47 Signal and noise through the LNA

All transistors will add some amount of noise to the input signal. Low Noise transistors are optimized so that they will add a minimum amount of noise to the signal. The signal at the output of a linear LNA is simply the signal level at the input plus the gain of the LNA in dB. However the noise at the output will be increased by the gain and the noise figure of the transistor.

The LNA noise figure is the degradation of signal to noise ratio of the LNA input to the signal to noise ratio of the output given by Equation (7-19).

$$NF_{dB} = 10 \cdot \log\left[\frac{\left(\frac{S_i}{N_i}\right)}{\left(\frac{S_o}{N_o}\right)}\right]$$ (7-19)

The noise is considered to be a white noise distribution meaning that it is constant with frequency and thermal in nature. Therefore any measurement of noise must be referred to a specific bandwidth. The thermal noise power is also a function of temperature and is defined by Equation (7-20).

$$P_n = kTB$$ (7-20)

Where,

k = Boltzmann's constant, 1.374×10^{-23} J/°K

T=Temperature of the input noise source (290 °K = room temperature)

B = Bandwidth of Measurement in Hz

If we normalize the measurement bandwidth to 1 Hz i.e., B=1 the thermal noise can be calculated using Equation (7-20):

$$P_n = \left(1.374 \cdot 10^{-23}\right)(290)(1) = 3.984 \cdot 10^{-21} \; Watts \, / \, Hz$$

Or, $$P_n = 3.984 \cdot 10^{-18} \; mW \, / \, Hz$$

Converting mW to dBm, we can express the thermal noise floor in dBm/Hz:

$$P_n = 10 \cdot \log\left(3.984 \cdot 10^{-18}\right) = -173.9 \; dBm \, / \, Hz$$

Working with the thermal noise floor normalized to a 1 Hz bandwidth, it is straight forward to calculate the amplifier output noise by using the amplifier's noise figure and gain as given by Equation (7-21).

$$P_{no}(1Hz) = kTB_{1Hz} + Gain_{dB} + NoiseFigure_{dB} \qquad (7\text{-}21)$$

We can normalize the noise power in a one Hertz bandwidth to any measurement bandwidth by using Equation (7-22).

$$P_n(B) = P_n(1Hz) + 10 \cdot \log(B) \qquad (7\text{-}22)$$

Where B = the measurement bandwidth in Hz

Noise Figure Circles

In order to perform noise figure simulation in ADS the device S parameter file must include noise parameters. Table 7-3 shows an S parameter file with noise parameters appended to the end of the file. The noise parameters include the optimum noise figure, NF_{opt} at a corresponding frequency in the left most column. The NF_{opt} is the lowest possible noise figure that can be achieved with this device when it is matched to Γ_{opt}. The third and fourth column gives the magnitude and angle of the Γ_{opt}. The final column gives the normalized noise resistance for the device. These noise parameters are usually provided by the device manufacturer on the data sheet, as shown in Table 7-3.

```
!S and NOISE PARAMETERS at Vce=2.7V   Ic=5mA.
# ghz s ma r 50
0.1    0.88   -11    13.32 169    0.01  83    0.97  -5
0.5    0.70   -48    10.49 134    0.04  64    0.82  -22
0.9    0.49   -72    7.73  111    0.05  57    0.70  -30
1.0    0.46   -77    7.15  107    0.06  55    0.69  -31
1.5    0.30   -100   5.27  89     0.07  53    0.62  -35
1.8    0.24   -112   4.52  81     0.08  52    0.59  -37
2.0    0.21   -120   4.13  76     0.09  52    0.58  -39
2.4    0.16   -140   3.52  67     0.10  50    0.57  -42
3.0    0.13   -172   2.88  55     0.12  48    0.55  -46
4.0    0.15   137    2.25  38     0.15  44    0.53  -55
5.0    0.21   106    1.87  22     0.18  39    0.52  -64
! Noise Parameters
!Freq NFopt   Γopt        rn=Rn/50
0.5    1.1    0.77  9     1.10
0.9    1.2    0.71  18    0.96
1.8    1.5    0.60  45    0.66
2.4    1.8    0.51  65    0.47
```

Table 7-3 Avago AT30511 S parameter file with noise parameters

Matching the device to Γ_{opt} can potentially lead to very poor input return loss and instability. Just as we have seen in the example of section 7.4.2 the designer must be aware of the location of Γ_{opt} with respect to the input stability circle. In LNA design we usually do not want to add resistive loading to the input of the device to improve the stability because this would increase the thermal noise power and increase the noise figure. In certain critical designs the poor input return loss is accepted and an isolator is added to the input of the LNA to provide a good input return loss. This also involves tradeoffs as the losses in the isolator add directly to the noise figure. A trade off is required among input return loss, stability, and accepting a higher noise figure than that which is provided by Γ_{opt}. A reflection coefficient can be chosen that corresponds to a noise figure that is greater than NF_{opt}. It is sometimes helpful to examine the constant noise figure contours on the Smith chart. The noise contours are a family of noise figure circles on the Smith chart that represent the reflection coefficients that correspond to a variety of resulting noise figures for a given device. To plot the noise figure circles in ADS, create a new workspace and a new schematic. Insert the S_Params Template and place the LNA on the schematic. Create a Smith chart graph and plot the noise circle contours. A family of eight circles is plotted as shown in Figure 7-48. These circles represent noise figure degradation from NF_{opt} in the increments of: NF_{opt} + 0.25, 0.5, 1, 1.5, 2, 2.5, 3 and 6 dB. Therefore the inner most circle represents (NF_{opt} + 0.25) dB, the second circle represents (NF_{opt} + 0.5) dB and so on. The circles can also be helpful when designing a wide band LNA. It is sometimes helpful to plot the stability circles along with the noise circles so that a given noise match reflection coefficient can be selected that is not too close to the stability circles. The resulting noise figure can be calculated for any source reflection coefficient, Γ_s, from Equation (7-23) [9].

$$NF = NF_{min} + \frac{4R_n}{Z_0\left|1 + \Gamma_{opt}\right|^2} \cdot \frac{\left|\Gamma_s - \Gamma_{opt}\right|^2}{\left(1 - \left|\Gamma_s\right|^2\right)} \qquad (7\text{-}23)$$

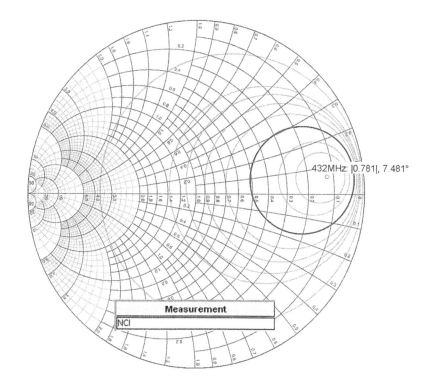

Figure 7-48 Noise Figure circles and Γ_{opt}

LNA Design Example

This section outlines the basic steps that are required to design a single stage Low Noise Amplifier for a UHF satellite downlink. The amplifier is intended to operate with a source and load impedance of 50 Ω. The design specifications are given as:

Center Frequency:	432 MHz
Gain:	20 dB minimum
Noise Figure:	1.2 dB maximum
Output Return Loss:	Less than -10 dB

The Avago AT30511 low noise transistor will be used for this design. The S parameter and noise parameter file for this device is shown in Table 7-3.

Figure 7-49 AT30511 with input and output matching

Example 7-10: Calculate the stability and noise parameters for the AT 30511 device.

Solution: Create a schematic in ADS with the device S parameter file as shown in Table 7-3. Make sure to select yes for calculating noise and setting Temp to IEEE standard of 16.85 degrees.

Figure 7-50 Avago AT30511 with input and output matching

Add a Table to display the stability parameters K, B1 and the noise parameters S_{opt} and Z_{OPT}.

Eqn K=stab_fact(S)   **Eqn** B1=stab_meas(S)   **Eqn** Gmax=max_gain(S)

freq	K	B1	Gmax
432.0 MHz	0.387	0.274	24.974

freq	NFmin	Sopt	Zopt1
432.0 MHz	1.100	0.761 + j0.120	283.259 + j167.624

Figure 7-51 Parameters K, B1, Gmax, NFmin, $S_{opt,}$ and Zopt1 at 432 MHz

Figure 7-51 shows that K < 1 meaning that the device is potentially unstable. This means that there are source and load reflection coefficients that can result in instability and oscillation.

Also add a Smith chart with S_{opt} and the stability circles. Then create a Smith chart and display the stability circles along with the noise circles.

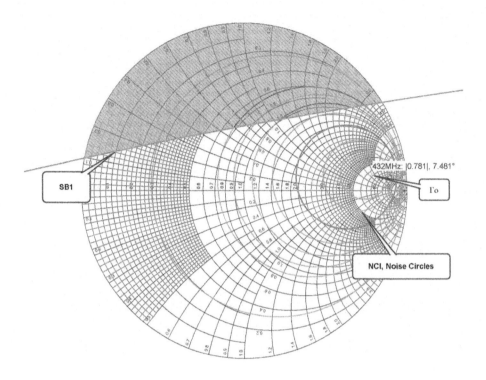

Figure 7-52 Input stability circle with noise circles

Figure 7-52 shows a plot of the input stability circle along with the noise circles and S_{opt}. In this example, the inside of the input stability circle, SB1, represents the region of stable source reflection coefficients. ADS shades the region of the stability circle that represents unstable reflection coefficients. Because the input reflection coefficient, S_{opt}, is well inside of the input stability circle, SB1, and we have no specification for input return loss, we can proceed with matching the input to S_{opt}. From the discussion of Specific Gain matching of Section 7.4 we can deduce that because a specific reflection coefficient is selected at the input of the device, the available gain circles can be used to determine the expected gain from the device when matched to S_{opt}.

Figure 7-39 shows the available gain circles plotted along with S_{opt}. The available gain circles are drawn for gains of 0, 1, 2, 3, 4, 5 and 6 dB less than maximum gain. Figure 7-39 shows the available gain circles for the AT30511 at 432 MHz. The 21.9 dB circle intersects S_{opt} therefore the expected gain of the device when matched to S_{opt} is 21.9 dB.

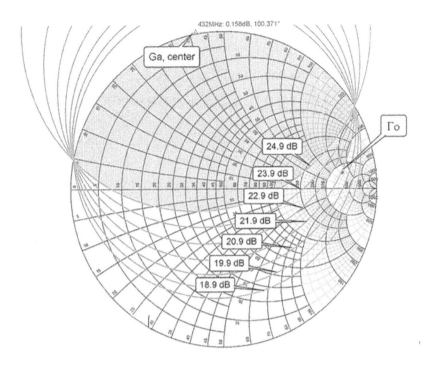

Figure 7-53   Available gain circles and Γ_{opt}

Design of the LNA Input Matching Network

The input and output matching circuits will be analytically designed using the single-stub matching networks. Because we are designing essentially a fixed frequency LNA, a simple single-stub matching network can be used. The equations developed in chapter 6 section 6.4 will be used to determine the input and output matching networks.

Example 7-11 Design a line and stub input matching network for the low noise amplifier using AT30511 device at 432 MHz.

Solution: We match the 50 Ω source impedance to the input impedance Z_{in} of the device. Z_{opt} is the impedance looking from the device back toward the 50 Ω source. Therefore, in the design of the input matching network, we must use the conjugate of Z_{opt} for the complex load impedance. The calculation gives $Z_{opt} = 318.4 + j166.1$ Ω, therefore, Z_{in} is defined as $Z_{opt}^* = 318.4 - j166.1$ Ω.

1. Enter design parameters and normalize the load

RS=50; RL=318.6; XL=-166.1; f=432e6; r=RL/RS; x=XL/RS

2. Calculate t1, t2, d1, d2, B1, B2, so1 and so2

t1 = (x + sqrt(r*(r^2 + x^2-2*r + 1)))/(r - 1)

t2 = (x - sqrt(r*(r^2 + x^2-2*r + 1)))/(r - 1)

d1 = 360*(pi + atan(t1))/(2*pi)

d2 = 360*(pi + atan(t2))/(2*pi)

B1 = (x*t1^2 + (r^2+x^2 - 1)*t1 - x)/(RS*(r^2 + x^2 + t1^2 + 2*x*t1))

B2 = (x*t2^2 + (r^2 + x^2 - 1)*t2 - x)/(RS*(r^2 + x^2 + t2^2 + 2*x*t2))

so1 = 360*(pi-atan(RS*B1))/(2*pi)

so2 = -360*atan(RS*B2)/(2*pi)

3. Calculation results show that d1 = 66.945, d2 = 105.58, so1 = 111.784, and so2 = 68.216. For the input matching network,

As the calculations show there are two single-stub matching networks that match the 50 Ω source impedance to the load impedance. we select the shorter open-stub length so2 = 68.216 degrees and the corresponding line d2 = 105.58 degrees, as shown in Figure 7-54.

Figure 7-54 Single-stub input matching network and simulated response

Design of the LNA Output Matching Network

The output load reflection coefficient, Γ_L, is defined in terms of the selected source reflection coefficient, Γ_S, as given by Equation (7-24) [4].

$$\Gamma_L = \left(S_{22} + \frac{S_{12}S_{21}\Gamma_S}{1 - S_{11}\Gamma_S} \right)^* \tag{7-24}$$

Equation (7-24) can be solved by letting $\Gamma_S = \Gamma_{opt}$ and calculating the load reflection coefficient, Γ_L.

To use the impedance matching utility we need the conjugate of Z_L or Z_{OUT} of the device or in this case: $Z_{OUT} = 71.9 - j54.4 \; \Omega$. Check the location of Γ_L with respect to the output stability circle to make sure that the impedance does not lie in the region of instability. Figure 7-55 shows the location of Γ_L with respect to the output stability circle, SB2.

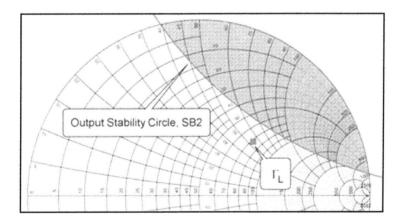

Figure 7-55 Location of Γ_L and the output stability circle

The impedance corresponding to Γ_L can be entered into an impedance element and plotted on the same graph as the output stability circle. The inside of the output stability circle is shaded which means that this area represents unstable output load reflection coefficients. Because Γ_L is safely outside of the SB2 circle we can use Γ_L as an acceptable output reflection coefficient.

Example 7-12: Design a single-stub output matching network for the low noise amplifier using AT30511 device at 432 MHz.

Solution: Now we can design a single-stub output impedance matching network. The procedure follows.

1. Enter design parameters and normalized load impedance

RS=50; RL=71.9; XL=-54.4; f=432e6; r=RL/RS; x=XL/RS

2. Use MATLAB script to calculate t1, t2, d1, d2, B1, B2, so1, and so2

t1 = (x + sqrt(r*(r^2 + x^2-2*r + 1)))/(r - 1)

t2 = (x - sqrt(r*(r^2 + x^2 - 2*r + 1)))/(r - 1)

d1 = 360*(atan(t1))/(2*pi)

d2 = 360*(pi + atan(t2))/(2*pi)

B1 = (x*t1^2 + (r^2 + x^2 - 1)*t1 - x)/(RS*(r^2 + x^2 + t1^2 + 2*x*t1))

B2 = (x*t2^2 + (r^2 + x^2-1)*t2 - x)/(RS*(r^2 + x^2 + t2^2 + 2*x*t2))

so1 = 360*(pi - atan(RS*B1))/(2*pi)

so2 = -360*atan(RS*B2)/(2*pi)

The calculation results show that there are two single-stub matching networks that match the 50 Ω load to the LNA output impedance. For the output matching network, we select the shorter stub length so2 = 44.364 degrees and the corresponding line d2 = 99.959 degrees.

Figure 7-56 Output matching network

Simulate the schematic and display the S11 and S21 response.

Figure 7-57 Output simulated response

Linear Simulation of the Low Noise Amplifier

Example 7-13: Assemble, simulate, and display the response of the low noise Amplifier.

Solution: Create a new schematic in ADS with the input and output matching networks attached to the device. Add a new S parameter simulation that sweeps the amplifier from 400 MHz to 500 MHz. Create a graph and plot the amplifier gain S21, as shown in Figure 7-58.

Figure 7-58 LNA schematic using single-stub matching networks

Simulate the schematic from 402 to 462 MHz and display S11, S22, and the gain, S21, in a rectangular plot.

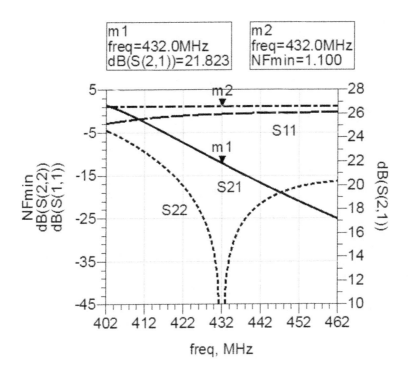

Figure 7-59 Marker showing LNA gain at 432 MHz

The reading at marker m1 shows that the amplifier gain at 432 MHz is 21.823 dB which is well within the acceptable range of the expected 21.9 dB. The simulated noise figure is 1.1 dB which is exactly the NFmin that was predicted in Figure 7-517.

Note that the Figure 7-58 is the ideal schematic of the LNA. The remaining design sequence should include the microstrip interconnecting lines and bias feeds. The circuit should then be optimized to bring the final response as close as possible to the ideal circuit results as was done in Section 7.2.

Figure 7-59 also shows that the LNA input is selectively mismatched to achieve the minimum noise figure while the output is perfectively matched to achieve maximum gain.

Amplifier Noise Temperature

Low Noise Amplifiers used at higher frequencies in the microwave region often have noise figure referred to in terms of noise temperature. Satellite engineers calculate the ratio of the antenna gain to the equivalent system noise temperature, G/T, as an important performance parameter. A higher system G/T indicates better signal to noise ratio and a better chance of receiving signals from space. Because the LNA is the first active component connected to the antenna it is convenient to also refer to its noise performance in terms of equivalent noise temperature. Noise Figure can be converted to noise temperature by first calculating the noise factor. The noise factor is simply the noise figure expressed in absolute units as calculated by equation (7-25).

$$NoiseFactor, \ F = 10^{\left(\frac{NF_{dB}}{10}\right)}$$

(7-25)

The equivalent noise temperature is then defined by equation (7-26).

$$NoiseTemperature, \ K = (F-1)T$$

(7-26)

Where,

T = Temperature of the input noise source (290 °K = room temperature)

Equation (7-26) gives us a good appreciation for the fact that Noise Temperature, or Noise Figure, is always a function of the temperature of the source of noise. It is not necessarily the temperature of the amplifier itself but the temperature of the source of the input noise. When measuring extremely low noise amplifiers it is important to account for the temperature of the noise source. Table 7-4 shows the conversion of noise figure in dB to noise temperature in degrees Kelvin.

NF_dB ( )	NoiseFactor ( )	NoiseTemp_K ( )
0.1	1.023	6.755
0.15	1.035	10.191
0.2	1.047	13.667
0.25	1.059	17.184
0.3	1.072	20.741
0.35	1.084	24.339
0.4	1.096	27.979
0.45	1.109	31.661
0.5	1.122	35.385
0.55	1.135	39.153
0.6	1.148	42.965
0.65	1.161	46.82
0.7	1.175	50.72
0.75	1.189	54.666
0.8	1.202	58.657
0.85	1.216	62.694
0.9	1.23	66.778
0.95	1.245	70.909
1	1.259	75.088
1.05	1.274	79.316
1.1	1.288	83.592
1.15	1.303	87.918
1.2	1.318	92.294
1.25	1.334	96.721
1.3	1.349	101.199
1.35	1.365	105.729
1.4	1.38	110.311
1.45	1.396	114.947
1.5	1.413	119.636
1.55	1.429	124.379
1.6	1.445	129.178
1.65	1.462	134.031
1.7	1.479	138.941
1.75	1.496	143.908
1.8	1.514	148.933
1.85	1.531	154.015
1.9	1.549	159.157
1.95	1.567	164.358
2	1.585	169.619

Table 7-4 Noise Figure to Noise Temperature conversion

7.7 Power Amplifier Design

The amplifier circuits described thus far have been designed using the measured S parameters that represent the active device. The S parameters are based on the small signal characteristics of the device. That is to say that the device is operating well below its maximum output power capability. This would suggest that the S parameters are defined for class A amplification, operating well within the linear portion of their power transfer characteristic. The S parameters can therefore be used to design an amplifier for specific values of gain but not output power. As we drive the transistor closer to its maximum output power the signal excursion is occurring over a much wider range of the transistor's load line. This is to say that the device is now operating under large signal conditions. There exists a specific source and load impedance into which the transistor can produce its maximum output power. Because the device S parameters are no longer defined under large signal conditions, they cannot be used to determine the optimum load impedance for maximum output power. These impedances are normally determined by performing a load pull measurement on the device. A typical load pull test setup is shown in Figure 7-60. This test setup empirically tunes the device for maximum output power using the input and output tuners. The load pull test creates a set of contours on the Smith chart that correspond to a given output power level. Selecting the impedance on the constant power contour will result in an impedance match that results in a power match. This is similar to the power gain circles that we seen in section 7.5 however power contours never form a circle. Power contours tend to have an elliptical shape when plotted on the Smith chart. Cripps has introduced a technique to approximate the optimum load impedance using linear design techniques [6]. This concept is based on determining an optimum load resistance from the classical load line theory. Once the load and source impedance are known, we can use the linear techniques developed earlier in this chapter to design the matching networks.

Figure 7-60 Load pull test for source and load impedance measurement

Data Sheet Large Signal Impedance

In many cases high power devices are intended for specific applications such as WiMAX, cellular base station, or mobile radio. In these applications the device manufacturer may perform the load pull analysis at specific frequencies and present the source and load impedance as an equivalent series circuit on the data sheet. This allows the designer to treat the power matching process as a simple impedance matching exercise. Figure 7-61 shows an excerpt of a data sheet for the Nitronex NPT25100 GaN HEMT device. As the data sheet shows the optimum source and load impedances are given in tabular and Smith chart forms.

Frequency (MHz)	Z_S (Ω)	Z_L (Ω)
2140	12.1 - j20.0	2.6 - j2.6
2300	10.0 - j3.0	2.5 - j2.3
2400	9.5 - j3.0	2.5 - j2.5
2500	9.0 - j3.0	2.5 - j2.7
2600	8.5 - j3.0	2.5 - j3.1
2700	8.0 - j3.0	2.5 - j3.3

Figure 7-61 Optimum source and load impedance (*courtesy of Nitronex*)

As Figure 7-61 shows the listed Z_S and Z_L is not the device impedance but rather the impedance that is presented to the device. This is analogous to the Γ_S and Γ_L that was calculated in section 7.2 for the simultaneous conjugate match. The actual device impedance is the conjugate of the given optimum source and load impedance. The designer must be cautious when interpreting the optimum source and load impedances from various vendor data sheets. Some manufacturers may list the actual device impedance as shown on the Freescale Semiconductor data sheet of Figure 7-48. We also need to read the impedance data from the tables rather than directly from the Smith chart. Because of the very low input and output impedance of power transistors, it is common to normalize the Smith chart to 10 Ω so that the impedance locus is not compressed on the left hand side of the Smith chart. The impedances given in the table are the actual impedance rather than the normalized impedance.

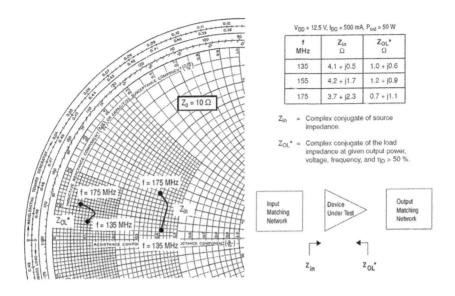

f MHz	Z_{in} Ω	Z_{OL}^* Ω
135	4.1 + j0.5	1.0 + j0.6
155	4.2 + j1.7	1.2 + j0.9
175	3.7 + j2.3	0.7 + j1.1

V_{DD} = 12.5 V, I_{DQ} = 500 mA, P_{out} = 50 W

Z_{in} = Complex conjugate of source impedance.

Z_{OL}^* = Complex conjugate of the load impedance at given output power, voltage, frequency, and η_D > 50 %.

Figure 7-62: Large signal series equivalent impedance (*courtesy of Freescale*)

Power Amplifier Impedance Matching Networks

In this section we will design the matching networks for the NPT25100 GaN power transistor at a frequency of 2.140 GHz. The matching networks of previous examples have all been based on two-element L-networks. In this example we will design three-element Pi network matching circuits. The Pi network is often preferred over a two element network because the component values are less sensitive when physically realizing the impedance match. It can also help to keep the circuit Q lower for improved bandwidth. We will illustrate both graphical techniques and synthesis techniques. The input matching circuit will be designed using graphical techniques while the output matching network will be designed using network synthesis techniques.

Design of the Input Matching Network

Example 7-14: Design a three elements Pi network to match the 50 Ω source impedance to the amplifier input at 2140 MHz.

Solution: Graphical matching techniques is employed for the input matching network using the Smith chart. We will design the matching circuit moving from 50 Ω at the center to the source impedance as given on the data sheet. A one port S parameter file can be created with impedance data as shown in Figure 7-63. Note the differences in line number 2 of the file. This line defines the format of the data contained within the file. The (Z) defines the file as containing impedance data. The number (1) means that the data is normalized to one, the actual device impedance.

```
!Optimum Source Impedance,Zs, presented to the NPT25100
# GHZ Z RI R 1
!Freq     REZ1       IMZ1
2.140     12.1       -20.0
2.300     10.0       -3.0
2.400     9.5        -3.0
2.500     9.0        -3.0
2.600     8.5        -3.0
2.700     8.0        -3.0
```

Figure 7-63: One port S parameter data file containing the Zs data

Setup a schematic with the one-port Z_S impedance data and sweep it at a fixed frequency of 2140 MHz. Then setup a second schematic with a 50 Ω resistor to represent the center of the Smith chart and begin the Pi network design. Plot the impedance of both networks on the same Smith chart. We know that the shunt inductors of a Pi network will travel clockwise on the conductance circles while the series inductor will travel clockwise on a resistance circle. Note the location of the conductance circle in which Z_S is located. The first capacitor and series inductor L section must move to the location of the Z_S conductance circle. Figure 7-50 shows the result.

Figure 7-64 Amplifier input matching Pi network

Simulate the schematic and display S11 and S21 in a rectangular plot.

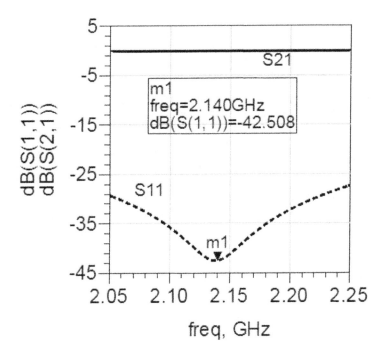

Figure 7-65 Amplifier input matching Pi network

Design of the Output Matching Network

Example 7-15: Design a three elements Pi network to match the 50 Ω load impedance to the amplifier output at 2140 MHz.

Solution: The output matching network will be designed using the one port S parameter file shown in Figure 7-66. Use caution when editing S parameter files on disk to be read into an ADS simulation. The first time that an S parameter file is read from disk it is loaded into the ADS Workspace. Subsequent simulations will not go back to disk to read the file but rather read the file from the Workspace for faster simulation speed. The file will not be read from disk again until the copy loaded into the Workspace has been deleted.

```
!NPT25100 Output Impedance
# GHZ Z RI R 1
!Freq       REZ1        IMZ1
2.140       2.6         2.6
2.300       2.5         2.3
2.400       2.5         2.5
2.500       2.5         2.7
2.600       2.5         3.1
2.700       2.5         3.3
```

Figure 7-66 S parameter data file containing the conjugate of Z_L

The Impedance Matching Utility program is used to design the output matching networks. The matching network is shown in Figure 7-67.

Figure 7-67 Output matching network

Simulate the schematic and display S11 and S21 in a rectangular plot.

Figure 7-68 Output matching network

Finally a two-port S parameter file can be created that contains the impedance data for the conjugate of Z_S and Z_L. This would be representative of the large signal input and output impedance of the device.

!Large Signal Impedances of the NPT25100								
# GHz Z RI R 1								
!Freq	REZ1	IMZ1	M(S21)	A(S21)	M(S12)	A(S12)	REZ2	IMZ2
2.140	12.1	20.0	0	0	0	0	2.6	2.5
2.300	10.0	3.0	0	0	0	0	2.5	2.3
2.400	9.5	3.0	0	0	0	0	2.5	2.5
2.500	9.0	3.0	0	0	0	0	2.5	2.7
2.600	8.5	3.0	0	0	0	0	2.5	3.1
2.700	8.0	3.0	0	0	0	0	2.5	3.3

Figure 7-69 S parameter data file containing the conjugate of Z_S and Z_L

Figure 7-69 shows the resulting matching networks attached to the large signal impedance data for the device. This allows examination of the return loss of the amplifier at the design frequency of 2140 MHz and the usable bandwidth. From Figure 7-69 note that the forward (S21) and reverse (S12) transmission parameters have been set to zero. Because we have no definition of the transmission parameters we cannot evaluate the gain of the circuit. If the manufacturer's data sheet includes an S parameter file along with the large signal impedance data, we could also examine the stability parameters to determine whether the device may require a stabilization network. The linear design techniques do provide a means of performing the matching network design from which the amplifier physical design can be realized. The circuit can then be built and empirically tuned and optimized on the bench for the desired performance. A thorough CAD design of the power amplifier requires a nonlinear physical model for the transistor. Under large signal conditions the strong nonlinearities will cause the gain to change as the drive (input) power changes. The gain of the device will go into compression and decrease as the input power is further increased. Harmonic energy is created by these nonlinearities that will further influence the behavior of the amplifier.

Example 7-16: Assemble, simulate, and display the response.

Solution: Create a new schematic in ADS with the input and output matching networks attached to the device. Add a new S parameter simulation that sweeps the amplifier from 2 GHz to 2.2 GHz.

Figure 7-70 Assembly and simulation of the power amplifier

Create a graph and plot the return loss S11 and S22 in a rectangular graph.

Figure 7-71 Resulting matching networks and return loss

The impedance matching techniques learned in Chapters five and six have been utilized to perform basic linear amplifier matching. These matching techniques have been solved analytically using the equations written in the MATLAB script as well as synthesis routines created in VBScript. Graphical techniques have also been applied to the design of multi-element impedance matching using the Smith chart. These techniques provide the engineer with a comprehensive set of tools to apply to amplifier impedance matching. These impedance matching techniques have been used to the introduce four of the primary RF and microwave amplifier circuits including: maximum gain, specific gain, low noise, and power amplifier circuits.

References and Further Readings

[1]   Dale D. Henkes, FAST: *Fast Amplifier Synthesis Tool*, Artech House Publishers, Norwood, MA. 2004

[2]   Chris Bowick, *RF Circuit Design*, Butterworth-Heinemann, Newton, MA, 1982

[3]   Keysight Technologies, Manuals for Advanced Design Systems, *ADS 2015.07 Documentation Set*, EEsof EDA Division, Santa Rosa, California www.keysight.com

[4]   Guillermo Gonzales, *Microwave Transistor Amplifiers – Analysis and Design*, Second Edition, Prentice Hall Inc., Upper Saddle River, NJ.

[5]   Randy Rhea, *The Yin-Yang of Matching: Part 1 – Basic Matching Concepts*, High Frequency Electronics, March 2006

[6]   Steve C. Cripps, *RF Power Amplifiers for Wireless Communications*, Artech House Publishers, Norwood, MA. 1999

[7]   David M. Pozar, *Microwave Engineering*, Third Edition, John Wiley & Sons, New York, 2005

[8]   R. Ludwig, P. Bretchko, *RF Circuit Design*, Theory and Applications, Prentice Hall, Upper Saddle River, NJ, 2000

[9]   Ted Grosch, *Noise Concepts and Design, Noble Publishing*, Atlanta, GA., 2003

[10]   Ali A. Behagi and Stephen D. Turner, *Microwave and RF Engineering, A Simulation Approach with Keysight Genesys Software*, BT Microwave LLC, State College, PA, March 2015

Problems

7-1. Design a Maximum Gain Amplifier

(a) For the Agilent HBFP0405 Transistor, calculate the stability factor, K, and the stability measure, B1 as well as Γ_{MS} and Γ_{ML} and conjugate match impedances at 2 GHz.

(b) Use ADS built in functions to determine the same parameters at 2 GHz.

(c) Sweep the frequency range of the device over the entire range of frequencies contained in the S parameter file.

(d) Plot of the stability parameters and GMAX for the Agilent HBFP0405 device from 100 to 4000 MHz.

(e) Employ a parallel RC circuit on the input of the device to stabilize the transistor. Make both the R and C values tunable. Tune the resistance and capacitor values until K > 1 for frequencies above 500 MHz.

(f) Add an RL network in shunt with the input of the transistor for additional low frequency stability. Tune the resistance and inductor values until K > 1 for frequencies above 500 MHz.

(g) Use the analytical impedance matching techniques developed in Chapter 5 to design the input and output matching L-networks. When performing the analytical match we are; matching 50 Ω source impedance to the impedance looking into the device; and 50 Ω load impedance to the impedance looking into output of the device.

(h) Complete the amplifier design in ADS by attaching the input and output matching circuits to the stabilized transistor. Use a linear sweep from 100 MHz to 4000 MHz to analyze the response of the amplifier, S11, S22, and S21 all in dB.

(i) Place a marker on S12 to measure the maximum gain of the amplifier at 2 GHz. Compare the maximum gain with the value originally calculated as G_{MAX}.

7-2. Design a Constant Gain Amplifier

(a) Use the Mitsubishi MGF0911a device to design a specific gain amplifier that achieves 10 dB gain at the frequency of 2 GHz. Examine the stability circles for the device in ADS by creating a schematic with the small signal S parameter file.

(b) Setup a linear analysis with both the start and stop frequencies set at 2 GHz. Add a linear analysis from 100 MHz to 3000 MHz with 100 MHz steps. Then add a Table to display K, B1, and GMAX.

(c) Plot a series of constant power gain circles on the Smith chart and choose the circle which is the closest to the design goal of 10 dB. The load reflection coefficient, defined as a reflection coefficient, Γ_L, is any point on the circumference of the circle that does not enter the unstable region. Choose a point that is not close to the unstable regions of the stability circles. Read the load impedance visually from the Smith chart at this point.

(d) Calculate the source impedance from Equation 7-18. The source impedance is therefore defined as a function of the chosen load reflection coefficient.

(e) Use the Smith chart to graphically design the simple two-element LC input and output matching networks.

(f) Create a new schematic and attach the input and output matching circuits to the device. Create a linear analysis that sweeps the amplifier from 1 GHz to 3 GHz. Display S11 and S21 in a rectangular plot.

(g) Place a marker on S12 to measure the gain of the amplifier at 2 GHz. Compare the gain with the value originally selected as specific gain.

7-3. Design a Low Noise Amplifier

Amplifier. Design a single stage Low Noise Amplifier using Agilent AT-32011 device. The amplifier is intended to operate with a source and load impedance of 50 Ω. The design specifications are given as:

Center Frequency:	500 MHz
Gain:	18 dB minimum
Noise Figure:	1.2 dB maximum
Output Return Loss:	Less than -10 dB

(a) Create an ADS schematic with the device S parameter file. Setup a Linear Analysis and add a Table to display the stability parameters K and B1 and the noise parameters Γ_{opt} and Z_{OPT}. Also add a Smith chart with Γ_{opt} and the stability circles. Then create a Smith chart and display the stability circles along with the noise circles.

(b) Drawn the available gain circles are for gains of 0, 1, 2, 3, 4, 5 and 6 dB less than maximum gain.

(c) Utilize the "L" Network Impedance Matching Utility to match the 50 Ω source impedance to Z_{opt} of the device at 500 MHz. In the impedance matching utility you must enter the conjugate of Z_{opt} for the complex load impedance.

(d) Use ADS to calculate the load reflection coefficient, Γ_{L}, from Equation (7-24). Convert Γ_{L} to output impedance Z_{L}. Z_{OUT} is the conjugate of Z_{L}. Check the location of Γ_{L} with respect to the output stability circle to make sure that the impedance does not lie in the region of instability. If Γ_{L} is safely outside of the SB2 circle, use Γ_{L} as an acceptable output reflection coefficient.

Chapter 8

Multi-Stage Amplifier Design

8.1 Introduction

In practical amplifier applications, a single stage amplifier is rarely adequate to meet the overall gain and output power requirements. Therefore we cascade multiple gain stages to achieve our gain specification. When several amplifiers are cascaded the inter-stage matching become an important task. Typically in amplifier design, the input-output impedance of the amplifier is matched to a 50 Ω resistor. In this chapter we design the inter-stage matching networks by directly matching the output impedance of the first stage to the input impedance of the second stage. This procedure helps to transfer more power and creates less reflections between stages. For simplicity much of this chapter will focus on ideal elements for inter-stage matching. Conversion of ideal elements to physical components were discussed in the previous chapter. Finally the gain and noise figure of the multi-stage cascaded LNAs are discussed in this chapter.

8.2 Two-Stage Amplifier Design

Figure 8-1 shows a block diagram of a two stage amplifier with the matching networks represented by a box. The input impedance of each device is designated as ZM1 while the output is designated as ZM2. We utilize transistors used in Chapter 7 to design a two stage amplifier cascade. The first stage uses SHF0189 and the second stage uses RT243. The design specifications are given as:

Center Frequency = 2350 MHz

Bandwidth: 2260 MHz to 2380 MHz

Gain: ≥ 34 dB

Input & Output Return Loss $\leq$ -10 dB

The cascade is designed as a maximum gain-conjugate matched amplifier. Therefore three conjugate matching networks must be designed in accordance with Figure 8-1. The first conjugate matching network is designed between the 50 Ω source and the first stage input impedance, ZM1. The second matching network is the inter-stage matching network. This network is designed to match the first stage output impedance, ZM2, to the second stage input impedance, ZM1. The third conjugate matching network is designed between the second stage output impedance, ZM2, and the 50 Ω load impedance.

Figure 8-1 Two-stage amplifier with impedance matching networks

Stability of the Amplifier First Stage

The first stage of the amplifier utilizes the SHF-0189 device. We know that the device must be unconditionally stable for the maximum gain conjugate matched amplifier [1]. Using the techniques of Chapter 7.2 a stabilizing network is designed around the SHF-0189.

Example 8-1: Measure the input-output impedance and the maximum stable gain of the first stage

Solution: Once the device is stabilized the maximum stable gain and the required input and output simultaneous match impedance is determined using the built-in functions in ADS. Create a new workspace and a new schematic in ADS. Use the stabilizing network developed in Chapter 7 for the SHF-0189 device as shown in Figure 8-2.

Figure 8-2 Stabilized first stage schematic

Simulate the schematic and display the response. Write the equations for source and load simultaneous match impedances in the data display window, as shown in Figure 8-3.

Eqn Zsource = sm_z1(S)   Eqn ZLoad = sm_z2(S)

freq	MaxGain1	Zsource	ZLoad
2.350 GHz	15.779	6.947 + j22.058	13.773 + j16.471

Figure 8-3 Maximum gain and simultaneous match impedances

As the Table in Figure 8-3 shows, the maximum gain and the input - output impedances are:

$$Zsouce = 6.947 + j\,22.058 \ \Omega$$

$$Zload = 13.773 + j16.471 \ \Omega$$

$$G_{max} = 15.779 \ dB$$

Design of the Amplifier Input Matching Network

Example 8-2: Design the cascaded amplifier inter-stage matching network

Solution: When designing the amplifier input matching network, we are matching the 50 Ω source impedance to the conjugate impedance looking into the SHF-0189 device. Therefore, the complex impedance that we are matching to is the conjugate of Zsource. Normalize the load impedance and use Equations (5-32) and (5-33) of Chapter 5 to calculate the element values of the matching network. The procedure follows.

1. Enter design parameters and normalize the load impedance

Z0=50; RL=6.947; XL=-22.058; f=2.35e9; r=RL/Z0; x=XL/Z0

2. Calculate the matching element values

B1 = sqrt((1 - r)/r)/Z0

X1 = Z0*(sqrt(r*(1 - r))-x)

L1 = X1/(2*pi*f)

C2 = B1/(2*pi*f)

The calculation results show that the series element is an inductor L1= 2.665 nH and the shunt element is a capacitor, C2 = 3.372 pF.

To display the response of the matching network, create a new workspace in ADS and open a new schematic window. Insert the S_Params Template and connect the input matching elements as shown in Figure 8-4.

Figure 8-4 Schematic of the input matching network

Simulate the schematic from 1350 MHz to 3350 MHz and display the insertion loss, S21, and return loss, S11, in dB, as shown in Figure 8-5.

Figure 8-5 Response of the input matching network

Stability of the Amplifier Second Stage

Example 8-3: Measure the simultaneous match input-output impedance and the maximum stable gain of the second stage of the cascaded amplifier.

The second stage with its stabilization network is shown in Figure 8-6.

Figure 8-6 Stabilized second stage schematic

As the Figure 8-7 shows, the stabilized RT243 device has a GMAX = 18.973 dB at 2.35 GHz.

| | Eqn ZLoud=sm_z2(S) | | Eqn Zsource=sm_z1(S) |

freq	MaxGain1	ZLoud	Zsource
2.350 GHz	18.973	2.094 - j1.780	0.689 - j4.270

Figure 8-7 Stabilized second stage with conjugate match impedance

According to Figure 8-7 the respective impedances maximum gain are given below.

$$Zsource = 0.689 - j4.27 \ \Omega$$

$$Zload = 2.094 - j1.78 \ \Omega$$

$$G_{max} = 18.973 \ dB$$

Design of the Inter-Stage Matching Network

One common method of inter-stage matching is to design each stage separately into a 50 Ω system and then cascade them directly with no additional matching. Many RF transistors have very low input and output impedance, much less than 50 Ω, making a low impedance interstage network desirable. In cascaded narrowband amplifier design a more efficient method of interstage matching is to conjugately match the two complex impedances directly together with a single L-network and thus reduce the number of interstage matching elements. Therefore, for the interstage matching network, we can use the equations developed in Chapter 5 to directly match together the two complex impedances.

Example 8-4: Design the interstage matching network between the SHF-0189 and the RT243 devices.

Solution: The procedure for the solution follows.

1. Enter design parameters and normalize the load impedance

RS=13.773; XS=-16.471; RL=0.688; XL=4.271; f=2.35e9

2. Calculate matching element values

B3 = ((RS*XL) + sqrt(RS*RL*(RL^2 + XL^2 - RS*RL)))/(RS*(RL^2 + XL^2))

X3 = (RS*XL - RL*XS)/RL + (RL - RS)/(B3*RL)

L2 = X3/(2*pi*f)

C1 = B3/(2*pi*f)

The calculation results show that the shunt element is an inductor C1= 17.91 pF and the series element is an inductor, L2 = 2.037 nH.

To display the response of the matching network, create a new workspace in ADS and open a new schematic window. Insert the S_Params Template and connect the matching elements as shown in Figure 8-8.

Figure 8-8 Schematic of the interstage matching network

Simulate the schematic from 1350 MHz to 3350 MHz and display both the return loss, S11, and the insertion loss, S21, in dB, as shown in Figure 8-9.

Figure 8-9 Response of the interstage matching network

Design of the Second Stage Output Matching Network

Example 8-5: Design the second stage output matching network.

Solution: Use Equations (5-24) and (5-25) to calculate the element values of the output matching network. The calculation results show that the shunt capacitor C1=6.48 pF and the series inductor L1 = 0.577 nH. Set up a new schematic in ADS and select the element values as shown in Figure 8-10. Simulate the schematic from 1350 MHz to 3350 MHz and display the insertion loss, S21, in dB.

Figure 8-10 Schematic of the output matching network

The simulated response is shown in Figure 8-11.

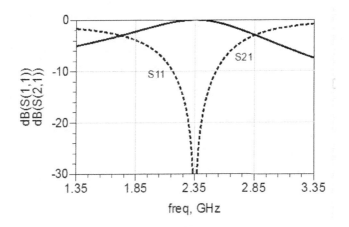

Figure 8-11 Response of the output matching network

8.3 Assembly of the Two-Stage Amplifier

Example 8-6: Simulate, and display the response of the cascaded amplifier.

Solution: The matching networks are attached to the stabilized devices to form a two stage amplifier. The input, inter-stage, and output matching networks are cascaded along with the devices as shown in Figure 8-12.
We will only deal with the ideal schematic at this point. The final design, of course, would include the physical models of the lumped element components and the interconnecting microstrip circuit elements.

Figure 8-12 Two-stage amplifier schematic with ideal matching networks

The gain and return loss are shown in Figure 8-13. The gain at 2.35 GHz is 34.754 dB which is very close to sum of GMAX for each stage. The amplifier gain is greater than 34 dB from 2260 MHz to 2380 MHz, satisfying one of the design specifications. The input and output return loss also satisfies the rest of amplifier design specifications.

Figure 8-13 Ideal amplifier cascade response

8.4 Multi-stage Low Noise Amplifiers

In practical amplifier applications, a single stage amplifier is rarely adequate to meet the overall gain and output power requirements of an amplifier design. Therefore it is necessary to cascade multiple gain stages to achieve a particular gain specification. In this section the gain and noise figure of the multi-stage cascaded LNA is discussed.

Cascaded Gain and Noise Figure

As we have seen in the example of Section 8.3 the overall gain of a cascaded amplifier is simply the algebraic sum of the gains (or losses) in dB. The gain of an amplifier cascade is then given by Equation (8-7).

$$Cascade\ Gain, G_{dB} = G1_{dB} + G2_{dB} + G3_{dB} + ... \qquad (8\text{-}7)$$

The overall noise figure is defined by the Friis formula [6]. As the Friis formula of Equation (8-8) shows, the overall noise figure of a cascade is influenced by all stages in the cascade. The noise figure contribution of the second stage is reduced by the gain of the first stage. Therefore, to maintain a low noise figure it is important that the first stage have high gain. The noise factor of a given stage is reduced by the gain of the preceding stages.

$$Noise\ Factor,\ F = F_1 + \frac{F_2 - 1}{G_1} + \frac{F_3 - 1}{G_1 G_2} + \frac{F_4 - 1}{G_1 G_2 G_3} + ... \qquad (8\text{-}8)$$

Where,

$$Noise\ Factor,\ F = 10^{\frac{F_{dB}}{10}}$$

$$Gain,\ G = 10^{\frac{G_{dB}}{10}}$$

In the solution of the Friis formula it is important to realize that the noise figure and gain must not be in dB format. This is referred to as the noise factor and related to the noise figure by the 10[log(F)] function.

For the three-stage LNA of Figure 8-14, the cascaded gain is easily calculated as 41 dB.

Figure 8-14 Three-stage cascaded low noise amplifier

Using the Friis formula to solve for the resulting noise factor leads to the following result.

$$F = 10^{\frac{0.7}{10}} + \frac{10^{\frac{1.1}{10}} - 1}{10^{\frac{15}{10}}} + \frac{10^{\frac{1.2}{10}} - 1}{10^{\frac{15}{10}} \cdot 10^{\frac{12}{10}}} = 1.1844$$

Converting the noise factor to noise figure we get 0.736 dB noise figure.

$$F_{dB} = 10 \cdot \log(1.1844) = 0.736 \ dB$$

The cascaded gain and noise figure can be calculated using the block diagram of Figure 8-14. The cascade uses the RFAmpHO system level model but can be used in linear simulation for gain and noise figure.

Setup a linear simulation for any frequency range as the frequency is independent for this use of the RFAmpHO model. The simulated cascade gain, S21, and noise figure, NF, are shown in Figure 8-15. We can see that the overall noise figure of the cascade is 0.736 dB which correlates with the solution of the Friis formula. The noise figure of the first stage dominates the overall noise figure and is slightly degraded by the 2nd and 3rd stages.

Figure 8-15 Simulated LNA cascade noise figure and gain

Impedance Match and the Friis Formula

A Low Noise Amplifier is typically used as the front end of a radio receiver. Therefore it is often attached to an antenna and filter combination. From Chapter 4 we have seen that the impedance of a filter can vary significantly across its passband as determined by the ripple and return loss. The same can be true of an antenna or the antenna feed network. Because the Noise Figure of an LNA is dependent on its source impedance, large errors can be obtained in the application of the Friis formula when calculating the overall noise figure of such a cascaded network. The Friis formula assumes that there is a perfect impedance match between each stage in the cascade and there are no variations in impedance across the frequency band. As an example consider a typical Low Noise Amplifier used in the Ku Band frequency range of 11.7 to 12.2 GHz. To eliminate any interference from the uplink signal or terrestrial sources a low loss waveguide filter is placed at the input of the LNA. This system level block diagram is shown in Figure 8-16.

Example 8-7: Consider a typical Low Noise Amplifier used in Ku band frequency range of 11.7 to 12.2 GHz. To eliminate any interference from the uplink signal, or terrestrial sources, a low pass waveguide filter is placed at the input of the LNA. The system level block diagram is shown in Figure 8-16.

Figure 8-16 Ku band LNA with bandpass filter

Note that a passive device's insertion loss is entered as a negative gain in dB in the Friis formula. The noise figure then becomes the absolute value of this loss or simply 0.2 dB in the case of the bandpass filter. Use the Friis formula to solve for the resulting noise figure.

Solution. Using the Friis formula to solve for the resulting noise figure we get the following result.

$$F = 10^{\frac{0.2}{10}} + \frac{10^{\frac{0.7}{10}} - 1}{10^{\frac{-0.2}{10}}} + \frac{10^{\frac{1.1}{10}} - 1}{10^{\frac{-0.2}{10}} \cdot 10^{\frac{15}{10}}} + \frac{10^{\frac{1.2}{10}} - 1}{10^{\frac{-0.2}{10}} \cdot 10^{\frac{15}{10}} \cdot 10^{\frac{12}{10}}} = 1.2402$$

Converting the noise factor back to noise figure gives a total cascaded noise figure of 0.935 dB.

$$F_{dB} = 10 \cdot \log \ (1.2402) = 0.935 \ \ dB$$

Based on this simple application of the Friis formula the engineer would expect the system noise figure to be 0.935 dB. Simulating the block diagram of Figure 8-14 in ADS reveals a vastly different result. The simulated noise figure of Figure 8-17 shows that there is significant ripple in the noise figure. The worst case noise figure is actually greater than 2 dB across the passband of the amplifier. The 0.5 dB ripple in the filter actually results in greater than 1.5 dB ripple in the noise figure. This is due to the fact that the noise figure of the input device is very sensitive to the impedance that is presented to it. The 0.935 dB noise figure calculation is an erroneous result that is obtained when using the Friss formula or one of the many spreadsheet cascade analysis programs. By modeling the simple cascade in ADS we can quickly become aware of this condition.

Figure 8-17 Ku band LNA with bandpass filter simulated response

Reducing the Effect of Source Impedance Variation

In practice it is often desirable to place a low-loss isolator at the input of the LNA to buffer the effects of impedance variation due to the filter ripple. It is important that the isolator have very low loss as its insertion loss will also add to the overall noise figure. This can easily be modeled in ADS by adding an isolator to the block diagram as shown in Figure 8-18.

Example 8-8: Add an isolator with an insertion loss of 0.1 dB to the block diagram of Figure 8-16 and plot the LNA cascade insertion loss and noise figure from 11.6 to 12.3 GHz.

Solution: An isolator with 0.1 dB insertion loss reduces the noise figure by 0.8 dB. Perform an S parameter simulation over the range of 11.6 GHz to 112.3 GHz with 600 points. This puts the noise figure of the LNA closer to 1.5 dB, which is a better value for the reception of Ku Band satellite signals from space. The resulting cascaded gain and noise figure is shown in Figure 8-19. Note the decrease in the noise figure due to the addition of the isolator between the filter and the amplifier.

Figure 8-18 Ku band LNA with isolator and bandpass filter

Figure 8-19 LNA cascaded noise figure and gain

8.5 Summary

The example of Section 8.4 gives an introduction to the important subject of system, or block diagram, level simulation. As the previous example shows there are also system level computations that can be evaluated with linear simulation techniques. Linear simulation continues to be a very important topic and is the foundation for all RF and microwave CAD work. This volume provides the reader with a thorough coverage of the linear circuit design techniques that can be accomplished with linear simulation in ADS. As an applications manual this text forms a bridge between the classic theory and practical engineering problem solving.

References and Further Readings

[1]   Guillermo Gonzales, *Microwave Transistor Amplifiers – Analysis and Design,* Second Edition, Prentice Hall Inc., Upper Saddle River, NJ.

[2]   Randy Rhea, *The Yin-Yang of Matching: Part 1 – Basic Matching Concepts*, High Frequency Electronics, March 2006

[3]   Steve C. Cripps, *RF Power Amplifiers for Wireless Communications*, Artech House Publishers, Norwood, MA. 1999

[4]   David M. Pozar, *Microwave Engineering*, Third Edition, John Wiley & Sons, New York, 2005

[5]   R. Ludwig, P. Bretchko, *RF Circuit Design*, Theory and Applications, Prentice Hall, Upper Saddle River, NJ, 2000

[6]   D. Roddy, J. Coolen, *Electronic Communications*, Second Edition, Reston Publishing Company, Inc., Reston, Virginia, 1981

[7]   Ali A. Behagi and Stephen D. Turner, *Microwave and RF Engineering, A Simulation Approach with Keysight Genesys Software*, BT Microwave LLC, State College, PA , March 2015

[8]   Keysight Technologies, Manuals for Advanced Design Systems, *ADS 2015.07 Documentation Set*, EEsof EDA Division, Santa Rosa, California www.keysight.com

Problems

8-1. Design a Two–Stage maximum gain amplifier

(a) Use the Agilent HBFP0405 and the Mitsubishi MGF0911a transistors to design a two-stage maximum gain amplifier at 2.2 GHz. All the input, output, and interstage impedance matching networks should be analytically designed using two-element L-networks.

(b) Design the stabilizing network for the first stage using Agilent HBFP0405 transistor

(c) Using the HBFP0405 stabilized transistor create a tabular output of the simultaneous match source and load impedance and Gmax

(d) Design the first stage input matching network by matching the 50 Ohm source impedance to the conjugate impedance looking into the stabilized HBFP0405 device, ZM1.

(e) Design the stabilizing network for the second stage using the Mitsubishi device

(f) Using the MGF0911a stabilized transistor create a tabular output of the simultaneous match source and load impedance and Gmax

(f) Design the second stage output matching network by matching the 50 Ohm load impedance to the conjugate impedance looking into the output of the stabilized MGF0911a device, ZM2

(g) Design the interstage matching network between stage one ZM2 and stage two ZM1.

(h) Cascade the two amplifiers and display the overall response of the cascaded network. The cascaded gain of the amplifier must be the sum of the maximum gains of the two single-stage amplifiers.

8-2. Increase the bandwidth of the matching networks

(a) Increase the bandwidth of the input matching network by selecting a virtual resistor R_M between the input resistor of the matching network, R_S, and the output resistor of the matching network, R_L, such that $R_M = \sqrt{R_S R_L}$

and then conjugately match the input and output impedances to the virtual resistor R_M with L-networks.

(b) Cascade the two matching networks and measure the fractional bandwidth at 20 dB return loss.

(c) Compare the measured fractional bandwidth with the fractional bandwidth of the original matching network at 20 dB return loss and calculate the percentage of the increase in the bandwidth.

(d) Repeat the above procedure for the interstage and output matching networks.

8-3. LNA Cascade Using the Friis Formula

(a) Consider a typical Low Noise Amplifier used in the X Band of 8.7 to 9.2 GHz. Using the Friis formula calculate the overall noise figure of the following LNA cascade.

LNA #1	G1 = 15 dB	F1 = 1.1 dB
LNA #2	G1 = 14 dB	F1 = 1.2 dB
LNA #3	G1 = 13 dB	F1 = 1.3 dB

Appendix A

Straight Wire Parameters for Solid Copper Wire

Wire Size (AWG)	Diameter in Mils	Resistance Ohms/1000 ft.	Area in circular Mils	Suggested Maximum Current Handling, Amperes[1]
0000	460.0	0.049	211600	1000
000	409.6	0.062	167800	839
00	364.8	0.078	133100	665
0	324.9	0.098	105500	527
1	289.3	0.124	83690	418
2	257.6	0.156	66360	332
3	229.4	0.197	52620	263
4	204.3	0.249	41740	208
5	181.9	0.313	33090	165
6	162.0	0.395	26240	131
7	144.3	0.498	20820	104
8	128.5	0.628	16510	83
9	114.4	0.793	13090	65
10	101.9	0.999	10380	52
11	90.7	1.26	8230	41
12	80.8	1.56	6530	32
13	72.0	2.00	5180	26
14	64.1	2.52	4110	20
15	57.1	3.18	3260	16
16	50.8	4.02	2580	13
17	45.3	5.05	2050	10
18	40.3	6.39	1620	8.0
19	35.9	8.05	1290	6.0
20	32.0	10.1	1020	5.0
21	28.5	12.8	812	4.0
22	25.3	16.2	640	3.0
23	22.6	20.3	511	2.5
24	20.1	25.7	404	2.0
25	17.9	32.4	320	1.6
26	15.9	41.0	253	1.2
27	14.2	51.4	202	1.0
28	12.6	65.3	159	0.80
29	11.3	81.2	123	0.61
30	10.0	104.0	100	0.50
31	8.9	131	79.2	0.40
32	8.0	162	64.0	0.32
33	7.1	206	50.4	0.25
34	6.3	261	39.7	0.19
35	5.6	331	31.4	0.16
36	5.0	415	25.0	0.12
37	4.5	512	20.2	0.10
38	4.0	648	16.0	0.08
39	3.5	847	12.2	0.06
40	3.1	1080	9.61	0.05
41	2.8	1320	7.84	0.04
42	2.5	1660	6.25	0.03
43	2.2	2140	4.84	0.024
44	2.0	2590	4.00	0.020
45	1.76	3350	3.10	0.016
46	1.57	4210	2.46	0.012
47	1.40	5290	1.96	0.010
48	1.24	6750	1.54	0.008
49	1.11	8420	1.23	0.006
50	0.99	10600	0.98	0.005

Current Handling based on 1 Amp/200 Circular Mils-no insulation and free air conditions. Insulated and stranded Copper wire must be de-rated from the values in the Table

Index

A

Admittance circles, 135-136,148,323
ADS Filter DesignGuide, 201-203, 206-207, 210, 212
ADS Impedance Matching Utility, 227, 290-291, 293, 299, 403, 416,
ADS Momentum Simulation, 217
ADS Optimization, 169-175, 376-378
ADS Simulation Wizard, 362-364
ADS Smart Components, 201-202, 291
ADS Smart Simulation, 360, 364-365, 367-368
ADS Transportation Assistant, 212
ADS Tuning, 165-169, 199
Amplifier design,
   Low noise, 382,393,397
   Maximum gain, 347-348
   Power, 347, 410
   Specific gain, 347, 380, 383
Amplifier noise, 408
Artwork replacement, 370, 373
Attenuation constant, 57, 60, 64, 67

B

Band pass filter, 221-222, 292, 438-440.
Bias feed networks, 102-104, 115, 370
Broadband matching networks, 227, 266-267, 274, 286, 332, 334, 336-338, 340-341

C

Capacitors,
   Multilayer chip, 46, 47, 49, 204
   Single layer, 42-44, 46,
Cascaded gain, 434-436, 440, 443
Cascaded L-network, 267 271, 281-282
Cascaded matching network, 274, 295, 331, 333
Coaxial transmission line 76-77, 80, 85
Conductor Q factor, 183
Coupled line filter, 221
Coupling coefficient, 189-191

D

Dielectric loss, 84, 181, 184

Directional coupler,
   Directivity, 108-111; 113, 115
Distributed bias feed, 14, 115

E

Edge coupled filters, 107,
Edge coupled lines, 106-108, 221
Effective capacitance, 51
Effective dielectric constant, 82, 86, 95, 100, 181-182
Electric field, 1, 41, 57, 74-75, 87, 107
Electromagnetic spectrum, 2-3
Electromagnetic wave, 1, 53, 57
Equal-Q L-networks, 274-275, 280, 299
External Q, 267, 274, 275, 280, 299

F

Filter order, 193-194, 197-198, 203, 207
Filter return loss, 196
Filter ripple, 198, 440
Filter synthesis, 200, 223
Filter topology, 192, 212
Filter type, 192-197, 200
Flat ribbon inductance, 3, 12
Free space, 1, 4, 10, 59-60, 73, 86, 91-93, 223, 225, 288
Friis formula, 435-439, 444

H

High pass filter, 88, 91, 193, 200, 206, 208-210, 225, 288
High pass matching L-network, 290

I

Impedance matching,
   Utility, 227, 290-291, 293, 299, 403, 416, 423
Incident power, 66, 68, 110, 123

About the Author

Ali A. Behagi received the Ph.D. degree in electrical engineering from the University of Southern California and the MS degree in electrical engineering from the University of Michigan. He has several years of industrial experience with Hughes Aircraft and Beckman Instruments. Dr. Behagi joined Penn State University as an associate professor of electrical engineering in 1986. He has devoted over 20 years to teaching RF and microwave engineering courses and directing university research projects. While at Penn State he received the National Science Foundation equipment grant to establish a high frequency measurement lab, and the Keysight/Agilent software grant to establish a computer lab and use the software in teaching RF and microwave engineering courses. After retirement from Penn State he has been active as an educational consultant. Recently he has authored and published textbooks on RF and microwave circuit design using the Keysight ADS and Genesys software. Dr. Behagi is recognized as a Keysight Distinguished Author and a Certified Expert. He is also a Senior Member of the Institute of Electrical and Electronics Engineers (IEEE), and the Microwave Theory and Techniques Society.

CPSIA information can be obtained
at www.ICGtesting.com
Printed in the USA
BVOW08*1347290118
505530BV00018B/287/P